THE DICTIONARY OF

Ethology and Animal Learning

THE DICTIONARY OF

Ethology and Animal Learning

EDITED BY

Rom Harré and Roger Lamb

ADVISORY EDITORS

R. D. Attenborough
D. J. McFarland
V. Reynolds

BLACKWELL REFERENCE

BRITISH LIBRARY CATALOGUING IN PUBLICATION DATA

The Dictionary of ethology and animal learning.
1. Animal behavior — Dictionaries
I. Harré, Rom   II. Lamb, Roger
591.51'03'21   QL750.3

ISBN 0-631-14606-7
ISBN 0-631-14607-5 Pbk

Typeset in 9 on 10pt Linotron Ehrhardt
by Oxford Publishing Services, Oxford
Printed in Great Britain by Page Bros (Norwich), Ltd

CONTENTS

PREFACE

The highly successful and comprehensive *Encyclopedic dictionary of psychology* included a dozen psychological specialities. The editors have selected, updated and supplemented material from the original dictionary to provide in this and similar volumes a compact but compendious coverage of the most widely studied of these specialities. In preparing the independent dictionaries we have had in mind the needs of both students and practitioners in many branches of psychology and allied fields. In addition to this volume which concentrates on ethology and animal learning, three further volumes cover physiological and clinical psychology, personality and social psychology, and developmental and educational psychology.

The selected articles have been brought up to date, and the bibliographies have been revised to include the most recent publications. Many new entries have been added to fill the inevitable gaps of the first edition. The number of biographies of great psychologists has been increased to help to bring the research process and its scientific findings to life.

Psychology has developed within several different conceptual frameworks, often treating the same subject matter with very different assumptions and methods. We have tried, we hope without being uncritically eclectic, to reflect a wide range of approaches to human thought and behavior, including those popular in academic, applied and clinical branches of psychology.

Rom Harré and Roger Lamb

ACKNOWLEDGMENTS

The Editors and Publisher are grateful for permission to reproduce the following illustrations:

autonomic nervous system

Blackwell Scientific Publications. (Redrawn from J. F. Stein, *Introduction to neurophysiology*, (1982), p. 316.)

communication

Cornell University Press. (Redrawn from K. von Frisch, *Bees, their vision, chemical senses and language* (1950).)

Cambridge University Press. (After van Hoof, in P. A. Hinde, ed., *Non-verbal Communication.*)

display

Oxford University Press. (After S. Cramp and K. E. L. Simmons, *Birds of the western Paleartic* (1977).)

drugs

Blackwell Scientific Publications. (Redrawn from R. Passmore and J. S. Robson, eds. *Anatomy, biochemistry, physiology and related subjects*, vol. 1, 2nd. edn. (1976), p. 25.15.)

hormones

Academic Press. (Redrawn from *Hormones and behavior*, ed. Seymour Levine (1972), p. 4.)

locomotion

Weidenfeld & Nicolson. (Redrawn from J. Gray, *Animal locomotion* (1968), p.278.)

recognition

Oxford University Press. (Redrawn from N. Tinbergen, *The study of instinct* (1951), p.78.)

RNA, DNA

Churchill Livingstone. (After G. H. Haggis et al., *Introduction to molecular biology* (1964), p.217.)

CONTRIBUTORS

Jeffrey R. Alberts   JRAl
Indiana University

Pamela J. Asquith   PJA
University of Alberta

R. D. Attenborough   RDA
Australian National University

Suzanne Benack   SBe
Union College, Schnectady

George E. Butterworth   GEB
University of Southampton

Michael R. A. Chance   MRAC
University of Birmingham

Jeremy Jon Cherfas   JJCh
University of Oxford

David D. Clarke   DDC
University of Oxford

Richard J. Davidson   RJD
State University of New York, Purchase

Marian Stamp Dawkins   MSD
University of Oxford

Richard Dawkins   RD
University of Oxford

D. W. Dickins   DWD
University of Liverpool

E. A. Gaffan   EAG
University of Reading

Carl F. Graumann   CFG
University of Heidelberg

T. R. Halliday   TRH
Open University

Rom Harré   RHa
University of Oxford

Paul H. Harvey   PHH
University of Oxford

R. W. Hiorns   RWH
University of Oxford

Gary P. Horowitz   GPH
State University of New York, Binghamton

Robert A. Jensen   RAJ
Southern Illinois University of Carbondale

Alison Jolly   AJ
The Rockefeller University

Hans Kummer   HK
University of Zurich

Roger Lamb   RL
University of Oxford

Barbara B. Lloyd   BBL
University of Sussex

D. J. McFarland   DJM
University of Oxford

Robert McHenry   RMcH
University of Oxford

N. J. Mackintosh   NJM
University of Cambridge

Aubrey W. G. Manning   AWGM
University of Edinburgh

Andrew P. Ockwell   APO
University of Oxford

G. A. Parker   GAP
University of Liverpool

T. K. Pitcairn   TKP
University of Edinburgh

Robert Plutchick   RP
Albert Einstein College of Medicine, New York

Benjamin E. Reese   BER
University of Oxford

Peter C. Reynolds   PCR
Corporate Anthropology, California

V. Reynolds   VR
University of Oxford

Mark Ridley   MR
University of Oxford

Richard C. Saunders   RCS
University of Oxford

Steve J. Simpson   SJS
University of Oxford

W. T. Singleton   WTS
University of Aston

Peter K. Smith   PKS
University of Sheffield

Nancy C. Waugh   NCW
University of Oxford

Andrew Whiten   AW
University of St Andrews

Gordon Winocur   GWi
Trent University, Ontario

Andrew R. Woodfield   ARW
University of Bristol

Joseph L. Zinnes   JLZ
University of Illinois, Urbana-Champaign

EDITORIAL NOTE

Asterisks against titles in the bibliographies indicate items suitable for further reading. The convention 1920 (1986) indicates a work first published in 1920 but widely accessible only in an edition of 1986, to which the publication details given refer.

Cross references to other entries are printed in small capitals in the text. Leads to further additional information can be found from the index.

A

abnormal behavior Behavior resulting from STRESS or from a pathological condition. Experimentally induced anxiety was investigated by PAVLOV who discovered that well-trained animals subjected to difficult problems often showed extreme signs of emotion. Prolonged exposure to stressful situations can lead to experimental neurosis and to physiological symptoms such as gastric ulcers. Animals subject to stress generally show loss of appetite, increased aggression and stereotyped behavior. These types of abnormal behavior sometimes occur in animals in zoos, especially if their natural behavior patterns are interrupted.   DJM

Bibliography
Grier, J.W. 1984: *Biology of animal behaviour.* Part 4. St Louis: C.V. Mosby; Oxford: Blackwell Scientific Publications.

activity A term used to denote general muscular activity without making any distinction between particular behavior patterns. Methods of measurement are usually automatic and involve placing the animal in a cage with a device for monitoring differences between activity and rest. Such devices may include infra-red beams of light which are invisible to the animal, each breaking of the beam by the animal being recorded by a photocell. Stabilimeter cages use a pivoted floor that tips as the animal moves across it. The movement of the floor is recorded electrically. Sometimes a particular activity, such as running, is recorded by means of a specially designed device. Running in rodents can conveniently be measured by a vertically mounted circular cage that rotates freely about its axis, called a running wheel: the animal runs inside the wheel, causing it to rotate, and the rotations are measured automatically. Measurements of general activity are sometimes useful in the study of CLOCK-DRIVEN BEHAVIOR, drugs, or other factors that influence sleep and wakefulness. Such measures give only a crude indication of the effects of experimental manipulations and are generally used only as part of routine testing.   DJM

adaptation in evolutionary biology The process whereby the biological (including behavioral) characteristics of individuals come to be ones which favor survival and reproduction in their particular environment, through the long-term action of NATURAL SELECTION on the genetic constitution of the population in question. Alternatively it sometimes refers to a general state of adaptedness, or to a specific adaptive feature, that results from this process. In principle, the benefit conferred by an adaptive feature can be assessed in terms of its contribution to Darwinian FITNESS. In practice, however, difficulties may arise in identifying truly adaptive features, and in relating them securely to the solution of particular survival (or reproduction) problems, since these are essentially *post hoc* procedures. These difficulties are emphasized by those who argue that adaptation is an over-used concept, attractive to invoke but easily yielding empty Panglossian explanations, but these critiques generally constitute arguments for the more rigorous application of the concept rather than its abandonment (see Williams 1966, Lewontin 1978, Maynard Smith and Holliday 1979).

In other contexts adaptation is used in a variety of less restricted ways. The sense common to most of these is that of successful adjustment to some external factor, though the terms in which this adjustment is assessed vary widely.   RDA

Bibliography

Lewontin, R.C. 1978: Adaptation. *Scientific American* 239 (3), 156–169.

—— 1982: Organism and environment. In *Learning, development and culture*, ed. H.C. Plotkin. Chichester: Wiley.

Maynard Smith, J. and Holliday, R. eds. 1979: The evolution of adaptation by natural selection. *Proceedings of the Royal Society of London*, Series B, 205, 435–604.

Williams, G.C. 1966: *Adaptation and natural selection: a critique of some current evolutionary thought*. Princeton: Princeton University Press.

aggression

Conceptual issues

The quest for a unitary definition of aggression has been both prolonged and largely unresolved. Some authors declare that a unitary concept is not viable. Johnson (1972), for example, maintains that 'it is difficult if not impossible to produce a satisfactory definition'. He goes on to conclude that 'there is no single kind of behavior which can be called "aggressive" nor any single process which represents "aggression"'. Definition is further complicated by the fact that there are different concepts and theoretical stances in the three related disciplines of psychology, ETHOLOGY and anthropology; there are more than 250 different definitions of aggression in the psychological literature alone. It is therefore appropriate to isolate those components of definitions for which there is broad support.

Firstly, aggression may be said to occur only between members of the same species. In other words it is distinguishable from predation, anti-predator behavior and encounters arising from competition for the same ecological niche. Writers such as Ardrey (1979) have argued that Man's hostility to his fellows derives from his emergence as a predatory hominid. His use of primitive weapons for the killing of prey were also used in conflicts with rivals and, coupled with territoriality, led to the evolution of a "killer" species. Many theorists, however, have argued that aggression and predation should be seen as quite separate processes – hunting

behavior being quite different in form from patterns of conspecific fighting and display in both animals and humans. In cats, for example, predatory behavior is shown in a silent crouch whereas a DISPLAY of fight/flight aggression involves hissing, bristling and arching the back. The two forms of behavior can be produced in the laboratory by stimulating different areas of a cat's hypothalamus. Stimulation of the *lateral* hypothalamus produces predatory behavior toward a rat. Stimulation of the *medial* hypothalamus produces defensive attack. Marsh (1978) suggests that the unique ability of Man is to manipulate symbols and thereby *dehumanize* rivals who are thereby demoted to the role of prey.

Secondly, there is the notion that aggression involves the delivery of a noxious stimulus. Such a definition would allow a wide range of behavior to be classed as aggressive, and this stance is to be preferred to those which limit aggression to the perpetration of physical injury. It is, however, not a *sufficient* condition for aggression since noxious stimuli can clearly be delivered without any aggression present.

Clearly the concept of *intention* seems an essential component of any satisfactory definition. It is at this point that the most severe difficulties arise. While it might be philosophically legitimate to talk of *intentionality* in a discussion of human behavior it would be absurd to use such a concept in relation to aggression in animals. To ask whether one cat *intended* to injure another is to engage in a quite untenable form of ANTHROPOMORPHISM.

So, on the one hand we have an apparent desire to define aggression in terms which accord with the frames of reference of traditional, empirical psychology – i.e. overt behavior. On the other, in order to meet the constraints of simple logic and everyday human experience, mentalistic criteria are introduced (often apologetically). What is lacking is any indication of how intention or expectation may be determined in general or specific examples of aggression.

Because of these problems we might be

forgiven for adopting Johnson's position. At the same time there exists in everyday language and conceptualization the notion that aggression does indeed have a unitary nature, although the range of psychological states and patterns of behavior might be rather wider than is commonly assumed by psychologists. What unites them is the presence of competition, establishment of DOMINANCE and the subjugation of perceived rivals – a broad but meaningful constellation of psychological processes. It is suggested that this might provide the starting point for a more relevant and useful definition of aggression. Such an approach is in keeping with some ethological perspectives, and allows for comparative study.

From this standpoint acts of violence may be distinguished clearly from the aggression process itself. Aggression, under certain circumstances, may result in acts of physical injury. Violence, however, is not a *necessary* consequence of aggression, other means for the expression of dominance and the subjugation of rivals being readily available.

Major fields of research

Research directly concerned with the antecedents of aggression has occupied the bulk of the literature over the past thirty years. The work of Freud and his "hydraulic" concept was later mirrored by the ethological theory of LORENZ (1966). Subsequent ethological work (e.g. Eibl-Eibesfeldt 1971) refined some of the more mechanistic assumptions of the earlier approaches, and emphasized more strongly the plasticity of inherited characteristics.

Numerous studies have shown that animals can be bred for aggressiveness. This has been found for laboratory mice (Lagerspetz 1961) and chickens (Guhl et al. 1960), and is visible in established breeds of dogs (see Scott 1958). Cross-fostering does not affect the genetic contribution, as the animals' aggressiveness is predictable from their biological rather than adoptive parents. There are clear neurochemical differences between aggressive and non-aggressive strains (Lagerspetz et al. 1968).

There is now a good deal of experimental work on hormones and aggression, particularly in rodents. Injection of the male hormone, testosterone, in infancy increases aggression in adult males in many species. Edwards (1968) was able to elicit male patterns of fighting from female mice which had been treated with testosterone immediately after birth. Administration of testosterone to adult, sixty-day-old female mice did not have this effect. It therefore appears to be the impact of the hormone on the animal's development which is decisive, rather than its presence in the body (see Svare 1983).

Apart from developmental plasticity under the influence of hormones, there is also experimental evidence for the effect of experience on later aggression. It is clear that isolation during rearing may heighten later aggressiveness (see Johnson 1972). Cairns et al. (1985) found age at the time of isolation, as well as length of isolation, affected subsequent aggression in mice, although isolates were generally more aggressive than the group-reared animals with which they were paired. Cairns et al. also noted that the behavior of the other animal was a factor in occasioning aggression. If the partner showed "mild investigatory activity" towards them, the isolates frequently attacked. It is clear that situational factors, especially the nature or behavior of the (potential) opponent play a major role. Lagerspetz (1961) demonstrated that mice paired with much more aggressive mice for ten days showed a marked reduction in aggression. When paired with much less aggressive mice for a further ten days, their aggression increased.

Concern with payoffs of aggression is assumed to be an important determinant of whether contests escalate into violence (see Maynard Smith 1981). Aggression involves risk of injury, which is only worthwhile if victory will increase one's FITNESS for survival and reproduction (Parker 1974). Intraspecific contests are a means to the end of controlling economic and reproductive resources (territory and mating partners; see TERRITORIALITY. Wynne-Edwards (1968) found that male

3

grouse contest suitable moorland territories in late September and thereby fix a pattern of holdings which last for ten or eleven months. Those birds which fail to establish territory have very little chance of survival. Riechert (1979) showed that spiders (*Agelenopsis aperta*) fight longer and more energetically when scarcer and higher quality resources are at stake. Aggression also occurs during the establishment of a HIERARCHY (see, for example, Chase 1985). But competition for status in primates such as chimps involves the formation of coalitions, and one-to-one fighting has only a minor role (De Waal 1982).

As with Lagerspetz's mice, contests are often asymmetric. One animal may have more RESOURCE-HOLDING POTENTIAL (be larger and fiercer). Otronen (1984), for instance, found that relative size was a good predictor of success in territorial struggles in the fly *Dryomyza anilis*. Equally, however, one contestant may have more to lose, and hence a greater incentive to fight. A third asymmetry is that one contestant may be the "owner" of the resource. There might be a rule that owners generally win (see Parker 1974; Maynard Smith 1982; TERRITORIALITY).

Ritual aggression

Work on ritual aggression has developed in ethology and anthropology. In ethology the term ritualization was coined by HUX-LEY and used to refer to the adaptive formalization or canalization of emotionally motivated behavior, under the telenomic pressure of NATURAL SELECTION. It has been employed in particular in the area of aggressive behavior by writers such as Lorenz (1966), Eibl-Eibesfeldt (1979) and others. Evidence suggests that patterns of fighting behavior are modified to the extent that intra-species agonistic encounters result in relatively little injury to the protagonists. Potentially lethal attacks take on the nature of "tournaments" involving threat signals such as color changes or bristling of fur.

Because of the asymmetries mentioned above, these THREATS are important for the contestants in deciding how far to escalate

the struggle. On the assumption that a stronger animal will defeat a weaker, it pays if the contestants can assess their relative strength without actually fighting. Many ritual displays seem to make animals look larger and fiercer. It might seem, in fact, that it would pay an animal to deceive an opponent into believing it to be a tougher proposition than it really was. Nevertheless it is debatable whether such "cheating" would pay off in the long run, and whether it could be an EVOLUTIONARILY STABLE STRATEGY. There is, however, controversy about the degree to which economic, cost-benefit analyses fit observed aggressive communications among animals (see Maynard-Smith 1982; Krebs and Dawkins 1984).

In anthropology ritual refers to patterned routines of behavior involving a system of signs and conventional relations between the actions in which the ritual is performed and the social act achieved by its successful completion. Many examples of tribal warfare have been described in these terms. The Dani of New Guinea, for example, were described by Gardner and Heider as engaging in highly ceremonial and ritual patterns of inter-group hostility.

More recently, writers such as Fox (1977) have brought these two major approaches together. Here the assumption is that patterns of ritual aggression in man have essentially the same (largely biological) origins and perform the same adaptive functions. Work by Marsh (1978), however, which has focused on ritual aggression among youth in Britain, suggests that the common origins argument is unnecessary.   PEM/RL

Bibliography

Ardrey, R. 1979: *The hunting hypothesis*. London and New York: Methuen.

Cairns, R.B., Hood, K.E. and Midlam, J. 1985: On fighting mice: is there a sensitive period for isolation effects. *Animal behaviour* 33, 166–80.

Chase, I.D. 1985: The sequential analysis of aggressive acts during hierarchy formation. *Animal behaviour* 33, 86–100.

De Waal, F. 1982: *Chimpanzee politics*. New York: Harper and Row.

Edwards, D.A. 1968: Mice: fighting by neonatally androgenized females. *Science* 161, 1027–8.

Eibl-Eibesfeldt, I. 1971: *Love and hate*. London: Methuen; New York: Holt, Rinehart and Winston.

Fox, R. 1977: The inherent rules of violence. In *Social rules and social behavior*, ed. P. Collett. Oxford: Basil Blackwell; Totowa, N.J.: Rowman and Littlefield.

Guhl, A.M., Craig, J.V. and Mueller, C.D. 1960: Selective breeding for aggression in chickens. *Poultry science* 39, 970–80.

Johnson, R.N. 1972: *Aggression in man and animals*. Philadelphia: W.B. Saunders.

Krebs, J.R. and Dawkins, R. 1984: Animal signals: mind-reading and manipulation. In *Behavioural ecology*. 2nd edn., eds. J.R. Krebs and N.B. Davies. Oxford: Blackwell Scientific Publications.

Lagerspetz, K. 1961: Genetic and social causes of aggressive behaviour in mice. *Scandinavian journal of psychology* 2, 167–73.

Lagerspetz, K.Y.H., Tirri, R. and Lagerspetz, K.M.J. 1968: Neurochemical and endocrinological studies of mice selectively bred for aggressiveness. *Scandinavian journal of psychology* 9, 157–60.

Lorenz, K. 1966: *On aggression*. London: Methuen; New York: Harcourt, Brace and World.

Marsh, P. 1978: *Aggro: the illusion of violence*. London: Dent.

Maynard Smith, J. 1982: *Evolution and the theory of games* Cambridge: Cambridge University Press.

Otronen, M. 1984: Male contests for territories and females in the fly *Dryomyza anilis*. *Animal behaviour* 32, 891–8.

Parker, G.A. 1974: Assessment strategy and the evolution of fighting behaviour. *Journal of theoretical biology* 47, 223–43.

Riechert, S.E. 1979: Games spiders play: II. Resource assessment strategies. *Behavioral ecology and sociobiology* 6, 121–8.

Scott, J.P. 1958: *Animal behavior*. Chicago: University of Chicago Press.

Svare, B.B. 1983: *Hormones and aggressive behavior*. New York: Plenum.

Wynne-Edwards, V.C. 1968: Population control and social selection in animals. In *Genetics*, ed. D.C. Glass. New York: Rockefeller University Press.

agonic This term together with the term HEDONIC refers to one of two extreme mechanisms of social cohesion and at the same time to the corresponding modes of mental operation.

Agonic social cohesion is typical of the general features of baboon and macaque societies, where social cohesion is maintained by predominant persistent attention to the dominant individual (usually a male) at the center of a group. This prevents continuous uninterrupted periods of attention to other matters. The low threshold of AGGRESSION of the dominant male means that all members of the group are liable to become the target of his aggression which in the form of threats can cause the individuals, after momentary withdrawal, to return to the source of the threat. This threat is responded to by spatial withdrawal and return (equilibration, see Mason 1965 for an explanation of this phenomenon), by submission, displacement, redirection, and CUT-OFF (which prevents visual exploration) or by appropriate organized counter-threat. These responses are immediately available as a means of avoiding punishment. Hence, the monkeys of these societies must be in a high state of AROUSAL, which, since they only manifest these types of behavior from time to time, must be simultaneously inhibited. A state of high arousal combined with inhibition is, therefore, the main feature of this hypothesized mental mode. The term agonic was chosen to label this state of latent defensive responsiveness to ally it with, but distinguish it from, "agonistic" which is the active state of social conflict taking place from time to time in agonistic social episodes. (See also ATTENTION STRUCTURE.)   MRAC

Bibliography

Chance, M.R.A. 1962: An interpretation of some agonistic postures: the role of "cut-off" acts and postures. Reprinted from *Symposia of the Zoological Society of London* No. 8, pp. 71–89.

——— 1967: Attention structure as the basis of primate rank orders. *Man* 2, 4.

Mason, W.A. 1965: Sociability and social organization in monkeys and apes. In *Advances in experimental social psychology*, vol. 1, ed. L. Berkowitz. New York: Academic Press.

altruism: biological

An act, or some other property, of one organism (the altruist) which increases the chances of survival of another organism while decreasing its own. Defined less formally, it is self-destruction to benefit others. Ethologists have taken the word from everyday use, where it has a rather broad meaning, and given it a narrower, technical meaning: confusion results if the common meaning is read in to a technical ethological discussion. In common usage, altruism not only refers to the transfer of goods from altruist to recipient; it also implies a kindly intent in the altruist. The non-ethological usage is as much motivational as economic. Ethologists have stripped the word of all connotations of subjective intent, and recognise altruism only by its effects. An altruistic act is one that has the *effect* of benefiting another organism at the altruist's expense.

The ethological meaning, as well as some of its peculiarities, can be illustrated by some examples. The commonest form of altruism is parental care, in all its forms from the most rudimentary protection of eggs to its most extreme development in viviparity and lactation. The parental animal decreases its own survival, but increases that of its offspring. But parental care is not the only behavior which fits the definition. A development from parental care is the activity of the "helper at the nest".

In many species of birds (the Florida scrub jay *Aphelocoma coerulescens* is an example) the offspring of earlier broods remain after fledging at the parents' nest and help to rear later broods. The later broods are the siblings, not the offspring, of the "helpers"; but helping at the nest conforms to the definition of altruism. Helping at the nest, and analogous forms of cooperative breeding, are being discovered in a rapidly lengthening list of species of birds and mammals. But for the most extreme developments we must look to the social insects (ants, bees, wasps, and termites). In fully social species some "worker" individuals are completely sterile, and devote all their energies to rearing the offspring of another individual (the "queen"). The poisonous sting of the honey bee worker illustrates a further point about the definition of altruism. The definition does not only refer to behavior. The sting, once inserted into the victim, cannot be removed; sting and abdomen are wrenched apart, and the individual worker dies. But her nestmates will benefit from the sacrifice: the sting is an altruistic ADAPTATION.

Let us now turn to theoretical principles. Altruism is of great interest to evolutionary theorists. On the first page of his book *Sociobiology* (1975) E. O. Wilson described it, without exaggeration, as "the central theoretical problem of sociobiology". But why is it so central a problem? To answer this question we must look closely into the theory of evolution: the theory of NATURAL SELECTION.

Natural selection, according to a simple and usually accurate interpretation, can only favor adaptations that cause their bearers to bear more offspring. It should favor individual selfishness. If we temporarily exclude parental care, altruism appears to be exactly what natural selection will oppose. Altruists (by definition) leave fewer offspring than non-altruists. So by natural selection the non-altruists should come to prevail in all natural populations. Darwinians believe that natural selection is the only cause of adaptation. Natural selection cannot (it seems) cause altruism. But altruism exists. That is the paradox. It has elicited four main kinds of solution, but only three of them are even in principle valid.

The one of the four which is in principle invalid is the theory of "group selection" (though according to some, in principle it is valid but in practice implausible – see NATURAL SELECTION and SOCIOBIOLOGY). We have so far supposed that natural selection produces only adaptations that make individual organisms live longer and leave more offspring. The group of organisms only benefits incidentally, when group benefit happens to be identical with individual benefit. The theory of group selection reverses this formula. It supposes that natural selection benefits groups, and if individual and group interests come into conflict, the group interest will, under natural selection, prevail. Group selection will favor characteristics that decrease the rate at which the group becomes extinct. Altruism is just such a characteristic, so it can be expected to evolve if natural selection favors groups rather than individuals.

But does it? When the evolutionary conflict between individual and group advantage has been mathematically modeled it has been found that the conditions for group selection to operate are so restrictive that they are probably rarely realized in nature (Maynard Smith 1976). Natural selection is much more powerful on individuals than on groups because the rate of turnover of individuals is so much higher than that of groups.

Group selection can be ruled out in principle. Nor do we need it, because we have three theories which are not incoherent in principle, and which can explain altruism. They are kin selection, reciprocal altruism, and manipulation. Kin selection is the most important. It is a theory that we mainly owe to W.D. Hamilton (1964). For exposition, it is convenient to work outwards from the case of parental care. Parental care presents no theoretical paradox. If an organism leaves more offspring by caring for them than by not, parental care will evolve, since genes which cause their bearers to care for their offspring will be found in more copies in the next generations than genes which do not cause parental care. The "parental care" genes are favored because the offspring share genes (with a known probability) with their parents.

But an organism's offspring are not the only ones to share its genes. All its relatives do, according to a certain probability which is called a "coefficient of relatedness" (see table). Consider again the case of helpers at the nest. An animal shares genes with a sibling with exactly the same probability as with its offspring. Natural selection will therefore favor helping at the nest if, by helping, an animal increases the number of its siblings by more than the number of offspring it would on average leave if it bred alone.

These two quantities are measurable, and the tests that exist so far, although preliminary, do suggest that kin selection is a major part of the explanation of helping at the nest (Emlen 1984).

Coefficients of relatedness (r = probability that a gene in one organism is also in the listed relative.)

Relatives	r
offspring	1/2
parent	1/2
full sibling	1/2
half sibling	1/4
grandchild	1/4
uncle or aunt	1/4
first cousin	1/8
second cousin	1/32

The second valid theory is called "reciprocal altruism" (Trivers 1971). It differs from kin selection in that it can explain altruistic acts among non-relatives. According to this theory, altruism is favored provided that it is repaid. It can be explained by one possible natural example. Packer (1977) found that male olive baboons often form pairs to consort with females in estrus. The pairs are better at defending the female from competing males than is a single male. But Packer observed that only one male of the pair mates with any particular female. So the other male is behaving altruistically: he is defending the female but receiving no benefit for his effort. Packer found that the altruism is favored because, when another female comes into estrus, the same pair of males tends to reform, but this time the males change roles. The olive baboons provide just one example. The process could work in many other cases. It is necessary that the animals can (in effect at least) recognize individuals so that acts of altruism can be reciprocated, and cheats (who do not reciprocate) discriminated against.

Manipulation is the third explanation. Animals carry a set of responses, which are normally appropriate. But they can be subverted. A cuckoo, for example, exploits the normal response of a parental bird to a

7

gaping chick's bill. Examples of manipulated altruism are particularly common among the relationships of parasite and host species: but natural selection can in principle favor manipulation in intraspecific interactions as well.

There are, in sum, three theories which can in principle explain the evolution of altruism. When confronted by an actual example the ethologist may study it in detail to work out which (or which mixture) of the three is the correct explanation in that case. Few such detailed studies have been yet carried out. But ethologists have reached the stage of being reasonably confident which theories are, and which are not, valid applications of the theory of natural selection.

(See also BEHAVIOR GENETICS; PARASITISM.)   MR

Bibliography

*Dawkins, Richard 1976: *The selfish gene*. Oxford and New York: Oxford University Press.

——— 1979: Twelve misunderstandings of kin selection. *Zeitschrift für Tierpsychologie* 51, 184–200.

——— 1982: *The extended phenotype*. New York: Freeman.

Emlen, S.T. 1984: Cooperative breeding. In *Behavioural ecology*. 2nd edn., eds. J.R. Krebs and N.B. Davies. Oxford: Blackwell Scientific Publications; Sunderland, Mass.: Sinauer Assoc.

Grafen, A. 1982: How not to measure inclusive fitness. *Nature* 298, 425–6.

——— 1984: Natural selection, kin selection and group selection. In *Behavioural ecology*. 2nd edn., eds. J.R. Krebs and N.B. Davies. Oxford: Blackwell Scientific Publications.

Hamilton, W.D. 1964: The genetical evolution of social behaviour. *Journal of theoretical biology* 7, 1–52.

Maynard Smith, J. 1976: Group selection. *Quarterly review of biology* 51, 277–83.

Packer, C. 1977: Reciprocal altruism in *Papio anubis*. *Nature* 265, 441–3.

*Ridley, M. and Dawkins, R. 1981: The natural selection of altruism. In *Altruism and helping behavior*, eds. J. Philippe Rushton and Richard M. Sorrentino. Hillsdale, New Jersey: Erlbaum.

Trivers, R.L. 1971: The evolution of reciprocal altruism. *Quarterly review of biology* 46, 35–57.

*Wilson, Edward O. 1975: *Sociobiology: the new synthesis*. Cambridge, Mass.: Harvard University Press.

analogy *See* homology and analogy.

anthropomorphism The attribution to an animal of psychical capabilities like those of men and the supposition that it acts from similar motives. Among many others Darwin (1872) and one of the founders of ethology, Lorenz, assumed that animals have mental experiences and emotions similar to those of humans, and at times described their behavior in anthropomorphic terms. However, another pioneer of ethology, TINBERGEN (1951), argued that there is no basis for inferring subjective experiences in other species. It is generally thought to be erroneous and unscientific to attribute human mental experiences to animals. The recent development of COGNITIVE ETHOLOGY (Griffin 1976), which attempts to study mental experiences in animals, is contrasted to anthropomorphism in that it does not assume that the experiences are the same as those of humans.   PJA

Bibliography

Darwin, Charles 1872: *The expression of the emotions in man and animals*. London: John Murray.

Dawkins, M.S. 1980: *Animal suffering*. London: Chapman and Hall.

Griffin, D.R. 1981: *The question of animal awareness*. 2nd edn. New York: Rockefeller University Press.

——— 1982: *Animal mind — human mind*. Berlin: Springer-Verlag.

Tinbergen, Niko 1951: *The study of instinct*. 2nd edn with new introduction, 1969. Oxford: Clarendon Press.

appeasement A ritualized gesture (including vocalizations and scents) of submission. It is commonly the opposite of threat gestures, taking the form of stances such as crouching which reduce apparent size and hide markings of sex and species. Many appeasement gestures mimic female or infantile behavior. (See also AGGRESSION, RITUAL AND RITUALIZATION.)   AJ

Bibliography
Poole, T. 1985: *Social behaviour in mammals.* Glasgow: Blackie.

appetite A psychological aspect of hunger which combines various influences upon the animal's overall tendency to eat. In addition to the animal's basic hunger, the tendency to eat can be influenced by the time of day and the nature of the feeding situation including social factors. Thus an animal may appear to have little appetite if there are signs of a predator in the vicinity; on the other hand, appetite can be increased by the presence of other members of the species, especially if they are themselves feeding.

Appetite can have an important influence upon FOOD SELECTION, and is itself influenced by the quality of the food available. Thus highly palatable food tends to increase appetite as does the presence of vitamins and minerals for which the animal has a specific physiological need (see HUNGER AND THIRST). Low appetite is generally associated with high selectivity or finickiness, whereas very hungry animals tend to be less selective and to eat foods that they would not otherwise take.
                                                      DJM

appetitive behavior The active exploratory behavior that precedes CONSUMMATORY BEHAVIOR. The term was introduced by Wallace Craig (1918) to describe the animal's response to the absence of a stimulus, such as food or a mate. For instance a hungry rat may actively forage for food and this appetitive behavior ceases when food is obtained.

Appetitive behavior is often exploited by scientists investigating animal learning and discrimination. Maze running and operant behavior are examples of appetitive behavior that are commonly manipulated in laboratory experiments (see operant CONDITIONING). However, although favored by LORENZ and TINBERGEN, the concept of appetitive behavior has not proved to be very useful in the study of natural behavior. Many animals do not show active foraging when hungry, but employ an ambush strategy. Moreover, there are many aspects of behavior to which it is not clear that the term is appropriate. Its use in connection with AVOIDANCE, and AGGRESSION, is controversial.   DJM

Bibliography
Craig, W. 1918: Appetites and aversions as constituents of instincts. *Biology bulletin* 34, 91–107.

approach/avoidance conflict The conflict shown when identical or similar objects or places have been associated with both attractive and aversive consequences. In the classic demonstration a hungry rat is trained to run down a runway for food in the goal box until it reliably approaches the goal whenever placed in the start box. If the rat is then punished whenever it reaches the goal box, by being given a brief electric shock, it may show a characteristic pattern of conflict, running part of the way down the runway after being placed in the start box, but then hesitating, stopping, retracing and going forward again. Given the opportunity, it will now escape altogether from the situation by jumping out of the runway.

The rat will also engage in DISPLACEMENT ACTIVITY, and ethologists have recorded similar approach/avoidance conflicts, for example during COURTSHIP, when the male is both (for obvious enough reasons) attracted to the female, and also afraid of her – for example because she resembles a male conspecific who would attack if approached too closely.   NJM

Bibliography
Baerends, G.P. 1975: An evaluation of the conflict hypothesis as an explanatory principle for the evaluation of displays. In *Function and evolution in behaviour*, eds. G.P. Baerends, C. Beer and A. Manning. Oxford: Clarendon Press.

arousal Generalized responsiveness to stimulation, may range from deep SLEEP, through various waking stages, to great excitement. The term is also used to denote the degree of responsiveness to particular types of stimulation. Thus the responsiveness of a male rat to a female is often described in terms of sexual arousal.

The concept of general arousal presents considerable difficulties of measurement and interpretation. Behavioral indices are inevitably specific to the type of behavior employed and physiological indices, such as the rate of the heart beat, are difficult to interpret. Thus although aroused animals generally have an elevated heart beat rate, this also occurs in other situations, such as exertion. Hebb (1955) suggested that arousal level, as measured by brain activity (electroencephalograph), is the physiological equivalent of the behavioral concept of general drive (see MOTIVATION), and that there is an optimal arousal level for performance of particular behavior patterns. The numerous attempts to substantiate this theory have not been particularly successful, and the arousal concept is no longer widely used.   DJM

Bibliography

Hebb, D.O. 1955: Drives and the C.N.S. *Psychological review* 62, 243–54.

association An aspect of learning in which two stimuli, events or ideas become connected by virtue of their temporal contiguity. (See CONDITIONING.)

Bibliography

Dickinson, A. 1980: *Contemporary animal learning theory*. Cambridge: Cambridge University Press.

attention An aspect of perception in which the animal exercises choice in respect of the types of stimuli that influence its behavior. It is related to the searching image phenomenon in which animals searching for food concentrate upon a particular food type while ignoring other equally palatable foods. The animal may pay attention to one food at one time and to a different food at another time.

Selective attention in animals can be studied by means of learning experiments in which the animal is required to solve problems involving stimulus classification. A rat may be required to discriminate between a large vertical rectangle and a small horizontal rectangle. The problem can be solved in terms of the size or the orientation of the stimuli. In order to discover which cues the rat actually used, unrewarded transfer tests can be given, in which the animal is presented either with two stimuli of the same size but differing in orientation, or with two stimuli of the same orientation but differing in size. The first problem could be solved only if the animal had attended to, and learned about, orientation during the original training. The second problem could be solved only if the animal had attended to the size differences between the original stimuli.   DJM

Bibliography

Rizzolati, G. 1983: Mechanisms of selective attention in mammals. In *Advances in vertebrate neuroethology*, eds. J.-P. Ewert, R.R. Capranica and D.J. Ingle. New York and London: Plenum.

attention structure The principle of social organization based on information flow (mainly through visual attention) among members of a group.

The ways in which individual animals pay attention (visual or in other modalities) to stimuli, or select them for attention from the mass of input bombarding the senses, has long been recognized as an important variable in explaining interindividual and inter-specific differences. For example, butyric acid is the important stimulus which a tick uses in searching for a mammalian host – for a crotaline snake (pit-viper) it is the body temperature which helps detection through the remarkable sensory pit on each side of the head, between eye and nostril. Thus these two groups of animals attend to quite different stimuli, which for each of them represents "mammal".

Similarly, within one species attention may be paid differentially among the stimuli presented to an individual – they exhibit selective attention. Perhaps the most extreme example of this is to be found in the ORIENTING RESPONSE investigated by Sokolov and his colleagues, which takes the form in many mammals of a cessation in breathing and an increase in heart rate to a sudden low frequency or rustling sound. That the same sort of thing occurs at the social level forms the basis for theories about attention structure:-that is, that animals pay greater or lesser attention to certain particular stimuli in the social environment. These stimuli are of course other members of the group. An early example of observations in this field came in Konrad Lorenz's work (1937) on jackdaws, which indicated that alarm calls are responded to differentially by the flock, only those given by dominant birds resulting in the rising of the group.

A general theory of attention paid among group members was formulated by Michael Chance (1967), who used the idea of selective visual attention paid to other (primate) group members primarily as a framework to describe status among members of the group; but he also suggested that the way in which the attention of the animals was distributed underlay all social processes occurring within the group. The patterns of attention form what Chance called an attention structure, which served as more than simply an index of social status. This extension of attention structure forms the basis of Hinde's criticism of the theory (1974).

In all analyses done to date on attention structure (e.g. Scruton and Herbert 1970, Pitcairn 1976, Hold 1976), the focal point of the research has been on measuring visual attention. So attention has come to mean visual attention, but it is clear from Chance's 1967 paper that this was not the original meaning. Primate attention, although primarily a question of visual awareness, is more precisely awareness dependent upon visual information; the latter is simply the most convenient observational measure of such information. The emphasis is upon awareness, not visual orientation. That information flow from general awareness is the basic unit of study was also evident in Chance's (1962) theory of CUT-OFF which predates atten-

tion structure theory by some five years. The basic proposition in this earlier article was that the animal regulates its own arousal level during social interaction by manipulating its visual attention and hence information input. The basic unit of information flow was also delineated by Pitcairn (1976, p. 53): 'to be able to maintain a spatial relationship with others, information must be available concerning the position, movements and behavior of conspecifics. Further, certain animals . . . will be of greater importance . . . than others . . . These statements form the logical basis of Chance's (1967) attention structure hypothesis . . . .'

Information flow is therefore the important central concept of attention structure. It is related to the selective attention among individuals and gives rise to the attention structure as an emergent property of the system:

ATTENTION STRUCTURE
↑
INFORMATION FLOW
↑
SELECTIVE ATTENTION

Attention structure emerges as an organizing principle (of the social structure of the group) because of the set of biases which operate on individual assessment of the relative importance of others within the group. Two of the many possible roles for the determination of this relative importance have been outlined by Pitcairn (1976). The first involves the gradations of information given by the actions of different individuals. For example it was noted that differently ranked female monkeys in a troop reacted in differing ways to the quiet (non-threatening) approach of the dominant male. Those (high-ranking) females which sat unconcernedly in that case, but moved off rapidly when the male was displaying, provided more information for onlookers about possible future events than did those who always retreated, no matter what the male was doing. The amount of attention paid to the high-ranking females is a result of their discriminant responses.

The second rule concerns the differential behavioral responses of animals themselves, which allow them to gather more or less information and hence to be able to make more or less discriminating judgments, and to modify their own future behavior. The retreating low-ranked female, for example, is not able to modify her behavior toward the dominant male because she does not receive differential information from his types of approach due to her own cut-off behavior. She is fixed in her way of behaving which lacks flexibility.

These rules of operation illustrate the ways in which a set of biases about individuals which comprise the group are ordered into a set of priorities which relate to the importance (or relevance) each individual has to the other members. The important feature then is the members' "attention-focusing quality . . . based on the adaptive strategy of securing the most relevant social information on which to base their own behaviour" (Chisholm 1976, p. 245). Some individuals may then act as "referents" (Pitcairn 1976), providing the model for others' behavior, exhibiting both an attention-focusing quality and acting as a resource in the sense of Seyfarth's model (see below).

Chance also suggests that different species exhibit different types of hierarchical action. What he calls AGONIC species have a rigid hierarchy in which the important lines of communication and information flow coincide with agonistic dominance. These species show inflexibility in behavior and the dominance hierarchies remain stable over considerable periods of time. In HEDONIC species, on the other hand, information flows along different lines, such as affiliation, and the group exhibits much greater flexibility as the social spacing of the individuals is not controlled by the agonistic (fight/flight) relations of agonic species. These principles seem to relate variations in group organization to the underlying principles of information flow and attention structure.

Another theory which relates social structure to the interest an individual arouses is Seyfarth's model (1977; 1980)

of the attractiveness of high rank. In this case, however, the model is strictly a resource model, rather than an information one. The central idea is that high-ranking individuals (in Seyfarth's work, females in a troop of vervet monkeys) win the highest proportion of disputes they enter and have relatively free access to scarce resources such as food. Other females, therefore, compete for access to these high-ranking females, in particular through grooming as this may lead to the development of close bonds with their superiors, which will in turn lead to their being tolerated at food sites and supported during disputes. This model is really the corollary of Chance's attention structure, concentrating on the functional component of close bonds, rather than the causal component of the information available to members of the group through others' actions.   TKP

Bibliography

Chance, M.R.A., 1962. An interpretation of some agonist postures. *Symposium of the Zoological Society of London* 8, 71–89.

——— 1967. Attention structure as the basis of primate rank orders. *Man* 2, 503–18. (Reprinted in Chance and Larsen, 1976).

——— and Larsen, R.R., 1976. *The social structure of attention.* London and New York: Wiley.

Chisholm, J.S., 1976. On the evolution of rules. In Chance and Larsen.

Hinde, R.A., 1974. *Biological bases of human social behaviour.* New York and London: McGraw Hill.

Hold, B.C.L., 1976. Attention structure and rank specific behaviour. In Chance and Larsen.

Lorenz, K., 1937. The companion in the birds' world. *Auk* 54, 245–73.

Pitcairn, T.K., 1976. Attention and social structure in *Macaca fascicularis.* In Chance and Larsen.

Scruton, D. and Herbert, J., 1970. The menstrual cycle and its effect on behaviour in the talapoin monkey (*Miopithecus talapoin*). *Journal of the Zoological Society of London* 162, 419–36.

Seyfarth, R.M., 1977. A model of social grooming among adult female monkeys. *Journal of theoretical biology* 65, 671–98.

——— 1980. The distribution of grooming and related behaviours among adult female vervet monkeys. *Animal behaviour* 28, 798–813.

Smuts, B.B. et al. 1985: *Primate societies.* Chicago: University of Chicago Press.

autonomic nervous system The portion of the peripheral nervous system that innervates visceral organs, glands, and blood vessels in the control of basic vegetative functions. Its cell bodies are arranged in ganglia outside the spinal cord. It consists of sympathetic and parasympathetic divisions. The sympathetic division receives preganglionic fibers from motor cells in the thoracic and lumbar sections of the spinal cord, while the parasympathetic division originates in the cranial and sacral sections. The sympathetic division is responsible for mobilizing bodily resources and organizing physical activity appropriate to exciting or emergency conditions. Sympathetic activation leads, for example, to increases in cardiac activity, blood flow to skeletal muscles, respiration rate, oxygen intake, and sweat gland activity to cool the body during exertion. Digestive processes and activities associated with a relaxed state are inhibited. In contrast, the parasympathetic division acts to conserve bodily resources and maintain a state of relative quiescence. Thus the effects of parasympathetic activation are opposite to those of sympathetic activation. In general, the two systems work in a correlated but antagonistic fashion to maintain an internal equilibrium. Autonomic activity is controlled by a part of the brain called the hypothalamus. It is closely associated with the action of various hormones, particularly the epinephrines and is important in aggression, fear and all aspects of emotion. DJM/GWi

Bibliography

Bullock, T.H. 1977: *Introduction to nervous systems.* New York: Freeman.

avoidance If a particular action or response causes the cancellation or postponement of an event that would otherwise have occurred, the action may be said to be an avoidance response. Avoidance of unpleasant or harmful consequences has obvious adaptive value, but has long seemed to pose a serious problem for theories of learning. A successful avoidance response is one which is followed by the absence of an aversive event; but, it was asked, how can the absence of an event, i.e. no event, be responsible for reinforcing conditioning? One solution is to point out that there is an important difference between no event occurring and no event occurring at a time when one was expected to occur (see EXPECTANCY). Another, adopted by TWO-FACTOR THEORIES (see LEARNING), is to assume that avoidance responses are reinforced because they reduce a state of FEAR classically conditioned to stimuli signaling the occurrence of the aversive event. A third, adopted by some radical behaviorists, is to describe the operations that appear to be required to reinforce avoidance responding and to eschew speculation about the inner processes of learning responsible. NJM

Bibliography

Mackintosh, N.J. 1983: *Conditioning and associative learning.* Oxford and New York: Oxford University Press.

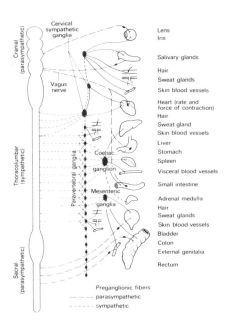

The autonomic nervous system

B

behavior genetics Is concerned with the effects of genes on the expression of behavior. Any form of genetic analysis requires the identification of differences. This may take the form of a clear distinction between the behavior of two individuals, or there may be continuous variation in the expression of some type of behavior within a population. Breeding tests or examination of relatives can then be made to establish how far such differences are genetic. Behavior genetics is not a unified field of investigation and within this broad outline are to be found a diverse set of aims and approaches which may have little contact with each other. Fuller and Thompson (1978) provide much the best survey of the whole field.

On the one hand, much research is directed toward the nature of gene action upon behavior. Single gene mutations are studied in convenient organisms such as *Drosophila* or mice, and attempts are made to relate behavioral differences between mutant and normal individuals to gene action on physiology, neural structure or neurochemisty. At the other end of the range the techniques of quantitative genetics are used to analyze the variation within a population for a complex trait like learning ability. This will certainly involve many genes and there is no possibility of identifying the action of any one; the aim may be to use genetic analysis to help partition the trait and distinguish between variation of genetic and environmental origin.

There is an inevitable diversity imposed on the field by the nature of the character being studied. Some branches of genetics are concerned with systems whose control is quite well known and where it is possible to relate the known action of genes (i.e. controlling the synthesis of proteins) to the end product. It is no coincidence that the most spectacular recent advances in genetics have come at its interface with molecular biology. Behavior presents many more problems for genetic analysis. Firstly, the phenotype itself is extremely diverse and indeed demands many completely different levels of analysis. We may be interested in the phototactic behavior of fruit flies, the control of balance and locomotion in mice, the maze-learning of rats, levels of aggression in different breeds of dog, courtship displays in chickens or spatial components of intelligence tests in human beings (all of which have been the subject of behavior-genetic analysis). Secondly, for many such phenomena the gap between gene action at the cellular level and the end-product we are studying is maximal. Nor can we expect to be able to generalize about the pathways along which genes operate to exercise their effects on such diverse behavioral phenotypes. Not all the pathways are of much interest in any case – a mutant mouse may show inferior avoidance learning, but turn out to have an elevated pain threshold to the electric shock which serves as reinforcer in the learning situation. It will always be necessary to screen out trivial effects of this type.

It has been argued that since behavior is usually manifested only intermittently as a sequence of events through time, its genetic basis exists only in so far as we can identify some underlying structure upon which it is based. Certainly some people feel that only by working with identified single genes of known effect can we hope to make any progress (see Quinn and Gould 1979 for an extreme statement of this reductionist position). However this type of approach is scarcely possible, except in one or two favored invertebrates whose genetics are well known, and much more that is of interest to psychologists has been achieved by behavior genetic analysis at other levels. We can consider some examples of each type.

Single-gene studies

There has been extensive work on *Drosophila melanogaster* where hundreds of mutant stocks are easily available, but these may have diverged genetically in other ways over generations of culturing, so it is often more useful to treat normal flies with a mutagen and screen the progeny for behavioral changes. Using this technique mutants have been isolated which affect a wide variety of behavioral phenotypes — phototaxis, locomotor activity, circadian rhythms, courtship behavior and learning ability (see Benzer 1983). Screening for behavior mutants requires some ingenuity and many trivial effects will have to be discarded along the way, e.g. flies which fail to respond because they cannot walk properly. The mutants affecting learning were mostly derived from a screening test in which flies learnt to avoid an odor which had been associated with electric shock. As their names, *dunce, amnesiac* and *turnip*, suggest their effect is to reduce learning and retention. It is obviously important to discover whether such mutants affect only olfactory CONDITIONING, or whether they act more generally. It is not easy to get a range of learning situations for *Drosophila* but some visual, and simple operant conditioning has proved possible; *dunce* and *amnesiac* flies show some learning ability in these situations but certainly reduced from normal (see Folkers 1982). The genes appear to have both general and specific effects and attempts are being made to link them with changes to brain biochemistry. Using special stocks of *Drosophila* it is possible to generate flies some of whose cells express the effects of a mutant gene while others are normal. Study of such mosaic individuals helps to reveal in which parts of the body the gene acts to produce its effect – its "primary focus"; (see Hotta and Benzer 1972).

Behavioral analysis involving many genes

The great majority of behavioral charac- ters will be affected by many genes and we may not be able to identify the effects of any particular locus. Nevertheless the study of different strains of breeds or inbred lines of animals has often yielded interesting results. Nearly always they show differences on a wide variety of behavioral measures which can be shown to be of genetic origin, but the scale and sometimes direction of such genetic effects can be markedly affected by the environment. For example Henderson (1970) compared mouse strains reared in complex or standard cage environments in a feeding situation which involved exploratory behavior and agility. The genetic contribution to variance between the strains was four times greater in mice from complex cages, indicating extreme gene/environment interaction. We must expect such interactions to be the rule in behavioral development.

Artificial selection for behavioral char- acters has often been successful and reveals that natural populations are vari- able for genes affecting behavioral traits. Aggression in mice, mating speed in *Drosophila*, maze learning in rats – all have responded strongly to selection. Tryon's experiment with maze learning was one of the first of its type. He produced "maze-dull" and "maze-bright" rats with virtually no overlap in performance. However when tested in other types of learning situation the brights performed no better or even less well than the dulls. Analysis showed that Tryon's selection had isolated factors relating to the main cues the rats responded to when learning the maze. The brights were genetically predisposed to concentrate on kinaesthetic cues in which Tryon's original maze was rich; the dulls' behavior was more visually control- led. Such a result contributed to our understanding of learning and illustrates the use of genetics as a tool for the study of behavior itself over and above its intrinsic genetic interest (see Manning 1976). By separating and exaggerating the effects of components which are normally associated together behavioral analysis is facilitated.   AWGM

15

Bibliography

Benzer, S. 1983: The Croonian Lecture. Genes, neurons and behaviour in *Drosophila*. *Proceedings of the Royal Society*, Series B.

Ehrman, L. and Parsons, P.A. 1976: *The genetics of behavior*. Sunderland, Mass.: Sinauer Associates.

Folkers, E. 1982: Visual learning and memory of *Drosophila melanogastor* wild type C-S and the mutants *dunce, amnesiac, turnip* and *rutabaga*. *Journal of insect physiology* 28. 535–39.

Fuller, John L. and Thompson, William R. 1978: *Foundations of behavior genetics*. St Louis: C.V. Mosby.

Henderson, N.D. 1970: Genetic influences on the behavior of mice can be obscured by laboratory rearing. *Journal of comparative physiological psychology*. 72. 505–11.

Hotta, Y. and Benzer, S. 1972: The mapping of behavior in *Drosophila* mosaics. *Nature* 240, 527–35.

Manning, A. 1976: The place of genetics in the study of behavior. In *Growing points in ethology*, eds. Paul P.G. Bateson and Robert A. Hinde. Cambridge and New York: Cambridge University Press.

Quinn, W.G. and Gould, J.L. 1979: Nerves and genes. *Nature* 278, 19–23.

Winter, R.E. and Wimer, C.C. 1985: Animal behaviour genetics: a search for the biological foundations of behaviour. In *Annual review of psychology*, vol.36, eds. M.R. Rosenzweig and L.W. Porter. Palo Alto: Annual Review Inc.

behaviorism *See* Skinner; Watson.

bond A relationship in which an individual maintains and restores proximity to an inanimate object (such as a nest) or to an animate object (such as a parent or mate) towards which certain behavior is exclusively or preferentially directed (Lorenz 1966; Wickler 1976). Ethology has been concerned mainly with bonding among conspecifics, which generally is mutual though not necessarily symmetric. Bonding partners recognize each other as individuals. Bond formation occurs rapidly between parent and young (see IMPRINTING). Among adults, it requires extended inter-actions (see COURTSHIP) and may then be regarded as an investment (Kummer 1978). Bonded partners tend to defend one another. Attachment theory holds that evolved behavioral and motivational systems underlie the differential preferences of individuals for forming particular bonds (Reynolds 1976).   HK

Bibliography

Gottlieb, G. 1971: *Development of species identification in birds*. Chicago: University of Chicago Press.

Hinde, R.A. 1983: *Primate social relationship: an integrated approach*. Oxford: Blackwell Scientific Publications.

Kummer, H. 1978: On the value of social relationships to nonhuman primates: a heuristic scheme. *Social science information* 17, 687–705.

Lorenz, Konrad Z. 1966: *On aggression*. New York: Harcourt, Brace and World Inc.; London: Methuen.

Reynolds, P.C. 1976: The emergence of early hominid social organisation: I. The attachment systems. *Yearbook of physical anthropology* 20, 73–95.

Wickler, W. 1976: The ethological analysis of attachment. *Zeitschrift für Tierpsychologie* 42, 12–28.

C

chimpanzee language *See* language, anthropoid ape.

classical conditioning *See* conditioning.

clock-driven behavior Rhythmic behavior driven by an endogenous clock is widespread in the animal kingdom. It is found in primitive single-celled animals and in humans. Research in the laboratory and in the field shows that many of the annual, lunar and daily RHYTHMS of behavior found in animals are maintained by clock mechanisms that are endogenous in the sense that the rhythm persists when the animal is isolated from all possible environmental time cues. It is not sufficient, however, merely to isolate an animal in a laboratory under conditions of constant temperature, photoperiod, etc. Exogenous factors such as barometric pressure or cosmic radiation, could possibly be used by animals to keep time, and it is never possible to be sure that all such factors have been excluded. Before concluding that a rhythm is truly endogenous additional evidence is required. Experiments in which the rhythm is directly manipulated, or which control for environmental influences by transporting the experimental preparation around the globe, fall into this category.

In many cases an exogenous *zeitgeber* (time-giver) is responsible for maintaining synchrony between the endogenous rhythm and the cycle of environmental events. When an animal is isolated from the exogenous *zeitgeber* its endogenous clock drifts out of step with the environmental rhythm and is said to be free-running. Endogenous rhythms with a period of about one day are generally called circadian rhythms (*circa*, about; *dies*,

a day); those of about one lunar month are called circalunar, and those of about a year are called circannual rhythms. Strictly, these terms also apply to the free-running rhythms, because the rhythm is likely to be exactly a day, etc. when under the influence of a *zeitgeber*. The action of the *zeitgeber* in synchronizing the clock to the rhythm of the environmental events is usually called entrainment.

Many animals adjust to seasonal changes in their environment by behavior that is based upon an endogenous circannual clock. Endogenous circannual rhythms have been established in some migratory birds. For example the garden warbler (*Sylvia borin*), the subalpine warbler (*Sylvia cantillans*) and the willow warbler (*Phylloscopus trochilus*) spend the summer in Europe and migrate across the Sahara desert to winter in southern Africa. If these birds are hand-raised from a few days after hatching they can be maintained under constant laboratory conditions, and the seasonal changes normally associated with migration still occur. Such captive birds show marked seasonal changes in bodyweight, food preferences, molt, testis size and migratory activity. Birds kept in cages exhibit a directional restlessness at the time when they would normally be migrating. The warblers usually migrate at night and rest during the day: in the laboratory they show nocturnal restlessness, hopping back and forth in the direction in which they would normally be migrating. The pattern of nocturnal restlessness conforms remarkably well with the pattern of activity that the migrating birds would normally show. The evidence suggests that the pattern of alternating activity and rest shown by the migratory birds is dictated by an endogenous circannual clock.

Hibernating mammals show a similar

phenomenon. The golden mantled ground squirrel (*Citellus lateralis*) and the woodchuck (*Mammota monax*) show marked circannual rhythms of bodyweight and activity when maintained under constant laboratory conditions for a number of years. These animals normally build up their bodyweight before hibernation and lose weight during hibernation. This pattern persists under laboratory conditions of constant photoperiod and environmental temperature. Circannual rhythms are evidently widespread in the animal kingdom, ranging from single-celled animals to mammals. The physiological mechanisms underlying circannual clocks are not well understood, and the same is true for lunar and tidal rhythms.

A number of marine animals exhibit endogenous rhythms which correspond to lunar or tidal cycles. The sea hare (*Aplysia californica*) has nerve cells which have a rhythm of activity with a period close to the tidal cycle. The green crab (*Carcinus maenas*) has a tidal rhythm of activity, being most active at high water. This rhythm persists in constant laboratory conditions for about a week, after which it fades away. If the crab is then cooled for six hours at just above freezing point the tidal rhythm is restored.

The most investigated rhythms are the circadian rhythms which have a period of about twenty-four hours under constant laboratory conditions. As with other endogenous rhythms, the typical periodicity drifts slightly from the norm when the clock is free-running under constant laboratory conditions. Under natural conditions a twenty-four-hour periodicity is maintained by some exogenous *zeitgeber* which serves continually to reset the endogenous clock and prevent it from drifting out of phase with the cycle of environmental change. For example, lizards raised from eggs in the laboratory show a free-running rhythm of activity with a period of just under twenty-four hours. Small (amplitude 1.6° C) daily fluctuations in temperature (the *zeitgeber*) are sufficient to entrain the animals in synchrony with the exact twenty-four-hour rhythm.

The physiological nature of the circadian clock is not well understood. It can occur in single-celled organisms such as the protozoan *Euglena*, which shows a rhythm of swimming activity that is synchronized with the motion of the sun, but persists when the organism is maintained in continuous darkness in the laboratory. However, many of the properties of single-celled protozoans are not found in single cells of multi-celled animals, and some rhythmic phenomena may be the result of interactions between cells. This may be the case in cockroaches in which the electrical activity of cells in the optic lobe seems to be of prime importance in the maintenance of circadian rhythms of activity (Brady 1969; Roberts 1974).

Ideas about clock mechanisms are complicated by evidence that behavior can be influenced by more than one clock simultaneously. For example in one experiment green crabs (*Carcinus maenas*) were raised in the laboratory, from eggs to adulthood, under a twenty-four-hour day-night regime. The crabs showed a circadian rhythm of activity, being active during the daylight hours. However, when they were given a cold shock treatment (see above) a tidal rhythm of activity also appeared, the cold shock having started an endogenous tidal clock which had lain dormant. Rats can be trained to work for food both every twenty-four hours and every 25 hours at the same time. To do this the rat has to maintain simultaneous twenty-four and twenty-five-hour rhythms of behavior, which must be based on different clocks.

The ability to keep in step with rhythmic environmental events is of considerable survival value to animals. Many animals have alternating periods of rest and activity which are synchronized with the opportunities for foraging and mating that are characteristic of the environment. The differences between diurnal and nocturnal animals is an obvious example. Animals specialized for daytime vision are at a disadvantage at night, because they are not able to forage efficiently and are in danger from predators. They usually sleep during the night in a place that is warm and safe from predators. Nocturnal animals are able to be profitably active at night. They sleep during the day in places that enable them to avoid both predators and climatic extremes, such as the heat of the desert.

Endogenous clocks play an important role in direction finding and NAVIGATION. Many birds require considerable powers of navigation on long migrations. The golden plover (*Pluvialis dominicus*), for example, breeds in Alaska and migrates to Argentina via Labrador. Much of the 11,000 km journey is over the Atlantic ocean. The green turtle (*Chelone mydas*) migrates between Brazil and Ascension Island 2,000 km out into the Atlantic ocean. Because many of the navigational aids used by animals, such as the sun, stars and moon, shift their positions in a cyclical manner, an endogenous clock is essential for precise navigation. An accurate chronometer which could be used at sea was long sought by human navigators for the same reasons. DJM

Bibliography

Brady, H. 1969: How are insect circadian rhythms controlled? *Nature* 223, 781–84.

Cloudsley-Thompson, John L. 1980: *Biological clocks, their functions in nature*. London: Weidenfeld & Nicolson.

McFarland, D.J. 1985: *Animal behaviour*. London: Pitman.

Pengelley, Eric T. ed. 1974: *Circannual clocks: annual biological rhythms*. New York and London: Academic Press.

Roberts, S.K. de F. 1974: Circadian rhythms in cockroaches. Effects of optic lobe lesions. *Journal of comparative physiology* 88, 21–30.

cognitive ethology A branch of ETHOLOGY introduced by Griffin (1976) concerned with awareness or mental experience in animals and its effects on their behavior. Griffin has suggested that animal behaviorists should reconsider the evolutionary continuity of mental characteristics between man and other animals based on evidence that animals employ some sort of internal imagery of their surroundings. Evidence from studies of problem solving and tool using suggests that some animals are capable of forming a cognitive map or model of their environment. When a horse scratches itself with a stick held in its mouth, it is difficult to explain the behavior without implying that the animal understands the spatial relationships between different parts of the body. When a chimpanzee makes a detour to attain a safe place from which to solicit food from a human, it is tempting to suppose that the chimpanzee has a mental map of the objects in its immediate environment. Practitioners assume that man is not uniquely endowed with conscious awareness, and that it is more likely than not that mental experiences in people and animals share important properties without being completely identical. However, some scientists argue that it is not necessary, or even scientifically permissible, to endow animals with mental awareness or cognitive abilities (see Roitblat et al. 1984). Cognitive ethology can be contrasted to ANTHROPOMORPHISM which is the attribution of human thoughts and feelings to animals. Griffin's working definitions in referring to animals are: *mental experience* – thought about objects and events that are remote in time and space from immediate sensations; *awareness* – the set of interrelated mental images of the flow of events; *intention* – a mental image of future events in which the intender places himself as participant and makes a choice as to which image he will try to bring to reality; and *consciousness* – the presence of mental images and their use by an animal to regulate its behavior.

PJA

Bibliography

Dawkins, M.S. 1980: *Animal suffering*. London: Chapman and Hall.

Griffin, Donald 1981: *The question of animal awareness: evolutionary continuity of mental experience*. 2nd edn. New York: Rockefeller University Press.

——— 1982: *Animal mind – human mind*. Berlin: Springer-Verlag.

Roitblat, H.L., Bever, T. and Terrace, H. 1984: *Animal cognition*. Hillsdale, N.J.: Erlbaum.

color vision Color vision is widespread in the animal kingdom and is well developed in some insects (e.g. bees), reptiles, birds and primates. Some animals such as the squirrel have only two types of cone pigment and thus have imperfect color vision similar to that of a color-blind person. Some reptiles and birds have cones containing colored oil droplets in addition to the visual pigments. It is thought that these droplets act as filters, and that the wide variety of receptor types found in these animals is the result of different combinations of photopigment and oil droplet. It is difficult for us to imagine how such animals see colors, although it is possible that their perception of water differs from ours, because the proportions of the various kinds of oil droplets vary between birds which have aquatic and terrestrial habitats.   DJM

Bibliography

Lythgoe, J.N. 1979: *The ecology of vision.* Oxford: Clarendon Press.

communication The term communication has been defined as "the passing of information from one animal to another (and so influencing its behavior) by means of signals that have evolved for the purpose" (Deag 1980). Animals communicate with each other for a variety of reasons, in a variety of ways, and with a variety of effects. Always, however, the form their signaling takes can be assumed to be a direct or indirect outcome of NATURAL SELECTION: direct in the case of highly stereotyped innate signals, indirect in the case of variable signals in which a large learning component is involved.

In general, animals lower in the phylogenetic scale communicate by means of signals that are under direct genetic control and relatively free of learned inputs. Such for example is the olfactory communication of moths, by the use of PHEROMONES. Bird communication sometimes involves learning, as for instance in chaffinch song, in which the nestling adds to an innate basis elements of the song of the parent bird. The communications of mammals are under enough genetic control to result in clear-cut, species specific

signals but are often marked by individuality, and a subtle relationship to the prevailing context indicating an advanced level of cognitive control of signal emission.

Without communication animals would lack any means of collecting information about each other and passing on information to others. If we ask why animals should collect and transmit information, the answer is that such activities will tend to increase inclusive FITNESS. For instance a male's REPRODUCTIVE SUCCESS is directly enhanced if he can detect that a female is in a sexually receptive condition. Likewise, a female's reproductive success will be increased if she ensures that she will be mated at the most fertile period by emitting signals to surrounding males. Hence natural selection has, in most animal groups, favored olfactory, auditory, tactile and visual signals that enable females to communicate about their sexual condition, and males to respond appropriately.

Indeed in some species, such as great-crested grebes, communication about sexual condition has been greatly extended into what can be called COURTSHIP behavior mating and pair-bond behavior afterwards. The same is true of many other species in which natural selection has established prolonged caring for the young by a single male and a single female, or in some cases a single male and a number of females. Such monogamy occurs commonly in birds such as geese and swans, and also, though less commonly, in mammals such as badgers and some primates such as gibbons. In all these cases the maintenance of the individual relationships on which these animal "families" are based consists of a complex set of communicative signals, in which information about personal identity is important, strangers being rejected by the bonded pair. Polygamous species include lions, deer and certain primates such as Hamadryas baboons.

Communication as described above has evolved because of its direct contribution to the reproductive success of individuals. This is not always the case. For instance worker bees, which are non-reproducing sterile females, are capable of some of the most complex kinds of communication in the animal world. Such females, or "workers" fly out to locate flowers. Having discovered a food source they return to the hive. They then perform a "round dance" if the distance to the flowers is less than 100 m or a "waggle dance" if it exceeds 100 m. The speed at which the waggle dance is performed, and the number of tail waggles it contains, give the distance to the flowers, while the orientation of axis of the dance on the comb surface replicates the angle of the sun to the flight path which leads to the flowers (see illustrations below, from von Frisch 1970).

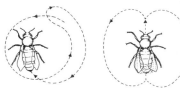

(a) round dance   (b) waggle dance

Such exceedingly precise communication is at first incomprehensible in the normal terms of natural selection, when we remember that worker bees do not reproduce. Why should it have evolved? The answer does not necessitate a recourse to theories of "mutual aid" as proposed by Kropotkin or to any other theory of group selection but can be understood as the outcome of genetic SELFISHNESS (Hamilton 1967, Dawkins 1976). Because of the nature of the reproductive process in bees, all workers are genetically very similar, and a successful genetic strategy is not for each female to reproduce individually but for one to reproduce while the rest become specialized feeders, nurses and so on. The latter has turned out, in some species, to be advantageous and in consequence the range of complex communicative processes that support it has evolved.

Besides communication within species, there are many curious features of communication that characterize prey-predator relations. These mostly relate to methods of deception or surprise. Since only prey that can avoid capture survive to reproduce, natural selection has produced extensive patterns of MIMICRY and camouflage. These are communicative in the sense that they relay and are received as false information by the predator. For its part, the predator's main problem is to avoid communicating its presence, owing to the existence of innate recognition reactions in the prey. Predatory activity often consists of slow, stealthy approach, or observation from a distance, followed by sudden attack before the prey can escape. This is true for both mammals such as cats and birds such as hawks, though not for some predators such as wolves or hyenas.

Finally we can consider the communication systems of our closest relatives and of ourselves. Group-living primates such as macaques and chimpanzees engage in a wide range of facial-visual signaling, as well as in a smaller range of tactile, auditory and olfactory signals. The facial expressions of these higher primates in many ways resemble those of man. Expressions such as the "silent bared-teeth" display have been linked in an

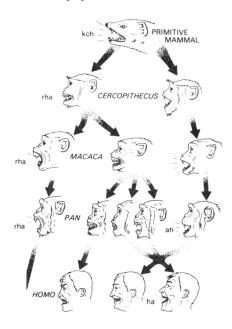

evolutionary progression to the human smile (see illustration, previous page from Van Hooff 1972). The rather spontaneous and world-wide distribution of some human facial expressions has led Eibl-Eibesfeldt (1970) to conclude that they are innate. Probably, indeed, we should assume an innate basis to some human non-verbal communicative signals, such as the laugh, the smile, the frown, the eyebrow-flash, and the facial expressions of weeping and fear. But it is a mistake to go on from this to assume that human communication is fundamentally non-verbal, with a mere linguistic overlay. Those non-verbal elements that have an innate basis provide the background, not the foreground, to human communication.

VR

Bibliography
Dawkins, R. 1976: *The selfish gene*. Oxford: Oxford University Press.
Deag, J.M. 1980: *Social behavior of animals*. London: Edward Arnold.
Eibl-Eibesfeldt, I. 1970: *Ethology, the biology of behaviour*. New York: Holt, Rinehart and Winston.
Halliday, T.R. and Slater, P.J.B. 1983: *Animal behaviour*, vol. 2. *Communication*. New York: Freeman.
Hamilton, W.D. 1967: The genetical evolution of social behaviour. *Journal of theoretical biology* 7, 1–52.
Van Hooff, J.A.R.A.M. 1972: The phylogeny of laughter and smiling. In *Non-verbal communication*, ed. R.A Hinde. Cambridge: Cambridge University Press.
Von Frisch, K. 1970: *Bees, their vision, chemical senses, and language*. Ithaca, N.Y.: Cornell University Press.
Sebeok, T. ed. 1977: *How animals communicate*. Bloomington, Indiana: Indiana University Press.

concept An animal can be said to have formed a concept if it can be shown that it responds consistently to a particular aspect of a variety of stimuli presented in many different contexts. For example it has been shown that pigeons can develop the concept of "human being" regardless of precisely what the humans look like or what they are doing. This was demonstrated by training pigeons to peck a key whenever they were shown a colored slide of a human being (which could be child, man, woman etc.) but not when they were shown animals, buildings or other pictures without human beings. The correct performance of pigeons on this and similar tasks shows an ability to form generalized concepts, not merely to respond to particular patterns.

MSD

Bibliography
Dickinson, A. 1980: *Contemporary animal learning theory*. Cambridge: Cambridge University Press.
Herrnstein, R.J., Loveland, D.H. and Cable, C. 1976: Natural concepts in the pigeon. *Journal of experimental psychology: animal behavior processes* 2, 285–302.
Lea, S.E.G. 1984: Complex general process learning in mammalian vertebrates. In *The biology of learning*, eds. P. Marler and H. Terrace. Berlin and New York: Springer-Verlag.

conditioning A form of associative learning which results in changes in an organism's behavior as a consequence of exposure to certain temporal relations between events. It is customary to distinguish two forms of conditioning, classical or Pavlovian conditioning on the one hand, and instrumental or operant conditioning on the other. In experimental studies of both varieties, the experimenter presents an event of biological or motivational significance usually termed a reinforcer; it may be food, water, or access to a sexual partner; or it may be a painful or distressing event such as a brief electric shock or the administration of a drug which causes nausea. Classical and instrumental conditioning differ in the other event with which this reinforcer is associated.

In classical conditioning (see PAVLOV) the occurrence of a reinforcer is signaled by the presentation of a particular stimulus. In Pavlov's original experiments (1927) the reinforcer was either the delivery of food or an injection of a weak solution of acid into the dog's mouth, both of which caused the dog to salivate.

Because they unconditionally elicited this response, they were called unconditional stimuli (abbreviated to US), and the salivation they elicited was an unconditional response (UR). The delivery of the reinforcer or US was preceded by the presentation of a neutral stimulus, a flashing light, a tone or buzzer or the ticking of a metronome. After a number of joint presentations of, say, the light and food, the dog would start salivating as soon as the light was turned on, before the food arrived. The light was referred to as a conditional stimulus (CS) and the response of salivating to the CS was called a conditional response (CR); the term refers to the fact that the CR is conditional upon the joint presentation of CS and US: if the light were now presented alone for a number of trials, it would lose its ability to elicit salvation. A mistranslation of "conditional" as "conditioned" meant that in English the CS and CR were referred to as a conditioned stimulus and conditioned response, and the verb "to condition" was derived to refer to the process responsible for the establishment of the new CR.

Classical conditioning experiments have employed a variety of events as CS and US, and have recorded CRs ranging from discrete, reflexive responses such as salivation to food or acid as the US, blinking to a puff of air directed at the eye or flexion of the leg to a shock to the foot, to more general changes in behavior such as approaching and contacting an object associated with the delivery of food, withdrawal from an object associated with danger, or rejection of a normally palatable food whose ingestion has been artificially associated with illness and nausea. The defining criterion for saying that these are all experiments on classical conditioning is that the experimenter's rules for delivering the reinforcer or US make no reference to the behavior of his subjects. In Pavlov's experiments the dog receives food on every conditioning trial regardless of its behavior when the CS is turned on; the puff of air is directed at the eye, the shock applied to the animal's foot, or the emetic drug injected after the animal has consumed some food, and

there is nothing the animal can do to prevent these things happening.

This marks the distinction between classical and instrumental conditioning. In an instrumental experiment the delivery of the reinforcer depends on the experimental subject's performance of a designated, instrumental response. The first systematic study of instrumental conditioning was by Thorndike (1911), who trained a variety of animals to escape from a puzzle box and thus gain access to food by pressing on a catch, pulling a loop of string or undoing a latch. The most commonly used procedure for studying instrumental conditioning is that developed by SKINNER (1938): a rat is placed in a small chamber and presses a bar or lever protruding from one wall in order to obtain a pellet of food delivered automatically into a recess in the wall. As in Pavlov's original experiments, the reinforcer is food, but here the delivery of the reinforcer is not dependent on the occurrence of a CS, but rather on the rat's performance of a particular response, that of pressing the lever. The experimenter may be said to be rewarding this response, or if the reinforcer is an aversive or painful event, punishing it, and instrumental conditioning has occurred if the subject's behavior changes as a consequence of these "contingencies of reinforcement" (in Skinner's phrase), that is to say if the subject comes to perform the rewarded response or refrains from performing the punished response.

The difference between classical and instrumental conditioning is thus defined in terms of the experimenter's rules for delivering a reinforcer. But this is hardly sufficient to prove that there is any fundamental distinction between the two. The fact that the experimenter can describe his experimental manipulations or operations in different ways does not imply that the subject's description matches the experimenter's or that fundamentally different processes are responsible for the changes in behavior observed in the two cases. But many psychologists have followed Skinner's lead in believing that the operational distinction may have some further significance. In the end the question is a theoretical one: whether a single theory of conditioning can encompass all the phenomena of both types of experiment.

An adequate theory of conditioning must explain why Pavlov's dog starts salivating to the CS. Pavlov's own explanation, expressed rather more clearly by his Polish successor Konorski (1948), was rather simple. Salivation is part of the set of responses unconditionally elicited by food; as a consequence of the experimenter's pairing a CS with the delivery of food the two events are associated by the subject; an association of the two events ensures that the presentation of one will activate a representation of the other; the presentation of the CS will activate a representation of food and this activation will elicit salivation just as it would have if generated by the presentation of the food itself. Classical conditioning thus depends upon the establishment of an association between CS and US, and the CS thereby acquiring the ability to elicit responses normally elicited by the US alone.

It does not seem easy to apply this explanation to a case of instrumental conditioning: when a rat is rewarded with food for pressing a lever, this new response, not previously elicited by food, increases in probability. It is true that the last thing that will normally happen before a pellet of food is obtained is that the rat will have been in contact with the lever, sniffing it or touching it with its paw, but it remains to show how any association between these stimuli and the delivery of food could generate, via the Pavlovian mechanisms outlined above, the efficient instrumental response that rapidly emerges from the rat's initially accidental or exploratory contacts.

In at least some cases, however, it turns out to be possible to apply a Pavlovian analysis. Another common instrumental procedure is to train pigeons to peck a small illuminated plastic disk on the wall of a Skinner box, rewarding them with food whenever they perform the required response. But pecking is, in fact, the pigeon's natural consummatory (or unconditional) response to food, and it turns out that the pigeon will peck the disk just as rapidly if the experimenter simply arranges to illuminate it for a few seconds before he delivers food regardless of the pigeon's behavior. The association between illumination of the disk (CS) and the delivery of food (US) is sufficient to ensure that the former comes to elicit the pecking response normally elicited by the latter alone. Here then is a purely Pavlovian explanation of what had always been regarded as a case of instrumental conditioning (Brown and Jenkins 1968).

But the fact remains that this analysis will not easily work for many cases of instrumental conditioning. It cannot easily explain why rats learn to press levers for food, still less why they can be trained to press the lever with a particular force (Notterman and Mintz 1965) or to hold it down for a particular length of time (Platt, Kuch and Bitgood 1973). It is equally unsuccessful at explaining why a dog should learn to flex a leg either to obtain food (Miller and Konorski 1928), or to avoid a puff of air directed at its ear (Fonberg 1958). Here and elsewhere instrumental conditioning occurs in accordance with Thorndike's law of effect which stated that responses are modified by the consequences, increasing in probability if followed by a satisfying consequence, decreasing if followed by an aversive consequence. Whether the law of effect is a theory or a circular description of observed data has from time to time been disputed, but it nevertheless captures what we intuitively see as the essential feature of voluntary actions – that they are performed because of their consequences.

If we cannot explain or describe instrumental conditioning without recourse to the law of effect, then the distinction between classical and instrumental conditioning can only be denied by dismissing Pavlov's account of classical conditioning and applying the law of effect here also. Several psychologists, notably Hull (1943), have attempted to do just this, but their attempts do not seem entirely successful. A pigeon conditioned to peck a disk whose illumination has served as a CS signaling food, will continue to do so even if the delivery of food is cancelled on those trials when the pigeon pecks at the disk. The only way for the pigeon to earn food now is to refrain from pecking when the disk is illuminated, but it is unable to do so. The association between light and food remains strong, so the pigeon cannot help approaching and pecking the light in spite of the adverse consequences of its actions (Williams and Williams 1969). There are many other examples of involuntary responses being conditioned by Pavlovian procedures in spite of their having adverse consequences. It is difficult to see how such conditioning could be analyzed in terms of the law of effect.

Unless a new, all-embracing theory is proposed, therefore, there is reason to believe that the distinction between classical and instrumental conditioning is real and important. This is not entirely surprising, for it corresponds roughly to the distinction we intuitively draw between involuntary and voluntary responses. Involuntary responses are evoked or elicited by stimuli which have been associated with, and thus make us think of, certain consequences: we cannot help salivating if we imagine someone squeezing a lemon into our mouth, or help blushing or sweating if we recall an embarrassing or frightening incident. Voluntary actions are those which we perform or refrain from carrying out because we have learned what their consequences are and because of the value we put on those consequences. We may often be mistaken in our belief that a particular response is voluntary or involuntary: the pigeon's pecking response seemed a voluntary act until experimental analysis suggested otherwise; and there is good evidence that responses we should normally regard as involuntary can sometimes be brought under voluntary control (this is the basis of biofeedback). It is possible that the difference is one of degree rather than of kind. But that does not diminish its importance, and this suggests that we should acknowledge the reality of the two types of conditioning. NJM

Bibliography
Brown, P.L. and Jenkins, H.M. 1968: Autoshaping of the pigeon's key peck. *Journal of the experimental analysis of behavior* 11, 1–8.

Fonberg, E. 1958: Transfer of instrumental avoidance reactions in dogs. *Bulletin de l'academie polonaise des sciences* 6, 353–56.

Hull, Clark L. 1943: *Principles of behavior*. New York and London: Appleton-Century.

Konorski, Jerzy 1948: *Conditioned reflexes and neuron organization*. Cambridge: Cambridge University Press. Reprinted 1968. New York: Hafner.

*Mackintosh, N.J. 1983: *Conditioning and associative learning*. Oxford and New York: Oxford University Press.

Miller, S. and Konorski, J. 1928: Sur une forme particulière des reflexes conditionnels. *Comptes rendus des séances de la Société de Biologie* 99, 1155–57.

Notterman, Joseph M. and Mintz, Donald E. 1965: *Dynamics of response*. New York and London: Wiley.

Pavlov, Ivan P. 1927: *Conditioned reflexes*. London: Oxford University Press. Reprinted 1960. New York and London: Dover.

Platt, J.R., Kuch, D.O. and Bitgood, S.C. 1973: Rats' lever-press durations as psychophysical judgments of time. *Journal of the experimental analysis of behavior* 19, 239–50.

*Schwartz, B. 1978: *Psychology of learning and behavior*. New York: Norton.

Skinner, Burrhus F. 1938: *The behavior of organisms*. New York and London: Appleton-Century.

Thorndike, Edward L. 1911: *Animal intelligence*. New York: Macmillan. Reprinted 1965. New York and London: Hafner.

Williams, D.R. and Williams, H. 1969: Automaintenance in the pigeon: sustained pecking despite contingent non-reinforcement. *Journal of the experimental analysis of behavior* 12, 511–20.

conflict A state in which an animal is simultaneously motivated in two or more incompatible ways. A hungry rat hesitates at a short distance from the end of a runway where it has sometimes received food, sometimes electric shock. Two rival male birds face each other across the boundary between their territories. In these cases the conflict can be expressed generally as approach/avoidance, or more specifically, in the case of the rival birds, as attack/escape. When in conflict an animal may adopt a compromise posture which reveals elements of both underlying motivations. The particular compromise posture held in territorial disputes is called "threat", and elements of postures adopted during aggressive attacks and during flight can be identified. This has been taken as evidence that aggressive and escape DRIVES are independent of each other but interact to determine the final form of a behavior pattern.

(See APPROACH/AVOIDANCE CONFLICT.)

AWGM

Bibliography
Hinde, R.A. 1970: *Animal behavior*. 2nd edn. New York and London: McGraw-Hill.

consummatory behavior The behavior that terminates a period of APPETITIVE BEHAVIOR. A period of FORAGING may be terminated by the consummatory behavior of feeding. Scientists differ in opinion as to the extent to which consummatory behavior *per se* is instrumental in bringing appetitive behavior to a temporary close. Episodes of copulatory behavior, for example, are clearly terminated by ejaculation, which may be regarded as the consummatory act. In other cases, however, the situation is not so clear. Behavior such as foraging, or nest-building may be punctuated by bouts of grooming or VIGILANCE on an apparently pre-programmed basis. It is not therefore always the case that episodes of appetitive behavior are terminated by a consummatory act. DJM

conventional and epideictic behavior These terms were given particular meanings by V.C. Wynne-Edwards (1962) in his carefully worked out theory of group selection. According to Wynne-

Edwards, animals control their own population densities and thereby avoid extinction. They do this by using a wide variety of homeostatic mechanisms, and these mechanisms involve competing for secondary resources such as territory instead of for food itself. It is these secondary resources that Wynne-Edwards described as "conventional", so "conventional behavior" includes territorial behavior and other behavior that leads to SPACING. The term "epideictic" refers to the effects of the DISPLAY which is involved in such activity. According to Wynne-Edwards's theory, population control comes about because when a certain number of individuals are displaying territorially, remaining potential breeders are deterred by the epideictic displays and forgo reproduction for the season.

Most ethologists now favor an alternative interpretation of such territoriality, stripping it of its group-homeostasis functions and regarding it as no more than a result of the normal inter-individual competition that forms the basis of natural selection.

(See also SOCIOBIOLOGY.) VR

Bibliography
Emlen, J.M. 1984: *Population biology: the coevolution of population dynamics and behavior*. New York: Macmillan.
Wynne-Edwards, V.C. 1962. *Animal dispersion in relation to social behavior*. Edinburgh: Oliver and Boyd; New York: Hafner.

cooperation Strong cooperation, individuals working together to achieve a common purpose, is found in social insects, and, to some extent, in a variety of other animal groups. It has been calculated that a termite mound, scaled up in relation to the size of a termite, is equivalent to a human skyscraper two miles high. As in great feats of human architecture, the termites achieve this by cooperation. NATURAL SELECTION favors cooperation among social insect workers because the workers do not reproduce themselves, but are close genetic relatives of the reproductive members of their colony. A worker has nothing to gain by working for itself. All the workers gain, genetically speaking, from the survival and reproduction of the whole colony. Colony survival is served by individual cooperation. Therefore natural selection favors cooperative tendencies among workers, to the point of total self-abnegation at the individual level. The same is not true of most animals other than social insects. Rudimentary cooperation occurs in, for example, hunting bands of carnivores like lions and wolves, but this is best seen as enlightened self-interest rather than cooperation for the benefit of the whole colony. An individual hyena gets more to eat if it hunts with a group than if it hunts alone. This is because a group can bring down much bigger prey, and each individual therefore gets more to eat than it would alone. Cooperation due to "enlightened self-interest" even occurs between members of different species. Honey guides are small African birds that have evolved the habit of leading ratels (honey badgers) or humans to wild bees' nests. The birds are good at finding nests but bad at breaking into them. The honey badgers and humans are good at breaking in but bad at finding bees' nests. Both partners benefit from the cooperation, the mammal eating the honey and the bird the grubs. Cooperation for mutual self-interest can also evolve if one partner does not benefit immediately, but only has a chance of benefiting at some time in the future, in which case it is known as "reciprocal altruism". There are theoretical problems with reciprocal altruism, but an adequate Darwinian rationale for it exists, and there is suggestive evidence that it occurs both within and between species. (See also ALTRUISM.)   RD

Bibliography
Brown, J.L. 1975: *The evolution of behavior.* New York: W.W. Norton.

*Dawkins, R. 1976: *The selfish gene.* Oxford: Oxford University Press.

Grafen, A. 1984: Natural selection, kin selection and group selection. In *Behavioral ecology.* 2nd edn, eds. J. Krebs and N.B. Davies. Oxford: Blackwell Scientific Publications.

coordination The harmonious control of muscular movements is achieved through two basic processes: central control and peripheral control. Central control involves a precise set of instructions issued by the central nervous system and followed by the muscles. The swallowing movements of humans are coordinated in this manner. Peripheral control involves FEEDBACK from sense organs in the muscles, which influences the instructions sent out from the central nervous system. For example, the coordination of limb movements in mammals is dependent upon the postural reflexes, which are based upon information from the muscles. In most cases coordination is achieved through a mixture of central and peripheral control. In the coordination of swimming movements in fish, for example, the central nervous system provides a rhythm that passes down the trunk in waves, determining the rhythmic movements of the tail and fins. In the bony fish (Teleostei), however, the fins can beat at different frequencies under certain circumstances, although they retain a degree of relative coordination.   DJM

Bibliography
Bush, B.M.H. and Clarac, F. 1985: *Coordination of motor behaviour.* Cambridge: Cambridge University Press.

Hinde, R.A. 1970: *Animal behavior.* 2nd edn. New York: McGraw-Hill.

courtship Behavior patterns, often very elaborate and conspicuous, that precede, accompany and sometimes follow the act of mating. The duration of courtship varies greatly, from several days to a few seconds, depending on the extent to which males and females establish durable pair bonds. Several functions may be ascribed to courtship, such as attraction of a mate, often over a considerable distance, stimulation of the mate to sexual receptivity, and the synchronization of mating activities so that the sexual act occurs at the optimum moment. Displays used in courtship tend to show typical intensity and a high degree of species specificity, features which enable animals to recognize and mate only with members of their own species. The form of some courtship behavior suggests that the motivation of the animal performing it involves a conflict between aggression, fear and sexual behavior. (See also COMMUNICATION; REPRODUCTIVE BEHAVIOR.)   TRH

Bibliography
Bastock, M. 1967: *Courtship; a zoological study.* London: Heinemann Educational Books.
Deag, J.M. 1980: *Social behaviour of animals.* London: Edward Arnold.

critical periods An ethological concept designating a fixed time in early development when the young organism is open to forms of learning that will be essential for social adaptation and adult life. A well known example is learning of conspecifics through IMPRINTING in newly hatched goslings. In recent years the concept has been broadened to a sensitive period, to suggest simply a susceptibility for learning at a particular time rather than a crucial occasion for it.   GEB

Bibliography
Bateson, P.P.G. 1979: How do sensitive periods arise and what are they for? *Animal behaviour* 27, 470–86.
Colombo, J. 1982: The critical period concept: Research, methodology, and theoretical issues. *Psychological bulletin* 91, 260–75.

culture Patterns of behavior within a species whose transmission is totally dependent on non-genetic processes. This definition can be compared with that found in social anthropology, in which "culture" means the ways in which a group has come to solve the problems of life and has brought into existence normatively sanctioned modes of action. It also differs from the lay definition in which "culture" implies intellectual sophistication. In ethology, culture is taken to refer to behavior patterns arising spontaneously by individual inventiveness and transmitted to others mainly as a result of learning. A well-known case is the potato- and seed-washing by Japanese macaques on Koshima Islet, S. Japan. McGrew and Tutin (1978) have suggested eight necessary criteria of culture: innovation, dissemination, standardization, durability, diffusion, tradition, non-subsistence, and natural adaptiveness.   VR

Bibliography
Boesch, C. and Boesch, H. 1983: Optimization of nut-cracking with natural hammers by wild chimpanzees. *Behaviour* 83, 265–86.
Bonner, J.T. 1980: *The evolution of culture in animals.* Princeton: Princeton University Press.
McGrew, W.C. and Tutin, C.E.G. 1978. Evidence for a social custom in wild chimpanzees? *Man* 13, 234–51.

curiosity A voluntary form of exploration. The term is not used for reflex forms of exploration such as the ORIENTING RESPONSE.

Animals tend to investigate novel objects or situations by making initially tentative exploratory acts, followed by more bold investigation as the animal becomes more confident. Curiosity thus involves an element of fear combined with motivation. Animals often approach other animals of which they are undoubtedly frightened. Black-headed gulls (*Larus ridibundus*) will approach the centre of disturbance caused by a fox entering the colony. Gazelle and wildebeest will often approach and stare at predators such as hyena and cheetah (Kruuk 1972). It seems that fear of the unknown is an important aspect of curiosity.

Exploratory behavior, including PLAY, may appear to be motivated by curiosity, but care is needed in interpreting this kind of behavior. For example monkeys will learn a puzzle task which enables them to look out of a window in their cage. Such behavior may be motivated by curiosity, but other experiments show that monkeys will learn to manipulate puzzle games without any obvious reward. Thus it may be that looking out of a window is regarded by the monkey merely as part of the puzzle game. Similarly, many animals tentatively explore and sample novel food. This may look like curiosity, but studies of FOOD SELECTION show that such sampling is an important part of learning to avoid poisonous foods, and is part of normal feeding activity.

Konrad Lorenz (1971) maintains that readiness for novel experience, defines curiosity and is characteristic of creatures which have evolved to be unspecialized. Creatures such as the raven, the rat and man can adapt to a wide range of environments and they also show the greatest curiosity. Humans often retain curiosity throughout the lifespan, in other species it may or may not be prevalent only in the earliest stages of development.   GEB/DJM

Bibliography

Kruuk, Hans 1972: *The spotted hyena: a study of predation and social behavior*. Chicago and London: University of Chicago Press.

Lorenz, Konrad 1970–1: *Studies in animal and human behavior*. 2 vols. London: Methuen; Cambridge, Mass.: Harvard University Press.

McFarland, D.J. 1985: *Animal behaviour*. London: Pitman.

cut off An ethological term for a posture which removes a social opponent, or partner, out of sight of the actor, thereby reducing the actor's arousal in a conflict situation and increasing the potential flexibility of its own behavior.

In the course of studies on the social behavior of laboratory rats Chance and Grant discovered that when an intruder rat was introduced to the home territory or cage of another rat an APPROACH/ AVOIDANCE CONFLICT was very evident. In close encounters the rats would adopt postures which involved raising the head so that they were unable to see each other.

The literature on the courtship of birds (e.g. several species of gulls, and especially the Booby (*Sula spp.*)), includes encounters in which either one or both of the participants could not see the other. Clearly, therefore, even if these postures were produced by conflict in the way that DISPLACEMENT ACTIVITIES are, the circumstances in which they occurred meant that they could have no effective signal value and hence an alternative explanation was sought in "cut off" which would enable the actor more readily to change its own behavior.

The concept is given added credibility from the known neurological facts about the separation of sensory (afferent) impulses in mammals along two pathways. On the one hand impulses pass via the medullary reticular and intralaminar nuclei into the cortex by a diffuse projection, bringing about arousal of the cortex and mid brain. On the other, there is a point-to-point projection to the cortex via the limniscal systems providing detailed information about the stimulus source. Hence, "cutting off" the stimulus will reduce arousal even if the price is a loss of information.

Kenneth J. Wilz, studying the action of dorsal pricking in the courtship of the three-spined stickleback (*Gasterosteus aculeatus L.*), concluded that by temporarily discouraging the female from approaching the nest the male prevents her from further arousing his own aggression towards her. In this way the male effectively controls his own conflicting tendencies in favor of leading her in courtship rather than being aggressive to her. Dorsal pricking, which involves the male rising up beneath the female with the spines of his back raised enabling him to fend her off without seeing her or approaching her directly as in an aggressive encounter, is a form of "cut off".

The possibility now has to be considered that what the performance of displacement activities does for controlling arousal in the motor system, "cut off" does for the control of arousal in the sensorium.
MRAC

Bibliography

Chance, M.R.A. 1962: An interpretation of some agonistic postures: the role of "cut off" acts and postures. *Symposia of the Zoological Society of London*, 8, 71–89.

Tinbergen, N. 1954: In *Evolution as a process*, eds. Julian S. Huxley, Alister C. Hardy, and Edmund B. Ford. London: George Allen and Unwin.

Wilz, K.J. 1970: Self-regulation of motivation in the three-spined stickleback (*Gasterosteus acculeatus L.*).*Nature*, 226, 465–466.

D

Darwin, Charles Born in Shrewsbury in 1809, the fifth child of a successful physician and Susannah, the daughter of the potter Josiah Wedgwood. Darwin had, as one might say, distinctly rural origins. His father tried him in various educational establishments, including Shrewsbury School and Edinburgh University. He began the study of medicine at the latter institution, but found the dissections unbearably disturbing. As a last attempt to find him a profession he was despatched to Cambridge to study for the church. There he came under the influence of J.S. Henslow who fired him with the enthusiasm for natural history which marked the rest of his life.

His thinking was greatly stimulated by his world-wide travels as a naturalist on HMS Beagle from 1831 to 1836. During the voyage geology was as much Darwin's interest as biology. He can be credited with building up extensive support for Lyell's "gradualist" view of geological change. But from hindsight, the most important single investigation of the voyage was Darwin's detailed mapping of the varieties of species found on the Galapagos Islands. It was here that the idea for a process of change towards environmental adaptation first began to become clear to him. However it was not until his return to England and his reading (on 28 September 1838) of Malthus' *Essay on population* that he came to a full understanding of the mechanism of natural selection.

His book, *The origin of species* published in 1859, was, together with Mendelian genetics, the foundation of the modern theory of organic evolution. It proposed the gradual evolution of distinct species from common ancestors via NATURAL SELECTION and the inheritance of minutely variable characteristics. Alfred Russell Wallace had independently formulated the same theory and the joint presentation of their papers to the Linnaean Society in 1858 has become legendary.

Darwin explicitly extended his evolutionary theory to human beings in *The descent of man*, published in 1871. Nevertheless the germinal ideas of both books can be traced back to the late 1830s in Darwin's unpublished notebooks (Gruber 1974). He probably delayed publication in order to build up evidence against the storm of scientific and religious controversy which he correctly estimated that the books would bring about. Darwin published the results of many other researches, including books on the effects of domestication on plants and animals, and the behavior of earthworms. Of most interest to psychologists have been *The expression of the emotions in man and animals* (1872), which foreshadows much later work on comparative ETHOLOGY and non-verbal communication; and *A biographical sketch of an infant* (1877), based on earlier diary observations of the behavior and development of his first child.

After returning from his voyages Darwin married his cousin, Emma Wedgwood. But he soon succumbed to a mysterious illness that obliged him to live the rest of his life almost wholly within the family circle. Once passed off as some form of neurosis it is now thought to have been Chaja's disease, endemic in those parts of South America that he had visited on his travels. He died in 1882.   PKS/RHa

Bibliography

Gruber, H.E. 1974: *Darwin on man: a psychological study of scientific creativity*. London: Wildwood House; New York: E.P. Dutton.

Thorpe, W.H. 1979: *The origins and rise of ethology*. London: Heinemann.

decision making The process of selecting a course of action from a behavioral repertoire. Animals usually have the motivation to perform more than one activity at a time, but are capable of only one. There must therefore be a process by which overt expression is given to one aspect of behavior while others are temporarily suppressed. This is the decision making process.

In investigating decision making in animals it is necessary to take account of the animal's motivational state, including its evaluation of external circumstances; the importance, utility, or notional cost, given by the animal to the relevant aspects of the situation; and the optimality criterion or set of decision-rules used by the animal to trade-off the various possibilities (McFarland 1977).

Research on decision making in animals is usually aimed at discovering the decision-rules employed and attempts to evaluate these in terms of the problems facing the animal in its natural environment. DJM

Bibliography

Krebs, J.R. and McCleery, R.H. 1984: Optimisation in behavioural ecology. In *Behavioural ecology*. 2nd edn, eds. J.R. Krebs and N.B. Davies. Oxford: Blackwell Scientific Publications.
McFarland, D.J. 1977: Decision-making in animals. *Nature* 269, 15–21.

delay-learning phenomenon (or delayed association) Denotes any case where associative learning depends on bridging a long interval between events. For example CONDITIONING usually proceeds with difficulty if the events to be associated (conditional and unconditional stimuli, response and reinforcer) are separated by an unfilled interval of more than a few seconds. However in certain cases, notably in associations between the quality of a food and later gastrointestinal symptoms, longer delays of minutes or hours can be tolerated. There is disagreement as to whether this phenomenon reflects a specialized adaptation of food-related learning, or unusually low levels of INTERFERENCE during the delay. Delayed-response learning, where a choice response must be made on the basis of a cue given some time previously, has been used as an assay of memory capacity and brain lesion effects in animals. (Not to be confused with Pavlov's term "delay conditioning" meaning any procedure where conditional stimulus onset precedes the unconditional stimulus without any gap between them.) EAG

Bibliography

Braveman, N.S. and Bronstein, P. eds. 1985: *Experimental assessments and clinical applications of conditioned food aversions*. New York: New York Academy of Sciences.

deprivation A specific lack of some essential kind of stimulation during the course of normal juvenile development. It is therefore to be distinguished from deprivation in experimental psychology, in which it refers to a period in which the subject has no access to an essential substance, usually food or water, so that the substance can later be used for conditioning. It also refers to the exclusion of normal sensory stimulation ("sensory deprivation") in order to study the disorienting effects of this on the subject.

The idea of deprivation in ethology is closely associated with the discovery that, in most species, normal behavioral development occurs by the unfolding of genetically based tendencies in the presence of suitable environmental stimulation. If the necessary environmental stimuli are absent the result is deprivation. A closely related phenomenon, therefore, is IMPRINTING, since absence of the stimuli involved in imprinting will disturb development. Studies of deprivation in mammals have been made on dogs and monkeys. In both cases, isolation of the newborn for several months from its mother leads to the development of aberrant avoidance behavior in later development, and leads also to a lack of social and sexual competence. VR

Bibliography

Harlow, H.F. and Mears, C.E. 1979: *The human model: primate perspectives*. Washington, D.C.: Winston and Sons.

Henderson, N.D. 1980: Effects of early experience upon the behaviour of animals: the second twenty-five years of research. In *Early behaviour: implications for social development*, ed. E.C. Simmel. New York and London: Academic Press.

development (evolutionary) Change in a characteristic over time due to organic evolution.

developmental psychobiology Also referred to as developmental biopsychology (e.g. Tobach et al. 1977) this is the study of biological processes that determine and constitute the development of behavior and its psychological components. As its name suggests, developmental psychobiology represents an amalgamation of *developmental psychology* and *psychobiology*. Developmental psychobiology encompasses all stages of life during which the foundations for behavior are established.

The roots of developmental psychobiology can be traced to the turn of the century when many ontogenetic issues were in the limelight of scientific debate. Experimental embryology had emerged as a discipline and from within it arose some model approaches to developmental studies that were to have broad and long-lasting influences. W. Preyer (1841–1897), in particular, attempted to unify developmental studies in physiology, neuroanatomy and behavior. Preyer's celebrated works included comparative studies of behavioral embryology and developmental studies of the maturation of children.

Charles DARWIN (1809–1882) can also be seen as an early advocate and practitioner of developmental psychobiology. In particular *The expression of the emotions in man and animals* (1872) reflects some of his views of developmental study as a tool to an understanding of comparative-evolutionary aspects of behavior, as well as the nature of brain-behavior relations. (See EMOTION: ETHOLOGICAL APPROACHES.)

Links with evolutionary theory and genetics

The Darwinian framework was incorporated into the thinking of many developmental psychologists (e.g. Baldwin 1895) during the later nineteenth century. Their acceptance of evolutionary views was influenced by those of contemporary embryologists who suggested that individual development (ontogeny) appears to replay (or recapitulate) the evolutionary development of the species (its phylogeny).

Ethological and comparative traditions, as articulated by Konrad Lorenz, Niko Tinbergen, T.C. Schneirla and Daniel Lehrman, placed great value on ontogenetic analyses. In particular, a goal of such behavioral approaches is to clarify *adaptive* or *functional* aspects of behavior, that is, to understand the means by which behavioral traits enable organisms to meet various environmental challenges and in the face of such forces of natural selection be maintained or reinforced in the species' repertoire. From this tradition comes interest in the behavior and behavioral development of young in relation to their social and physical environments. Parent-offspring relationships, affiliative behavior, the organization of motor patterns, play, imitation, recognition of parents, kin, food, prey, and basic vegetative activities have, for example, been involved in studies of the adaptive aspects of behavioral development.

The function of developmental processes is in general the achievement of adult competence. The adaptive significance of some aspects of the behavior of young, then, may lie in converting neonatal competence to adult competence: it is thought to be the case for infantile play, for example, that adaptive benefits are realized *in later life*. By contrast, some of the behaviors of young may not perform this function at all, but instead have survival value *at that point* in development.

The development of species-typical behavior and its evolutionary implications brings with it an appreciation of and interest in *heritable* factors that are expressed in behavior. Thus, the field of BEHAVIOR GENETICS has a relevant alignment with developmental psychobiology. Heritability, however, is a parameter of populations, not individuals, so the role of some aspects of behavior genetics exists most precisely on the level of population characteristics. The historical persistence of the so-called "nature – nuture" controversy in developmental psychobiology can be understood, in part, as a problem that has been difficult to resolve because the adversaries in the controversy are often confronting one another with analyses that are appropriate either to individuals or to populations. Behavior genetics is, however, increasingly influenced by revelations of modern molecular biology and genetics.

The complexity of modern psychobiology: parent-offspring relations

Although developmental psychobiology has a tradition of comparative study that ranges across many species, mammalian development is emphasized. This can be understood in terms of its relevance to humans, and because mammalian offspring tend to present interesting ontogenetic pictures for study – their life histories usually include dramatic transformations from infancy to adulthood. It is possible to make such a generalization because mammals are defined, as a group, on the basis of common reproductive – developmental features: live birth and the provision of milk via specialized glands on the female's body. Mammary glands are an anatomical signpost for maternal behavior. The developmental psychobiology of mammals, therefore, necessarily includes the analysis of maternal behavior or, more accurately, *parental* behavior since in many species, including man, nurturance is provided by adults other than, and in addition to, the mother. Parental behavior is, in fact, a prominent feature of the reproductive efforts of many non-mammalian animals, such as some species of fish and many species of birds.

The inclusion of parental behavior in the mandate of developmental psychobiology brings with it special conceptual and methodological demands. Parental behavior is not a static or fixed form of input. The quantity and quality of parental attention tends to change over time, usually in a manner suited to the developmental status of the offspring. It is important to recognize the *developmental* nature of parental care.

The concept of developmental synchrony is very important because it stimulates awareness of the existence of the different means by which such interindividual synchrony is achieved. The effect of a parent (caregiver) on the offspring and the effect of the offspring on the parent often must be analyzed separately in order to understand the nature of their *reciprocal* controls. Developmental studies have been enhanced considerably by ability to understand the mechanisms of interactions within dyads, such as parent-offspring units.

Links with neuroscience

The problems and methods of contemporary psychobiology, physiological psychology, and the neurosciences in general, contribute to the scope and conduct of developmental psychobiology. Developmental analyses continue to be applied as *tools* to study other processes. Thus, many topics of psychobiological interest, such as learning and memory, feeding and drinking behavior, sensory processes, sleep, reproductive behavior and communication, are studied developmentally, with the aim of learning more about each problem as a result of better understanding the factors that contribute to its development.

In addition, the *methods* of contemporary neuroscience have influenced the conduct of the developmental work. In some instances a new technology has been applied to a developmental problem. This would include, for instance, basic studies of the development of neurochemical systems of the brain, behavioral pharmacology in immature animals, and neuroanatomical studies of the developing nervous system. Some of these efforts

33

resemble or are identical to research in developmental neurobiology, a closely-aligned discipline which is best discriminated from developmental psychobiology by greater emphasis on intrinsic properties of neural tissue and systems, rather than in their relations to behavior.

The application of modern anatomical and physiological techniques of neurobiology to behaviorally-oriented investigations is usually done through "descriptive – correlative" studies, which are typical of preliminary analyses. In developmental psychobiology there are several significant examples of this approach. Neural changes during development have been described with the aid of numerous neurobiological measures, ranging from molar levels of analysis such as brain size, cortical depth and myelination patterns, to more molecular analyses such as neuronal counts, cell size and shape, or arrangement of dendritic spines. Such morphological measures are then correlated with onset of function or level of performance. Alternatively, the same kinds of neural measures can be used correlatively to assess the consequences of different early environmental conditions for rate or level of neural development.

Relevance of early experience

Ontogenetic stages during which behavior and/or morphology undergo rapid or dramatic changes are, generally speaking, especially attractive to developmental psychobiologists. It is generally believed that periods of rapid changes are more susceptible to extrinsic influences than are ontogenetic stages of stability. The assumption is that living systems in the process of reorganization or change are more easily affected by environmental events, natural or artificial, than are systems that are operating in a relatively steady state. It is for this reason, at least in part, that developmental psychobiologists are attracted to analyses of "early experience", because the "early" period is usually part of the postnatal phase when development is rapid and dramatic.

The same assumptions that highlight early life as an important period during which development is shaped, also apply to the study of the early influence of toxins or teratogens (substances that can have detrimental effects on the organism). Hence, the methods and data of developmental psychobiology are often relevant to toxicologists and teratologists interested in some organismic effects of a toxin. Toxicologists who study, for instance, potentially harmful effects of drugs on developing animals are particularly aware of the special interpretive problems, particularly in organisms that engage in extensive parent-offspring interactions. The problem is that a drug can directly affect the young organism in at least two different ways. First, the drug can act directly on the organ systems of the young animal, and perhaps have more dramatic effects than on an adult, whose tissue is less susceptible to perturbation. The second potential source of effect is less direct but can be as significant. Alterations in physical or behavioral characteristics of offspring can produce changes in the quantity or quality of parental care. Many aspects of parental care are determined partly by responses to proximate cues from offspring. Drug effects may affect the parent's response which, in turn, can alter the condition of the young. These chains of interaction can extend beyond the immediate drug effect, in time and in kind of action. JRA1/AW

Bibliography

Baldwin, J.M. 1895: *Mental development in the child and in the race*. London: Macmillan.

Bateson, P.P.G. 1981: Ontogeny. In *The Oxford companion to animal behaviour*, ed. D.J. MacFarland. Oxford and New York: Oxford University Press.

Darwin, C. 1877: A biographical sketch of an infant. *Mind. 2*, 285–94.

Gould, S.J. 1977: *Ontogeny and phylogeny*. London: Belknap.

Hall, W.G. and Oppenheimer, R. 1987: Developmental psychobiology. In *Annual review of psychology*, vol. 38, eds. M.R. Rosenzweig and L.W. Porter. Palo Alto: Annual Reviews Inc. (in prep.).

Tobach, E., Aronson. L.R. and Shaw, E. 1971: *The biopsychology of development*. London and New York: Academic Press.

discrimination Differential responsiveness to different stimuli. An animal can respond differently to different stimuli only when it can discriminate between them. Animals which do not initially discriminate between two stimuli can often learn to do so. For example, a pigeon given two types of grain may readily eat both. But if one type has been treated with lithium chloride and the bird vomits as a result, upon recovery it will not eat that type of grain. This form of discrimination is an important aspect of FOOD SELECTION.

Animals may have little difficulty in perceiving the difference between stimuli, but, nevertheless, behave towards them in the same way (see GENERALIZATION). This is the counterpart of discrimination. In learning to discriminate, the animal has both to pay attention to the relevant aspects of the stimuli, and to respond appropriately to these differences (Sutherland and Mackintosh 1971).   DJM

Bibliography

Krebs, J.R. 1973: Behavioral aspects of predation. In *Perspectives in ethology*, eds. P.P.G. Bateson and P.H. Klopfer. New York: Plenum Press, pp. 73–111.

Mackintosh, N.J. 1983: *Conditioning and associative learning*. Oxford and New York: Oxford University Press.

Sutherland, N.S. and Mackintosh, N.J. 1971: *Mechanisms of animal discrimination learning*. New York and London: Academic Press.

displacement activity An activity which may appear normal, and which may be directed toward its normal external stimulus, but which occurs at an inappropriate time. For example a hungry bird shown food behind glass will often preen its wing. This might be called "displacement" preening. The name comes from the particular motivation theory which, in classical ethology, was used to account for such inappropriate actions. A DRIVE, such as hunger, denied its normal outlet (in this case feeding), "sparks over" or is "displaced" into an alternative outlet (in this case preening). In a displacement activity, unlike a redirected activity, there was no obvious functional link between the behavior pattern that was used as the alternative outlet for a drive, and the behavior pattern that was normally activated by that drive. The surplus energy theory later became unfashionable, but the name displacement activities stuck even when other motivational theories such as the "disinhibition" theory came into favor.

(See also APPROACH/AVOIDANCE CONFLICT.)   RD

Bibliography

Tinbergen, N. 1969: *The study of instinct*. 2nd edn. Oxford: Oxford University Press.

display The term used to designate a pattern of social behavior that is species-specific and forms a part of the communicative system within or between social groups, or between individuals. An example is the "weed presentation display" of great-crested grebes which occurs between courting pairs: the partners waggle their heads, preen and then dive and rise vertically holding weeds in their beaks (see illustration, from Deag 1980). In

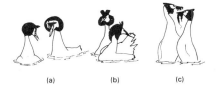

(a)   (b)   (c)

primates many displays involve facial expressions, such as the "bared-teeth display" of macaques and chimpanzees. Ethologists make efforts to link overt displays with their underlying motivations, moods, or emotions, by context analysis. In man, non-verbal communication consists largely of gestures and expressions some of which undoubtedly have their phylogenetic roots in the displays of our primate ancestors. (See also COURTSHIP.)

      VR

Bibliography

Deag, John M. 1980: *Social behaviour of animals*. London: Edward Arnold.

Edmunds, M. 1974: *Defense in animals*. Harlow, Essex: Longman.

Poole, T. 1985: *Social behaviour in mammals*. Glasgow: Blackie.

dominance Dominance has two meanings. It is usually the ranking of one animal over another in a fairly stable hierarchy of threats. It may also mean the priority of one animal over another for access to scarce resources, particularly food or mates. Much of the work on dominance deals with the relationship between the two meanings, that is, the question does high status in the threat hierarchy increase an animal's survival and reproduction?

Dominance originally seemed a unitary, and all-embracing idea. Schjelderupp-Ebbe (1931), working on peck-order in chickens and other birds, pictured dominance as a despotic ordering of the universe. Maslow (1936) realized that the apparently sexual mounting and presenting of macaque monkeys is often a ritualized gesture of threat or appeasement. Thus dominance relations apparently pervaded the monkeys' lives. Maslow studied monkeys competing for a piece of food. He found that the mounter or threatener obtained the food, except occasionally when a subordinate presented, and then was "allowed" to feed. A stable dominance hierarchy can, in fact, reduce tension, since only a few situations are contested (Hall and DeVore 1965). It soon became clear, however, that threat ranking and food and mating priorities are not always correlated. Their relation varies in different species and situations (Gartlan 1968).

In the most straightforward situations the threat hierarchy does correlate with access to food or mates. These threats may be a direct function of body size, as in bighorn sheep, which grow more massive and curly horns year by year. They can assess each other's appearance as a "threat", and do not challenge sheep better armed than themselves (Geist 1971). A similar signal is the roaring of red deer. The length and pitch of a stag's rutting roar is closely correlated to the size of his harem, presumably because the roar is an index of his size, stamina, and fighting ability (Clutton-Brock et al. 1979).

However, there are more complicated situations, such as when status has a geographical factor, when threat and food priority differ between the two sexes, or when the most advantageous strategy depends on the strategy of competitors.

If status has a geographical component, it verges on TERRITORIALITY. Territorial animals successfully chase rivals from their core areas, but at the territorial boundaries the rivals simply chase each other back to their own sides. In this case, winning the fight implies control of the territory's resources, whether food, nesting sites or other crucial resources. A classic intermediate case is Stellar's jay, which is territorial in summer but has a dominance hierarchy in winter. In winter flocks, however, both threat and food priority are determined by distance from the summer territory – the bird feeding nearest its own nest site dominates the others (Brown 1963). Several mammals, such as rabbits, also have geographical dominance, in which members of one clan overlap others, but proximity to the warren influences the hierarchy.

In several primate species the sexes are ranked separately, and females have priority to food while males maintain a threat hierarchy among themselves with little reference to the females. This is true in ringtailed lemur, brown lemur, and white sifaka on Madagascar. These lemurs suggest that female food priority may be a strongly inherited trait – it appears in all four social lemurs that have been studied, including the monogamous indri. Among the true monkeys and apes all but a few species apparently have male priority over females for food. The South American squirrel monkey, and the African talapoin and patas monkeys, at least show that the monkey stock can evolve female priority in exceptional circumstances. It is not clear quite what those circumstances are. Squirrel monkey and talapoin are very similar: small greenish river-edge species which forage in multi-male troops of 40–100 animals or more. The patas, however, is a large harem-forming monkey of the savannah and desert edge. Jones (1980) suggested that female dominance evolves in species which are highly food-limited. It may be that food priority is just one of a number of strategies open to females, such as foraging alone, out of immediate competition, like chimpanzees and orangutans (Wrangham 1979) or limiting body size, like, perhaps, Sykes monkeys and savannah baboons (Coelho 1979).

In still more complicated situations, the threat hierarchy is only loosely correlated with priority for resources. Hausfater (1975) found that in one baboon troop the first ranking male selectively mated on the third day of estrus, when a female baboon is most likely to conceive. However, individual preference also played a part: not all females mated with a first-ranking male. Other adult males formed consort bonds, and mated on as many cycle days as possible. Again, particular females were likely to consort with particular males. Finally, subadult males copulated behind bushes, particularly on the most fertile cycle days, whenever an estrus female escaped the adult males' vigilance. Hausfater (1975) points out that differing strategies are appropriate to different phases of the life cycle. Dominance must be understood over time, not just at a given moment. A similar conclusion emerges from Glander's study (1980) of howler monkeys. Young adult howler females dominate older ones in the threat hierarchy. However, the younger ones, like many primipares, had much lower survival of infants than the second-rank females, and they in turn than third rank, and so on, with the oldest and lowest ranked females raising fewer infants than any but the dominant. In this case, it may be an advantage to a young female to enter the hierarchy at the top, though the advantage only appears when she is displaced to second rank.

The costs and benefits of high rank depend on the strategies of one's opponents. In some species, or social situations, one may find an EVOLUTIONARILY STABLE STRATEGY (ESS), in which some animals achieve partial reproductive priority by social dominance, while others may "choose" to remain subordinates or avoid-ers. The advantages of being subordinate depend on both the number and ferocity of the dominants, while the advantages of being dominant depend on the number and meekness of subordinates (Maynard-Smith 1972, 1979). This is true both for the young baboons sneaking copulations behind bushes, and for species where the alternate behavior may be genetically programmed, as in solitary bees. Thus, threat-submission strategies form part of the general theory of SOCIOBIOLOGY and reproductive advantage, as well as bearing on the question of when it is advantageous to escalate threat into fighting (see AGGRESSION).

Finally, high threat rank may be transmitted from an animal to its descendants. This may be done genetically, as in inbred strains of aggressive rats. It may be done environmentally, as the young of social animals in good condition, with ample food supply, tend to be larger and survive better than those raised with poor food supply, and therefore at an advantage when the threat hierarchy corresponds to physical size and stamina. It may be done socially, as when a young Japanese macaque learns from its mother whom it may or may not threaten, and in maturing acquires a rank just below its mother (if female), or loosely correlated with hers (if male). Thus entire female lineages may dominate others in threat. During food shortage, this threat dominance does indeed translate, in the macaque, into differential food access, infant growth, and survival (Mori 1979).

In summary, dominance began in the 1930s as a simplifying and unifying concept. Now, the real interest is in analyzing "dominance" into its not-so-simple components, and in seeing how these components increase evolutionary fitness.   AJ

Bibliography

Brown, J.L. 1963: Aggressiveness, dominance, and social organization in the Stellar Jay. *Condor* 65, 460–484.

Chase, I.D. 1985: The sequential analysis of aggressive acts during hierarchy formation. *Animal behaviour* 33, 86–100.

Clutton-Brock, T.H., Albon, S.D., Gibson, R.M. and Guinness, F.E. 1979: The logical stag: adaptive aspects of fighting in red deer (*Cervus elaphus L.*). *Animal behaviour* 27: 211–225.

Coelho, A.M. Jr. 1979: Socio-bioenergetics and sexual dimorphism in primates. *Primates* 15, 263–269.

*Gartlan, J.S. 1968: Structure and function in primate society. *Folia primatologia* 8, 89–121.

Geist, V. 1971: *Mountain sheep: a study in behavior and evolution.* Chicago: University of Chicago Press.

Glander, K.E. 1980: Reproduction and population growth in free ranging mantled howler monkeys. *American journal of physical anthropology* 53, 25–36.

Hall, K.R.L. and Devore, I. 1965: Baboon social behavior. In *Primate behavior*, ed. I. Devore. New York: Holt, Rinehart and Winston.

Hausfater, G. 1975: Dominance and reproduction in baboons (*Papio cynocephalus*) *Contributions to primatology* 7.

Jolly, A. 1985: *The evolution of primate behavior.* 2nd edn. New York: Macmillan.

Jones, C.B. 1980. The functions of status in the mantled howler monkey. *Primates* 21, 389–405.

Marler, P. and Hamilton, W.J.III 1966: *Mechanisms of animal behavior.* New York, London and Sydney: John Wiley and Sons.

Maslow, A.H. 1936: The role of dominance in the social and sexual behavior of infrahuman primates III: a theory of the sexual behavior of infrahuman primates. *Journal of genetic psychology* 48, 310–38.

Maynard-Smith, J. 1972: *On evolution.* Edinburgh: Edinburgh University Press.

*———— 1979: Game theory and the evolution of behavior. *Proceedings of the Royal Society of London.* Series B, 205, 475–88.

McKinnon, J. 1978: *The ape within us.* London: Collins.

Mori, A. 1979: Analysis of population changes by measurement of body weight in the Koshima troop of Japanese monkeys. *Primates* 20, 371–8.

Schjelderupp-Ebbe, T. 1931: Die Despotie im sozialen Leben der Vögel. *Forschungsbericht Völkerpsychologische Sozialogie* 10: 77–140.

Smuts, B.B. et al. 1985: *Primate societies.* Chicago: University of Chicago Press.

Wrangham, R. 1979: Sex differences in chimpanzee dispersion. In *The great apes*, eds. D.A. Hamburg and E.R. McCown. Menlo Park, California: Benjamin/Cummings.

drive The output of a motivational system which energizes a specific, functionally-related set of behavior patterns. When its sexual drive is activated an animal is motivated to perform sexual behavior of all types, searching for a mate, courting, copulating, etc. when appropriate stimuli are present. Some drives are postulated to fluctuate in accordance with the internal state. Food deprivation stimulates the neural systems concerned with feeding motivation thereby ensuring that the animal's food seeking is initiated and persists until the imbalance is corrected. The drive concept is much less popular than formerly, its neural basis has remained elusive and many consider it to be impossible to define other than in terms of the observed behavior. It retains more usefulness in the consideration of conflict behavior. (See also VACUUM ACTIVITY.)   AWGM

Bibliography

Bolles, R.C. 1975: *Theory of motivation.* New York: Harper and Row.

Tinbergen, N. 1969: *The study of instinct.* 2nd edn. Oxford: Oxford University Press.

drugs Substances administered to a living organism which changes its internal environment in ways different from that of normal foodstuffs. Drugs may be administered orally or by injection into the bloodstream, muscle or peritoneal cavity. Most drugs are relatively small molecules which quickly become distributed throughout the body. Only very small molecules are capable of penetrating the blood-brain barrier to affect behavior in a direct manner.

Drugs alter brain function in a variety of ways which include (1) changing the blood supply to neurons; (2) altering the water and ion balance among neurons and their surrounding tissues; (3) blocking the transmission of nerve impulses; (4) altering the excitability of neuronal membranes. The last of these is probably the most important.

Neurons transmit information from one part of the nervous system to another by

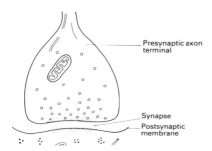

Diagram of a synapse. The presynaptic fiber swells to form a terminal bouton. This contains the chemical transmitter. The bouton membrane is polarized. The action potential depolarizes the membrane and the transmitter is released.

means of changes in electrical potential that travel along the long protrusion called the neuronal axon. These potentials are called nerve impulses. They are generated by electrical changes in the membrane of the cell body of the neuron called generator potentials. Communication between neuron occurs at the points where the branching dendrites at the end of the axon, and on the cell body, form junctions. The cells' membranes are not contiguous but come very close together, leaving a small gap called a synapse. Transmission across the synapse may be electrical but is usually chemical. Chemical substances, called neurotransmitters are released on one side of the synapse and received on the other, where they give rise to a generator potential.

Many types of neurotransmitter are known to exist in the brain. Of these the most important are probably the following: acetylcholine (ACL), dopamine (DA), gamma-amino-butyric acid (GABA), norepinephrine (NA) and serotonin

(5HT). Different brain pathways involve different transmitter substances, so that chemical coding plays an important part in brain function. Many drugs exert their primary action by interfering with the release or reception of transmitter substances.

Drugs may be classified in accordance with their primary effects on behavior. This is usually done in relation to their clinical application to human beings. Thus it is common practice to refer to anti-anxiety drugs, anti-depressant drugs, anti-psychotic drugs, depressant drugs and stimulant drugs. This type of classification does not readily correspond with a chemical classification of drugs, although there is some correlation between mode of action and clinical effect. The effects of drugs on animal behavior is studied primarily as an aid to the pharmaceutical industry, especially in the evaluation and testing of possible new products. In some screening tests mice and rats are simply injected with the chemical and observed for a standard period of time. Obvious changes in behavior, and particularly abnormal behavior are noted. In other tests the animals are rated according to the extent to which they struggle when handled, for their general activity, for motor coordination, etc. Drugs are also widely used in brain research, though here it is usually their physiological effects that are monitored.

In addition to their use in investigations aimed at furthering our understanding of pharmacology and neurochemistry drugs may also be used as a tool in psychological experiments. For example one of the minor tranquilizers (sodium amytal) has

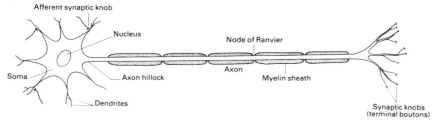

A typical neuron

been used to test the theory that the continued responding of animals that have been only partially rewarded during training is due to their greater tolerance of frustration, compared with animals that were consistently rewarded (see EXTINCTION).

The idea is that an animal that has been trained to expect a reward (see REINFORCEMENT) in particular circumstances becomes frustrated if the reward is not given. However, if the animal experiences such frustrative non-reward many times, say on 50 per cent of the trials, it will develop a tolerance of frustration. During extinction, when the animals are not rewarded at all, those which were previously partially rewarded (PR) continue to respond for much longer than those which were consistently rewarded (CR). The theory maintains that the frustration experienced by the CR animals at the beginning of extinction has a much more disruptive effect than in the PR animals, because the latter have already developed a tolerance of frustration. To test this theory Gray (1969) and his co-workers administered sodium amytal, a drug already known to have fear and frustration reducing effects in rats. In some experiments they gave the drug during training, while in others they gave it during extinction. When given during training the drug should have little effect upon CR rats because these do not experience frustration. The drug should ameliorate the effects of frustration in PR rats, thus preventing them from developing a tolerance to frustration. Therefore the administration of the drug during training should make PR animals extinguish quickly, as CR animals did during the subsequent extinction tests. This is exactly what is found.

When given during extinction the drug should have less effect upon PR animals than on CR animals, because the former (according to the theory) are already tolerant of frustration whereas the CR animals have yet to experience it. If the drug reduces the effects of frustration it should therefore have the effect of prolonging extinction in CR animals, but have little effect upon PR animals. This prediction is also confirmed by the results of experiments.

Here we have a good example of the use of a drug as a tool in experiments designed to test a psychological theory. It does not matter that the physiological action of the drug is not yet fully understood, because physiological details do not enter into the theory. The logic of the tests does not depend upon the exact action of the drug, but upon the fact that the theory predicts specified effects in different circumstances. The fact that these effects can be obtained lends support to the theory that frustration is important in the extinction of learned responses.   DJM

Bibliography

Gray, J.A. 1969: Sodium amobarbital and effects of frustrative nonreward. *Journal of comparative physiological psychology* 69, 55–64.

—— 1971: *The psychology of fear and stress*. London: Weidenfeld and Nicolson: New York: McGraw-Hill.

Panksepp, J. 1986: The neurochemistry of behavior. In *Annual review of psychology*, vol. 37, eds. M.R. Rosenzweig and L.W. Porter. Palo Alto: Annual Reviews Inc.

Silverman, Paul 1978: *Animal behavior in the laboratory*. London: Chapman and Hall: New York: University Books.

E

emotion: ethological approaches

One of four major historical traditions that have attempted to describe the nature of emotions. One of these, the psychophysiological tradition, reflects the thinking of the American philosopher William James, who was concerned with a chicken-and-egg problem: which comes first, the feeling of an emotion or the physiological changes that are associated with it? This approach led to contemporary research on autonomic physiology, lie detectors and arousal. The neurological tradition, reflecting the research of Walter Cannon, a physiologist, was concerned with the effects of brain lesions on emotional expressions. Cannon's work stimulated a great deal of research concerned with mapping the hypothalamus and the limbic system of the brain. The dynamic tradition stemmed from the work of Sigmund Freud, and was concerned mainly with the developmental changes that occur in emotions, and with their mixtures and derivatives. Freud concluded that emotions could be repressed, distorted or displaced and that their existence could only be inferred on the basis of a variety of indirect types of evidence.

The fourth major tradition, the evolutionary one, is based on the work of Charles DARWIN described in *The expression of the emotions in man and animals* (1872). This work is the source of contemporary ethological approaches to emotion.

Darwin assumed that the process of evolution applied not just to anatomical structures but to the "mind" and emotions as well. He gave numerous illustrations of the basic continuity of emotional expressions from lower animals to humans. For example he pointed out that the baring of the fangs of the wolf is related to the sneer of the human adult, and that most species of animals, including humans, show an apparent increase in body size during rage (or under threat) owing to erection of body hair or feathers, changes in posture or expansion of air pouches. On the basis of many such examples, Darwin concluded that emotional expressions serve several functions in the lives of animals. They act as signals of intentions, and they are aspects of the various preparations the body makes for emergency actions. Emotional expressions convey information from one animal to another about what is likely to happen and thereby influence the chances of survival. For example a cat confronted by an attacking dog opens its mouth and shows its long incisors, pulls back its ears, erects the hair of its body, arches its back and hisses. This pattern of expression, associated with mixed fear and anger, has value to the attacker: it signals the possibility of an attack in return. It makes the cat look larger and more ferocious and decreases the chances of a confrontation.

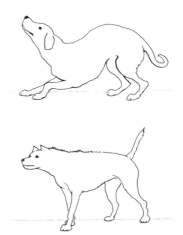

Darwin's Principle of Antithesis illustrated by the posture of a dog when submissive (above) and angry (below)

41

This, in turn, increases survival possibilities for the cat.

Darwin also stated that many, but not all, emotional expressions are innate, or unlearned. This conclusion was based on four types of evidence:
(1) some emotional expressions appear in similar form in many lower animals;
(2) some emotional expressions appear in very young children in the same form as in adults, before much opportunity for learning has occurred;
(3) some emotional expressions are shown in identical ways by those born blind and in those who are normally sighted; and
(4) some emotional expressions appear in similar form in widely distinct races and groups of humans.
Darwin also concluded that some emotional expressions are phylogenetically later than others. Expressions of fear and rage are quite primitive, while frowning and blushing are relatively recent evolutionary acquisitions.

Darwin's views deal with the key issues of ethological research on emotions. He was concerned with the usefulness of a given emotional expression in the life of the animal (adaptation), with the occurrence across species of different facial and postural expressions (phylogeny), with genetic factors in expression (mechanism), and with natural selection pressures that might help to account for the appearance of particular expressions (evolution). Darwin's judgment, as well as that of ethologists today, is that emotional expressions are as reliable characters of species as are body structures, and they serve adaptive, survival functions in all organisms.

Contemporary ethologists and sociobiologists have accepted these ideas and tried to extend them. One extension has been to show more detailed parallels between lower and higher animals in emotional and social behavior. Comparing termites and monkeys, Wilson (1975) wrote: 'Both societies are formed into cooperative groups that occupy territories. The group members communicate hunger, alarm, hostility, caste status, or rank and reproductive status among themselves . . . Individuals are intensely aware of the distinction between groupmates and nonmembers . . .'

In addition ethologists have devoted considerable research effort to studying, at many different phylogenetic levels, such emotional/social behavior as AGGRESSION, timidity, CURIOSITY, PLAY, COURTSHIP and sexuality. One well known list of basic adaptive, emotional patterns identifiable at most phylogenetic levels was proposed by Scott (1958). This consists of the following behavioral patterns: ingestive, agonistic, sexual, shelter-seeking, care-giving, care-soliciting, eliminative, allelomimetic (imitative), and investigative. An alternative view proposed by Plutchik (1980) is that there are eight basic behavior patterns which are the prototypes of emotions as seen in higher animals. These have been labeled with the following terms (with the subjective aspect in parentheses): protection (fear), destruction (anger), incorporation (acceptance), rejection (disgust), reproduction (joy), reintegration (sadness), orientation (surprise) and exploration (curiosity). These patterns may interact to produce the large variety of recognized emotional states.

Contemporary ethological approaches to emotion have at least four elements. As indicated above, they assume that emotions must be considered within an evolutionary context as adaptive classes of behavior. Secondly, they assume that emotions are complex chains of events that include more elements than expressive behavior alone, or subjective feelings. Emotions also include cognitive appraisals, states of physiological arousal, impulses to action, and overt behavior, all directed toward the particular events which triggered the emotional chain of response in the first place. Thirdly, it is recognized that the complexity of emotional reactions implies that their properties can be known only through a process of inference. An emotion may be conceptualized as a hypothetical construct which is known through various kinds of evidence. The types of evidence used include knowledge of: stimulus conditions preceding a reaction; an organism's behavior over an extended period of time;

the species-typical behavior; how the organism's peers or conspecifics react to it; the choices an individual makes in a comparative free-choice situation; and the effect of the organism's behavior on others.

Finally, contemporary ethological thinking recognizes that emotions often mix and interact thereby producing various indirect derivatives. An example of this is the appearance of "displacement" behavior. This consists of actions that appear totally out of context. For example, two birds fighting may suddenly stop to preen their feathers. This is interpreted on the basis of the assumption that tendencies to attack and to flee occur during fighting, and that at certain times the strength of these opposing motivations are equal and opposite. Since the two responses are incompatible, neither can occur, and other activities in the animal's repertoire, such as preening, suddenly and temporarily appear. Another example of derivative expressions is seen in the variation of posture of birds and animals as a function of the relative strength of competing emotional tendencies. The zebra finch may show an "aggressive" horizontal posture associated with threat, or a "frightened" sleek, vertical, posture, or a "submissive" fluffed posture, or a specific "courtship" posture.

Intermediate postures and expressions reflect the existence of conflicts between impulses to attack and to flee. Similar mixtures of attack and withdrawal impulses have been shown for cat postures and facial expressions in the dog and the chimpanzee.

In summary it may be said that emotions are genetically programmed responses to certain common survival-related problems such as dealing with prey and predators, food and mates, care-givers and care-receivers. Emotions are attempts of the organism to achieve control over these kinds of events related to survival. Emotions are the ultra-conservative, evolutionary, behavioral adaptations that have been successful (like amino acids, DNA and genes) in increasing the chances of survival of organisms. Therefore, they have been maintained in functionally equivalent form through all phylogenetic levels. RP

Bibliography

Chance, M.R.A. 1980: An ethological assessment of emotion. In *Theories of emotion*, eds. R. Plutchik and H. Kellerman. New York: Academic Press.

Griffin, D.R. 1981: *The question of animal awareness*. 2nd edn. New York: Rockefeller University Press.

Hinde, R.A. 1985: Was 'The expression of the emotions' a misleading phrase? *Animal behavior* 33, 985–92.

Plutchik, R. 1980: *Emotion: a psychoevolutionary synthesis*. New York: Harper and Row.

Scott, J.P. 1958: *Animal behavior*. Chicago: University of Chicago Press.

Wilson, E.O. 1975: *Sociobiology: the new synthesis*. Cambridge, Mass.: Harvard University Press.

emotion: satiation and starvation effects on Hunger and satiety activate emotions which complement the drive state. Drives unamplified by emotion will not activate learning or sustain behavior, but emotions are sufficient motivators in the absence of drives. For example, during periods of intense emotion, DRIVE signals may go unnoticed, as when excitement over work inhibits or attenuates hunger pangs. The apparent urgency of hunger is a joint product of both the drive state and emotion. If a competing emotion is not present, the drive state of hunger may facilitate the activation of a relevant emotion such as interest, which will in turn amplify the drive state. In this way, emotions and drives affect one another. RJD

epideictic behavior *See* conventional and epideictic behavior.

ethical problems of experiments with animals Whether described as the study of behavior or of mind, the nature of psychological research and professional practice makes ethical problems inevitable: for example, some psychologists engage in research programs that have as their goal the prediction and control of behavior; engage in therapies that aim to change thought and behavior; engage in constructing, administering, and interpreting tests that are used to determine people's life chances (Noble 1980).

Ethical issues arise in psychology, as elsewhere, when it is thought that serious good and bad are bound together in the same activity. When harm or wrong is done to animals or humans subjected to or participating in research an outsider might consider it both reasonable and humane to abandon the project. Researchers find it less simple, for they believe that harm and wrong are an incidental but inescapable part of the benefits flowing from scientific activity. It is undeniable that world-changing benefits have come from applying scientific method to problems. The belief that benefits follow all such practice sometimes seems to be a modern article of faith.

If, as psychologists typically claim, the decision to perform a potentially harm-inducing experiment is to be based on weighing scientific benefits against costs to participants, how are the benefits and costs to be assessed? American Psychological Association guidelines (1973) contain an admirably sensitive discussion of possible costs, but declare that benefits are insured by good research design and that, in turn, good design is assured by such things as graduate training, critical reviews and research proposal evaluation.

Psychologists experiment with animals because it is believed, for example, that learning processes in animals are similar to those in humans. As property, animals have no rights, so no balancing of benefits to others and costs to them can protect them. If we need not consider their suffering there are no ethical problems. For protection animals must rely on the sensitivity of researchers (members of a profession which values detachment and objectivity), laws against wanton cruelty (where they exist), or the intervention of animal protection activists.

Such activists sometimes claim that researchers do not do their best to minimize the sufferings of their animals, or see that they are properly looked after away from the laboratory. There are even claims that researchers connive at pet-stealing, or at least the recruitment of stray pets. The last point, although undoubtedly emotive, seems to raise questions about researchers' respect for other people's property, rather than their respect for animals' rights. But the serious objections to animal experiments are not based on any incidental misconduct of scientists. They are based on questioning whether the benefits justify the costs to the animals. The answer depends not on the legal rights of animals (although protesters may urge that animals ought not to be denied such rights), but on morality. Some argue that causing suffering to any sentient creature is so bad that no end justifies it. Others would say that the only justification for damaging or hurting animals lies in the potential reduction of human suffering, and not just any human suffering. When animals are used to test the safety of new cosmetics, there is a benefit to people because they are less likely to be offered a dangerous product which might cause disease or other harm. But some feel that new cosmetics pander only to human vanity and greed. The potential suffering of both animals and humans could be avoided if no one wanted the cosmetics. Arguments against the cost/benefit justification of animal experiments therefore depend on how much weight is given to animal suffering. Many people may be inclined to think that animals should not be abused in tests on cosmetics, but should be exploited in the effort to understand and combat human illness. This conclusion rests on the assumption that human happiness is more desirable than the happiness of other animals, but human self-indulgence is not.

Many animal experiments in psychology involve no obvious suffering; but others which employ electric shock or surgery may seem ethically dubious. Their purpose is often the increase of human knowledge rather than any immediate alleviation of human distress. The degree of suffering caused and the amount of potential benefit therefore become significant. Because both are difficult to quantify, it is hard to assess whether much of this work is morally defensible or not. This remains true even if such experiments have added and will continue to add to a worthwhile stock of knowledge. Some who have doubts about animal experiments in psychology may not be convinced of this.

On the other side, psychologists may feel that they are unjustly treated in being made the butt of moral obloquy. In a society that pens, plumps and slaughters animals for food or fancy clothing, the record of research scientists does not seem worse than most. When a man in a sheepskin coat and suede boots presumes to question whether the pursuit of knowledge is sufficient justification for abusing animals, the psychologist may feel himself confronted by an obnoxious self-deception. Such *ad hominem* arguments, however, are no closer to the issues outlined above than are the animal rights protesters' outcries about the theft of pets.

DLM/RL

Bibliography

American Psychological Association, Committee on Ethical Standards in Psychological Research 1973: *Ethical principles in the conduct of research with human participants.* Washington, D.C.

Dawkins, M.S. 1980: *Animal suffering.* London: Chapman and Hall.

Noble, W.G. 1980: Psychologists and ethics: Report of a working party. *Australian psychologist* 15, 393–411.

Regan, T. and Singer, P. eds. 1976: *Animal rights and human obligations.* Englewood Cliffs, N.J.: Prentice-Hall.

ethogram The complete behavioral vocabulary of a species, the listing of units of behavior whose occurrence in various contexts, and sequences, can be used in principle to provide a comprehensive description of behavior.

The ethogram has its origins in the theories of instinct which postulated specific innate units of behavior, and ethograms are easiest to compile for the lower species. Inevitable problems in compiling an ethogram are balancing the completeness of the listing against the frequency of occurrence of rare behavior; and the issue of the lumping or splitting of particular units. In the mammals the problem is compounded by the graded nature of many types of behavior, and, in the higher primates and humans, the possibilities of intra-species variations in behavior and the possibility of deception. Nevertheless, an ethogram is an important first step in the description of a species, and human ethograms have been attempted, notably for young children. Different researchers may not agree on the ethogram of a particular species, and the construction of an ethogram may be conceived of as a psychological process involving the researcher's aims, and the perceptions of the species being studied (Reynolds 1976). (See OBSERVATIONAL METHODS.)   PKS

Bibliography

Reynolds, V. 1976 The origins of a behavioural vocabulary: the case of the rhesus monkey. *Journal for the theory of social behaviour* 6, 105–42.

ethology The study of animal behavior, primarily in the natural environment of the species being observed. The domain of classical ethology was dominated by the theories of LORENZ and TINBERGEN during the 1940s and 1950s. Modern ethology has broadened both the range of theoretical concepts used, and of species studied, and is now less distinct from neighboring disciplines such as comparative psychology, neurophysiology, and the experimental study of animal behavior.

The origins and rise of ethology have been described by Thorpe (1979). The immediate origins of classical ethology lay in the work of zoologists such as Heinroth in Germany, Whitman in the USA, and Huxley in Britain. These researchers combined an interest in the observation of an animal's behavior in its natural surroundings, with a concern for the adaptive value of behavior. This concern stemmed from evolutionary theory and the work of DARWIN. By the late 1930s classical ethology was well under way; Huxley was instrumental in founding the Institute (now Association) for the Study of Animal Behaviour in Britain in 1936, while Lorenz and Köhler founded the German journal *Zeitschrift für Tierpsychologie* in 1937.

The work of Lorenz, Tinbergen and others led to a highly developed theory of animal behavior based on the concept of a number of DRIVES which affected responses to external stimuli; the simplest animals responded by reflexive, kinetic and taxic behavior, and more complicated animals by a chaining or hierarchy of rather stereotyped behavior forming "fixed action patterns". Tinbergen's book, *The study of instinct* (1951), was the culmination of this approach, which is now summarized.

A reflexive behavior is considered as an innate, relatively simple and stereotyped response involving the central nervous system and occurring very shortly after the stimulus which provokes it. Reflexive movements without orientation are referred to as kineses; the intensity of stimulation may affect rate of movement (orthokinesis) or rate of change of direction, such as turning (klinokinesis). Reflexive movements with orientation of the whole animal are referred to as taxes; for example swinging from side to side to compare stimulus intensities (klinotaxis); simultaneous comparison of two stimuli, and orientation towards one (tropotaxis); direct choice of or aversion to a source of stimulation (menotaxis); and orientation to a complex or patterned stimulus source (mnemotaxis).

Instinct theorists further postulated that such reflexive behavior units could be chained together in a sequence, or, more flexibly, considered as a hierarchical progression from higher to lower levels of APPETITIVE BEHAVIOR, ending in a consummatory act. The courtship and mating of the three-spined stickleback is a well-known example from Tinbergen's work. A fixed sequence, relatively uninfluenced by

learning, is referred to as a "fixed action pattern" (FAP).

The FAP is thought of as being set off by certain specific stimuli, called SIGN STIMULI. These "release" the behavior by means of an INNATE RELEASING MECHANISM (IRM) which detects key features of the sign stimulus and triggers off the relevant motor neurons to activate the FAP. A SUPERNORMAL STIMULUS is one which elicits an FAP even more strongly than natural stimuli.

In Lorenz's hydraulic model of motivation (1950), which Tinbergen took over, physical energy becomes nervous energy. An instinct for a particular behavior (such as nestbuilding or finding food) builds up a reaction-specific energy or drive state. This leads to appetitive behavior (with associated kineses and taxes) and, if an appropriate sign stimulus is found, the release of FAPs which lead to a consummatory act (such as feeding, or constructing a nest). The build-up of reaction-specific energy can lower the threshold of responsiveness to external stimuli. VACUUM ACTIVITY, the expression of an FAP in the absence of sign stimuli, could occur if the reaction-specific energy built up sufficiently without finding release. DISPLACEMENT ACTIVITY occurred if the normal outlet for reaction-specific energy was prevented and the nervous energy "spilt over" from one FAP to another.

The ideas of classical ethology came under attack during the 1950s, from ethologists and comparative psychologists, especially those studying mammalian and avian species and finding that learning and flexibility in behavior were substantially greater than could be accommodated within instinct theory. It became clear that even the relatively stereotyped behavior of lower species was not as "fixed" or invariant as predicted (for example, courtship in the stickleback). Behavior patterns in birds and mammals were not simple chains or hierarchies but could only be explained by more sophisticated models. An example is the reproductive cycle of canaries, which is controlled by an interaction of internal hormonal effects, external stimuli such as day length, the behavior of conspecifics, and the physiological effects of the behavior performed.

The hydraulic model of motivation, in particular, was criticized as exemplifying a misleading confusion of physical and nervous energy. Behavioral sequences could be brought to an end by the reception of certain specific stimuli, just as readily as by the supposed discharge of energy in action. Displacement activities received alternative theoretical explanations, such as disinhibition of a response. Indeed the fundamental concept of "drive" states as in any sense usefully simplifying very complex phenomena was criticized by Hinde (1959); though the term continues in use at least as a shorthand way of describing the organization of behavior toward certain biological goals.

The 1950s and 1960s saw a rapprochement between ethologists, comparative psychologists, and neurophysiologists, such that the present disciplines are not very distinct. Although Lorenz defended a modified version of the innate/learnt dichotomy, the conceptual and practical difficulties of any simple distinction along these lines have become increasingly recognized. IMPRINTING has been an example of a type of behavior initially thought of as a largely innate process, with only the object of imprinting being learnt. The complexities of the process are now better understood. The ideas of constraints on learning, and predispositions to learn more readily in certain ways, have also been developed.

Among more recent developments in ethology has been the rapid growth of studies in primates (e.g. Chalmers 1979), with specialist journals such as *Primates* and *Folia Primatologica*. There has been increased interest in RELATIONSHIPS AND SOCIAL STRUCTURE, and in more complex and flexible behavior patterns such as PLAY. Socioecology is a subdiscipline which relates social structure to the ecology of a species, notably its feeding resources and likely predators.

The growth of SOCIOBIOLOGY and behavioral ecology has led to vigorous new perspectives on animal behavior in general, and social behavior in particular. It has heightened the importance of observational studies of a sufficiently large scale to cover the behavior of a social group over several generations, so that KINSHIP relations and medium-term REPRODUCTIVE SUCCESS can be elucidated. It has also encouraged more detailed experimental studies of behavioral choices, for example of FORAGING, in terms of optimality theories. Ethological concepts and methods have also been applied to the study of human behavior, with a specialist journal, *Ethology and sociobiology* starting in 1979.

Particularly noticeable has been the advance of sophisticated quantitative models for the analysis of behavior (Colgan 1978). Two distinctive features have remained though from the earlier classical ethology. First, the emphasis on naturalistic, OBSERVATIONAL METHODS, at least in the initial stages of studying a new species/ behavior, and the construction of an ETHOGRAM. Second, the basic framework of Tinbergen's "four whys"; the study of the immediate causation of behavior, its development in ontogeny, the immediate adaptive value or function of the behavior, and its evolutionary history (Tinbergen 1963).   PKS

Bibliography

Bateson, Paul P.G. and Hinde, Robert A. eds. 1976: *Growing points in ethology*. Cambridge and New York: Cambridge University Press.

Chalmers, N. 1979. *Social behaviour in primates*. London: Edward Arnold; Baltimore: University Park Press.

Colgan, P.W. ed. 1978. *Quantitative ethology*. New York: Wiley.

Hinde, R.A. 1959. Unitary drives. *Animal behaviour*, 7 130–41.

*——— 1982: *Ethology*. Oxford and New York: Oxford University Press.

Lehner, P. 1979: *Handbook of ethological methods*. New York: Garland.

Lehrman, D.S. 1953. A critique of Konrad Lorenz's theory of instinctive behavior. *Quarterly review of biology* 28, 337–63.

Lorenz, K.Z. 1950: The comparative method in studying innate behaviour patterns. *Symposium of the society for experimental biology* 4, 221–68.

McFarland, D. 1985: *Animal behaviour*. London: Pitman Publishing Ltd.

Manning, Aubrey 1979: *An introduction to animal behaviour*. 3rd edn. London: Edward Arnold; Reading, Mass.: Addison-Wesley.

Morris, D. 1958. The reproductive behaviour of the ten-spined stickleback (*Pygosteus pungitius* L.) *Behaviour*, Suppl. No. 6, 1–154.

Thorpe, W.H. 1979. *The origins and rise of ethology*. London: Heinemann Educational.

Tinbergen, Nikolaas 1951. *The study of instinct*. Oxford: Clarendon Press.

—— 1963. On aims and methods of ethology. *Zeitschrift für Tierpsychologie* 20, 410–33.

eusocial Social organization with reproductive division of labor, such that some individuals do not themselves reproduce but rear the young of others. (See also ALTRUISM.) MR

evolution In biology, evolution refers to change from generation to generation in the genetic constitution of an animal (or plant) population. On the large scale, evolution may involve the appearance, transformation or disappearance of whole species over long spans of time, but smaller-scale changes are also forms of evolution (see Mayr 1963). The idea that species are changeable (rather than fixed, as once widely thought), has a considerable history, but was crucially strengthened by Darwin's argument for NATURAL SELECTION as a process which could bring about evolutionary change.

In the modern understanding of evolution, genetic variation may be widespread in a population and may be increased by mutation and migration: and evolutionary factors including natural selection act to change or stabilize gene frequencies in particular ways. Opinions vary as to the relative importance of different evolutionary factors – many biologists still consider natural selection in some form to be the most influential, but increasingly this has been questioned in view of the possible importance of mutation, migration, and especially genetic drift (gene frequency change at random) and founder effect (where a population's founders are unrep-resentative of their population of origin). A current controversy concerns the problem of whether evolution proceeds slowly and gradually or by the alternation of long periods of stability with short episodes of rapid change (e.g. during speciation: see Stanley 1979). RDA

Bibliography

Mayr, E. 1963: *Animal species and evolution*. Cambridge, Mass.: Harvard University Press.

Ridley, M. 1985: *The problems of evolution*. Oxford and New York: Oxford University Press.

Stanley, S.M. 1979: *Macroevolution: pattern and process*. San Francisco: W.H. Freeman.

evolutionarily stable strategies (ESS) In sociobiology a strategy is an ESS if, when adopted by most members of a population, it cannot be invaded by any alternative strategy. The "invasion" refers to evolutionary spread of an alternative strategy; thus an ESS is a strategy that cannot be replaced by alternatives once it becomes fixed in a population. The ESS concept was developed and formalized by Maynard Smith (1972, 1974), though several workers had independently used the same principle without emphasizing its general importance as a technique in evolutionary biology.

First, what is a strategy? A strategy is simply one of a series of possible courses of action, or allocations of effort. For an animal, "search for food" and "search for mates" could be two possible strategies. An ESS model would begin with a list of plausible strategies; precisely what is a plausible strategy must be decided by the modeler on a basis of what it seems feasible that the animal could do. The next step in the model would be an algebraic definition of how payoffs (measured in terms of FITNESS) will be allocated when individuals playing the various strategies interact. Finally, there will be a formal, mathematical analysis (based on the mathematics of game theory) to determine which strategy, if any, can be an ESS. It then remains to be established whether behavior observed in nature fits the ESS predicted by the model.

Maynard Smith pointed out that an ESS could be of two types:

(i) *pure ESS* – in a given condition always play one particular strategy.
(ii) *mixed ESS* – in a given condition play various strategies with prescribed probabilities.

There are two ways in which a mixed ESS could be achieved (Maynard Smith and Parker 1976). The population could be genetically polymorphic, so that strategy frequencies relate to genotype frequencies. (In general this poses considerable theoretical difficulty for most sexually reproducing organisms if several pure strategies must co-exist). More simply, the population could be genetically monomorphic; each individual "playing" the strategies randomly within the ESS probabilities. Some doubt exists as to whether mixed ESSs will exist in nature, rather than a set of appropriate "conditional strategies" (see below).

The formal requirements for a strategy to be an ESS have been defined by Maynard Smith (1974). For a strategy (call it strategy *I*) to be an ESS all alternative strategies must get lower pay-offs than *I* when the population consists mainly of *I*-type individuals. The mean fitness of all rare, alternative strategies must be lower than the mean fitness of the *I* strategy when *I* is common. *I* will therefore be stable, since the alternative strategies cannot spread after arising as mutations.

How does an ESS differ from a simple optimum? An ESS is in a sense a competitive optimum, or Nash equilibrium. The optimum strategy (to give highest REPRODUCTIVE SUCCESS) for an individual in an interaction against competitors often depends critically upon the strategy played by the competitors. It is under these circumstances (where payoffs to "self" depend on the strategy played by others) that the ESS approach is necessary. Two simple examples serve to illustrate this point. If an animal is constructing an overwintering nest, there may be a unique optimal solution for effort spent, reflecting the tradeoff between cost (effort = time and energy that is spent on nest-building)

and benefits (improvement in survival prospects due to protection by nest against cold weather). Essentially, the animal "plays" against the environment. On the other hand, if an animal is fighting a conspecific over a territory, the optimal strategy depends on what the opponent is likely to do. If the opponent is likely to back off quickly when challenged, it pays to be persistent. Alternatively, if the opponent will persist to a costly level, it may pay to retreat. The best strategy depends on the current frequencies in the population of strategies for persisting or retreating. Selection is *frequency-dependent*; it is here we need the ESS approach.

How does the ESS approach differ from the techniques used by population geneticists who work on frequency-dependent selection? Rather little in some cases. However, population geneticists tend to be interested, say, in the equilibrium properties of two alternative alleles at a locus. The mathematics becomes very tedious as more than one locus is included, and the strategy set is therefore often very restricted. ESS theorists usually omit the problems of diploidy (dominance and recessiveness of genes) from their models, and make the assumption that strategies reproduce asexually, or that the genetic system is haploid. This sacrifice of genetic rigor allows consideration of a much bigger array of alternative strategies than would be possible using standard techniques of population genetics. In short, ESS models usually sacrifice genetic precision in the interest of having wide strategic possibilities. This has attracted some criticism (e.g. Oster and Wilson 1978) but there is reason for optimism that even with sexually-reproducing diploidy, populations can indeed evolve to an ESS (Maynard Smith 1981).

For some games there can be more than one ESS. Which ESS is achieved depends on the frequencies of strategies at the start of selection. This contrasts with simple, non-frequency dependent optimization, where there is only one solution (optimism). A further contrast is that at an ESS, the *mean fitness of the population* may well be lower than at some alternative solution though *individual fitness* is maximized in the sense that deviant mutants do worse. (In simple optimization, both mean population fitness and individual fitness are maximized at the optimum). There is no paradox in this phenomenon; characteristics do not spread because they aid the reproduction of species or populations, but because they enhance the replication rate of the genes that determine them (see e.g. Dawkins 1976, 1982).

Many ESSs are likely to be "conditional" upon circumstances. A *conditional ESS* (Dawkins 1980) prescribes what to do in alternative circumstances. For instance the conditional strategy: "retreat if smaller than opponent, escalate if larger than opponent" can be an ESS for contests between a pair of opponents over a disputed resource (Maynard Smith and Parker 1976, Hammerstein 1981). There are doubts as to whether ESSs will ever be mixed strategies, in the sense that an animal plays strategies randomly within the ESS probabilities, on the grounds that selection would favor some form of conditional ESS. The argument can be formulated as follows. If each component-pure strategy of a mixed ESS has the same expected fitness, then any mutant that behaves non-randomly can spread if it can profit by linking a given strategy with a given phenotypic state (Parker 1982). However, cases where animals have imperfect information about states, or roles, in a contest, can generate mixed ESSs that are also conditional upon an animal's estimate of its roles (Hammerstein and Parker 1981).

Difficulties with the ESS approach largely concern defining the appropriate strategy set for a particular game. It is not always easy to decide what mutant strategies may be possible, and what the payoffs would be. Further, it is not likely to be fruitful to attempt to test ESS models by trying to observe mutant strategies in nature! Despite this sort of difficulty, the fit between the predictions of many ESS models and behavior observed in nature is often encouraging, and the ESS concept must certainly be regarded as one of the major developments in SOCIOBIOLOGY.   GAP

Bibliography

Dawkins, R. 1976: *The selfish gene*. Oxford and New York: Oxford University Press.

*———— 1980: Good strategy or evolutionarily stable strategy? In *Sociobiology: Beyond Nature/Nurture?* eds. G.W. Barlow and J. Silverberg. Boulder, Colorado: Westview Press.

———— 1982: *The extended phenotype*. Oxford and San Francisco: W.H. Freeman.

Greenwood, P.J., Harvey, P.H. and Slatkin, M. 1985: *Evolution: essays in honour of John Maynard Smith*. Cambridge and New York: Cambridge University Press.

Hammerstein, P. 1981: The role of asymmetries in animal contests. *Animal behaviour* 29, 193–205.

Hammerstein, P. and Parker, G.A. 1981: The asymmetric war of attrition. *Journal of theoretical biology*.

Maynard Smith, J. 1972: *On evolution*. Edinburgh: Edinburgh University Press.

———— 1974: The theory of games and the evolution of animal conflicts. *Journal of theoretical biology* 47, 209–221.

*———— 1979: Game theory and the evolution of behaviour. *Proceedings of the Royal Society of London*, Series B, 205, 475–88.

———— 1981: Will a sexual population evolve to an ESS? *American naturalist* 117, 1015–18.

———— and Parker, G.A. 1976: The logic of asymmetric contests. *Animal behaviour* 24, 159–75.

Oster, G. and Wilson, E.O. 1978: *Caste and ecology in the social insects*. Princeton: Princeton University Press.

Parker, G.A. 1982: Phenotype-limited evolutionarily stable strategies. In *Current problems in sociobiology*, ed. King's College Sociobiology Group. Cambridge: Cambridge University Press.

———— 1984: Evolutionarily stable strategies. In *Behavioural ecology*. 2nd edn, eds. J.R. Krebs and N.B. Davies. Oxford: Blackwell Scientific Publications.

expectancy Anticipation of some future event. Tolman developed a theory of learning based on the notion of expectancy, the fundamental idea being that organisms exposed to regular sequences of events came to expect or anticipate later members of the sequence as soon as the earlier occurred. A rat that had learned to run through a maze to obtain food was said to expect that food would be delivered if it performed certain responses, or if certain stimuli (those associated with the correct path through the maze) appeared.

It can hardly be doubted that animals are sensitive to regularly repeating sequences of events. A simple demonstration is provided by an experiment on HABITUATION. If an animal is repeatedly exposed to a particular stimulus (a tap, a noise, a light) presented at regular intervals, the reaction initially elicited by that stimulus will soon habituate. But if the regular sequence is interrupted, e.g. simply by omitting the stimulus at a time when it would normally have occurred, the animal will show, by an abrupt change in its behavior, pricking its ears, turning its head towards the source of the stimulus, that it has detected this omission. To do so, it must presumably have formed some representation of the regular sequence: it must, in other words, have been expecting the stimulus to occur and been surprised when it did not.

The resistance to an expectancy theory arises from a doctrinaire adherence to a strong form of BEHAVIORISM, which requires the psychologist to study and predict only what his subject does, and does not allow him to appeal to any inner mental life to explain that behavior. But it soon became apparent that, even with inarticulate organisms (perhaps particularly with them), what an animal has learned or may be said to know is not always immediately evident in its behavior. Although it may have been true that in Tolman's theory as Guthrie said, "the rat is left buried in thought", this is paradoxically a virtue if it means that the theory stresses the gap between knowledge and action. Recent trends in the theory of learning have marked a return to Tolman's views, and few theorists today are troubled by talk of expectancies of reinforcement, differences in the effectiveness of expected and unexpected reinforcement, or animals being surprised by the occurrence of an unexpected event or the omission of an expected one (Gray 1975).   NJM

Bibliography

Gray, J.A. 1975: *Elements of a two-process theory of learning*. London: Academic Press.

Tolman, Edward C. 1932: *Purposive behavior in animals and men*. New York: Appleton-Century-Crofts.

exploration A form of APPETITIVE BEHAVIOR by which it is assumed that the animal gains knowledge of its environment. Some forms of exploratory behavior seem to be aimed at a specific goal, but other forms sometimes appear to be motivated by curiosity, and to have no obvious relevance to more material aspects of behavior, such as feeding, sexual behavior or nest maintenance. Studies of such apparently motiveless aspects of exploration, which include play, show that learning does take place, and this may be a prime function of exploration.   DJM

Bibliography

McFarland, D.J. 1985: *Animal behaviour*. London: Pitman.

Tinbergen, N. 1969: *The study of instinct*. Oxford: Clarendon Press.

Toates, F.M. 1980: *Animal behavior – a systems approach*. Chichester: John Wiley.

extinction The process of decline in performance of learned activities which are no longer reinforced. Some aspects of learning require REINFORCEMENT for the establishment and maintenance of the response. If the reinforcement is removed the response will start to be extinguished. For example, a rat may learn to obtain food by pressing a bar. If reward is withheld, so that bar presses no longer result in food delivery, the rate of bar pressing will gradually decline to zero, and the response is said to have become extinguished.

Extinction is due to a learned inhibition of the original learned response, and not to forgetting. This can be shown by the spontaneous recovery of the original response that sometimes occurs when the animal is placed in the training situation some time after the response has been extinguished.

The rate of extinction is partly a function of the similarity between the learning situation and the conditions of extinction. The greater the difference between the two sets of circumstances the more quickly extinction occurs. This effect is known as the GENERALIZATION decrement. The rate of extinction is also affected by the reinforcement schedule that operates during learning. If the rat is rewarded for every bar press a consistent reinforcement schedule is in operation, but if only some bar presses are rewarded the animal is said to be on a partial reward schedule. Extinction proceeds at a lower rate following a partial reward schedule compared with a consistent reward schedule. This effect, known as the partial reinforcement effect, has been the subject of a large amount of research, and it remains the subject of considerable controversy (Mackintosh 1974, 1983).

DJM

Bibliography

Mackintosh, Nicholas J. 1974: *The psychology of animal learning*. London and New York: Academic Press.

——— 1983: *Conditioning and associative learning*. Oxford: Clarendon Press.

F

fear A motivational state aroused by specific external stimuli and promoting avoidance, defensive and escape behavior. Fear may be aroused as an innate response to certain external stimuli such as loud noise, loss of support and pain. The influential behaviorist psychologist J.B. WATSON maintained (1924) that these were the only stimuli capable of invoking fear as an instinct, and that most fear responses were acquired through conditioning. However the work of ethologists such as LORENZ and TINBERGEN showed that there is a variety of SIGN STIMULI of which animals have an innate fear. These include hawk-like silhouettes (Tinbergen 1951), eye-like patterns (Blest 1957) and certain owl features (Hinde 1954). Fear of snakes seems to be innate in various primates including man (Hebb 1946), and detailed studies of the maturation of fear in children provide no evidence for the behaviorist view that fear is primarily acquired as a result of conditioning (Gray 1971).

On the other hand there is also plenty of evidence that fear can be acquired through learning. In addition to their innate repertoire of responses to frightening stimuli, many animals are capable of learning to fear previously neutral stimuli, and of learning new responses to avoid frightening stimuli. Fear of previously neutral stimuli may develop through the process of CLASSICAL CONDITIONING, or ASSOCIATION. When an animal responds to a frightening stimulus it does so in the presence of other neutral stimuli, such as background sounds and the visual features of everyday life. If one of these neutral stimuli is consistently paired with the frightening stimulus it is associated with it and eventually comes to elicit fear, even in the absence of the original frightening stimulus. J.B. Watson's well-known experiment in this field involved an eleven-month-old boy called Albert, who appeared to have no fear of animals. He did, however, show signs of fear at the sound of a steel bar being struck loudly. Albert initially showed no fear of a white rat, but when the rat was repeatedly presented together with the sound of the steel bar being struck he became frightened of the rat even when it was presented without any accompanying sound. Subsequent experiments have shown that although classical conditioning is undoubtedly important in the acquisition of fear it is easier to transfer fear (by a conditioning procedure) to some stimuli than to others. Albert may well have had a latent fear of animals (such fear develops rapidly during the second year of life) and would probably not have so readily acquired fear of a more neutral stimulus.

It is thought by many psychologists that the acquisition of new avoidance patterns is accomplished in two stages. In the first stage the animal learns to fear particular environmental stimuli, as a result of a consistent association with aversive situations. In the natural environment, for example, an animal might repeatedly see a predator when feeding in a particular locality, and might consequently acquire a fear of the feeding area as a result of conditioning.

In the second stage of avoidance learning the animal learns how to prevent or remove the fear. A bird which repeatedly saw a cat in a garden might acquire a fear of the garden, but could prevent the fear from arising simply by not visiting the garden. (See AVOIDANCE).

In addition to its role in MOTIVATION, fear also has an emotional aspect which is important in communication. The fearful animal has increased autonomic activity, including elevated heart beat rate, defecation, piloerection (hair standing up), and sweating. This activity is often accompanied by facial expressions and postures that are characteristic of the species.

The manifestation of such display varies with the circumstances. For example, radio-telemetry studies show that an incubating herring gull (*Larus argentatus*) has an increasing heart beat rate when approached by a human, even though there may be few outward signs of fear. In social situations, however, herring gulls incorporate outward signs of fear into their displays. This is particularly true of THREAT and of the conflict that arises in dispute over territory. At the territorial boundary there is usually a balance between aggression and fear which results in a classic APPROACH/AVOIDANCE CONFLICT. As the animal approaches its opponent the fear becomes greater than the aggression, so the tendency to retreat predominates. As the animal moves away the fear subsides and aggression predominates once more. In these circumstances, animals often show ambivalent, threat, redirected and DISPLACEMENT ACTIVITY. In some species these have become ritualized in such a way that their role in communication is enhanced and the direct involvement of fear is reduced.

Fear also provides a basis for social communication in the case of alarm. In many cases an alarm signal such as the call of a bird or the bobbing white tail of a rabbit is likely to attract the attention of a predator, and the individual that issues the alarm may be endangered. Such instances of ALTRUISM in which an individual disadvantages itself to the benefit of others, are thought to evolve only when the other animals are likely to be close relatives of the animal giving the alarm. Overt signs of fear, pain, or danger are generally absent when there is no clear benefit to the kin. The cricket (*Acheta domestica*) simply stops chirping when it senses danger. The chief beneficiaries of an alarm signal would probably be rival males. Similarly, antelopes that are pulled down by predators on the African plain suffer in silence. To call for help would only endanger other members of the herd.

Many of the physiological aspects of fear are also common to AGGRESSION. From the evolutionary viewpoint this is perhaps not surprising, because both are concerned with the protection and defense of the individual, its kin and resources. In vertebrates both involve *autonomic* activity which prepares the animal for emergency action. During sympathetic activation the blood supply to the brain, heart, lungs and muscles is increased, making the animal ready for "fight or flight". Mild fear may lead to increased vigilance which may give rise to aggression or defense, depending on whether a predator or rival is detected. Many aspects of defensive behavior are highly specialized and evolved to suit the animal's ecological niche. They sometimes involve elements of both fear and aggression. The scorpion uses its sting both to poison an attacker and against its prey. Similarly, snakes use their teeth and venom both for prey capture and for defense. The horns and antlers of antelopes and deer are primarily used in aggressive encounters between rivals, but may also be used in defense against predators. Some retaliatory defensive structures have evolved primarily as anti-predator devices. Examples include the spines of hedgehogs and porcupines, and of sticklebacks. The three-spined stickleback (*Gasterosteus aculeatus*), however, also uses its spines in encounters with rival males, and to ward off over-enthusiastic females during courtship. For some species the best form of defense is attack, while for others it is escape. In many species the mixture of fear and aggression is complex. Rats and pigeons usually show signs of fear when given electric shocks in the laboratory. If, however, another member of the species is present, it may well be attacked. DJM

Bibliography

Blest, A.D. 1957: The evolution of protective displays in the *Satumioidea* and *Sphingidae* (*lepidoptera*). *Behaviour* 11, 257–58.

*Edmunds, Malcolm 1974: *Defence in animals*. Harlow: Longman.

*Gray, Jeffrey 1971: *The psychology of fear and stress*. London: Weidenfeld and Nicolson; New York: McGraw-Hill.

Halliday, T.R. and Slater, P.J.B. eds 1983: *Animal behaviour*, vol. 1, *Causes and effects*. Oxford: Blackwell Scientific Publications.

Hebb, D.O. 1946: On the nature of fear. *Psychology review* 53, 259–76.

Hinde, R.A. 1954: Factors governing the changes in strength of a partially inborn response, as shown by the mobbing behavior of the chaffinch (*Fringilla coelebs*). *Proceedings of the Royal Society of London* 142, 306–31 and 331–58.

Tinbergen, N. 1951: *The study of instinct.* Oxford: Clarendon Press. Reprinted with new introduction Oxford, 1969.

Watson, John B. 1924: *Behaviorism.* New York: Norton. Reprinted 1958. Chicago: Chicago University Press; London: Cambridge University Press.

feedback The effect of the consequences of behavior on future behavior. Negative feedback occurs when the consequences diminish the level of performance of, or probability of, future behavior. The consequences of feeding (i.e. intake of food) have a diminishing effect upon hunger, and the animal is less likely to eat in the near future. Positive feedback occurs when the consequences increase the level of future behavior. In some cases, for instance, it is possible for feeding to have a temporary incremental effect upon appetite and so increase the apparent level of hunger. Positive feedback tends to be unstable, leading to escalation of the behavior, and in nature it is usually kept in check by simultaneous negative feedback (as in the case of feeding) or by environmental constraints.

Negative feedback processes tend to have a stabilizing influence and they are particularly important in those aspects of animal behavior, such as HOMEOSTASIS and ORIENTATION, in which maintenance of equilibrium is important. The essential elements of a negative feedback process are illustrated in the figure. The reference x represents the required level of output, and is usually supplied from some other part of the system. The error signal is the difference between the reference x and the feedback signal z. The error signal actuates the controlled device which produces an output y. In animal behavior studies y is usually some aspect of the behavior of the animal. The feedback mechanism monitors some aspect of the output and translates this into a signal z, which is subtracted from the reference x to give the error signal (x-z). For example, the body temperature $x = 39°C$

may be compared with a feedback signal (actual body temperature) of 38°C, giving an error signal of 1°C. This actuates the warning mechanisms of the body (controlled device) to increase heat output y. The consequent rise in body temperature is sensed by the feedback mechanism, and z consequently becomes larger. The feedback mechanisms that operate in real physiological and behavioral control systems are considerably more complex than that illustrated here, but the principle remains the same.   DJM

Bibliography

Hogan, J.A. 1980: Homeostasis and behaviour. In *Analysis of motivational processes*, eds. F.M. Toates and T.R. Halliday. London: Academic Press.

Toates, F.M. 1980: *Animal behavior – a systems approach.* Chichester: John Wiley.

fitness In evolutionary biology "fitness" refers to Darwinian fitness – that is, the evolutionary success of an individual organism, or the average evolutionary success of organisms sharing a particular biological characteristic. In principle evolutionary success is measurable in terms of survival and reproduction, though different aspects of this are stressed in different contexts: survival, total number of offspring, or number of surviving offspring (i.e. REPRODUCTIVE SUCCESS). In practice, there may be obstacles to the measurement of these, and less satisfactory indicators may be used instead. The Spencerian phrase "survival of the fittest", though accepted by DARWIN as a summary of natural selection, is apt to mislead unless it is appreciated that it is a tautological way of expressing a principle that is nonetheless far from trivial: by definition, the fittest are those that survive (and reproduce). The more recently developed concept of inclusive fitness is a modification of Darwinian fitness to take account not only of reproductive success but also of successful aid to relatives other than offspring (see ALTRUISM; NATURAL SELECTION).

In other contexts, fitness may refer to health, physical fitness or physiological capacities. Sometimes there may be correlations between fitness in these senses and Darwinian fitness, but they are not synonymous. RDA

Bibliography

Ridley, M. 1985: *The problems of evolution.* Oxford and New York: Oxford University Press.

fixed action pattern (FAP) Recognizable pattern or sequence of behavior which, once begun, is completed independently of external influence. (See ETHOLOGY.)

food selection The tendency for animals to choose among available food items and so achieve a diet that is characteristic of the species. Some animals, such as the rat, are omnivorous and will eat almost anything. Others (feeding specialists) eat a single type of food, for example the koala bear (*Phascolarctos cinereus*) which eats only eucalyptus leaves. Among grazing animals food selection occurs partly as a result of the feeding technique. The buffalo (*Syncerus caffer*) selects plants on the basis of the leaf-stem ratio, preferring species with the most leaf. The plant is drawn into the mouth by the action of the tongue and lips and then pressed against the palate. A short pull of the head results in the leaves being stripped from the more fibrous stem. Feeding specialists generally have innate recognition of suitable foods and often have physiological specializations designed to cope with the restricted diet.

Omnivorous animals are more likely than feeding specialists to encounter poisonous foods and they also require more elaborate procedures for ensuring a balanced diet. Rats are notoriously good at avoiding poisoned food, and their success is achieved partly by initially avoiding novel foods. Faced with a shortage of familiar foods the rat will sample a small amount of a novel food and wait a number of hours before proceeding further. Garcia et al. (1955) discovered that if rats were fed a harmless substance and afterwards made to vomit they rapidly developed an aversion to the substance. Subsequently it was shown that a rat can learn in a single trial to avoid a novel food if consumption of the food is followed by vomiting. Such rapid and specific learning seems to be restricted to certain kinds of association, such as that between the cues that normally accompany feeding and the physiological consequences of food ingestion. A similar principle applies to specific hunger. Rodgers and Rozin (1966) found that thiamine deficient rats show an immediate, marked preference for new food, even when the new food is thiamine deficient and the old food has a thiamine supplement. The preference is short-lived. If however consumption of a novel food is followed by recovery from dietary deficiency, the rat rapidly learns to prefer the novel food. Such rapid learning on the basis of the physiological consequences of ingestion enables the rat to maintain a degree of food selection by avoiding novel foods and yet to adapt quickly and relatively safely to changing circumstances. DJM

Bibliography

Braveman, N.S. and Bronstein, P. 1985: *Experimental assessments and clinical applications of conditioned food aversion.* New York: New York Academy of Sciences.

Garcia, J., Kimeldorf, D.J. and Koelling, R.A. 1955: Conditioned aversion to saccharin resulting from exposure to gamma radiation. *Science* 122, 157–58.

Rodgers, W. and Rozin, P. 1966: Novel food preferences in thiamine-deficient rats. *Journal of comparative physiological psychology* 61, 1–4.

foraging Or searching for food, has several components. Before they can actually eat anything most animals must locate the area where food is to be found and then discriminate food items from inedible objects. Where food is unpredictably distributed in space, a predator may have to cover quite long distances in its search for food, expending time and energy in the process. Animals might therefore be expected to forage as efficiently as possible (gaining maximum energy in the form of food but expending as little as possible in searching for it). This is the assumption behind "optimal foraging" models, which have attracted particular attention. On investigation, many animals including birds, fish and insects have been found to forage optimally, or nearly so.　　　　MSD

Bibliography

Kagel, J.H., Green, L. and Caraco, T. 1986: When foragers discount the future: constraint or adaptation? *Animal behaviour* 34, 271–83.

Krebs, J., Stephens, D.W. and Sutherland, J. 1985: Perspectives in optimal foraging. In *Perspectives in ornithology*, eds. A.H. Brush and G.A. Clark. Cambridge: Cambridge University Press.

Rodman, P.S. and Cant, J.G.H. eds. 1984: *Adaptations for foraging in nonhuman primates*. New York: Columbia University Press.

frustration A state of motivation that occurs when an animal's actions do not lead to the expected consequences or rewards. A hungry animal is likely to be frustrated if an expected food reward is delayed, if the food is less palatable than usual, or if the animal is physically prevented from obtaining food although it can see it.

The frustrated animal first tries harder to reach the goal, a phenomenon sometimes called the frustration effect (Amsel 1958). It may then indulge in irrelevant DISPLACEMENT ACTIVITIES such as grooming, or in AGGRESSION toward an innocent bystander.

Physiological changes during frustration are similar to those of fear, and these together with some of the behavioral manifestations of frustration are alleviated by tranquilizing drugs (Gray 1971). When animals are repeatedly frustrated in a particular situation they develop an anticipation which is aversive and leads to avoidance of the situation. This competes with the original approach motivations so that a conflict arises. When the conflicting tendencies are particularly strong and prolonged the animal may develop symptoms of acute anxiety, leading to a stress syndrome and abnormal behavior.　　　　DJM

Bibliography

Amsel, A. 1958: The role of frustrative nonreward in noncontinuous reward situations. *Psychological bulletin* 55, 102–19.

Gray, Jeffrey A. 1971: *The psychology of fear and stress*. London: Weidenfeld and Nicolson; New York: McGraw-Hill.

Toates, F.M. 1980: *Animal behavior – a systems approach*. Chichester: John Wiley.

G

generalization Absence of DISCRIMINATION. When an animal has been trained to respond to one stimulus it may or may not respond in the same way to another stimulus. When it does so respond it is said to generalize between the two stimuli, and when it does not do so it is said to discriminate between them.

When presented with a series of stimuli of which one is familiar, animals often produce a weaker response the greater the difference between the familiar and the test stimuli, giving rise to a generalization gradient. For example, Guttman and Kalish (1958) trained pigeons to peck at colored lights to obtain food rewards. A pigeon trained to peck at a yellow light showed a progressively diminishing response when presented with lights of a different color.

DJM

Bibliography

Guttman, N. and Kalish, H.I. 1958: *Scientific American* 198, 77–82.

Mackintosh, N.J. 1974: *The psychology of animal learning.* London: Academic Press.

goal The object, purpose, or aim of behavior. Apparently goal-directed behavior may arise in a number of different ways. Behavior which is clearly adaptation to the environment in the sense of being an appropriate product of evolution is sometimes said to be goal-directed. This does not mean that the animal is aware of any goal, but simply that the behavior appears to serve some end: namely survival or reproduction.

An alternative use of the term goal is the reference to an end-state which an animal appears to strive for. Thus a FORAGING animal may be said to have food as its goal. Some scientists believe that the goal is actually represented in the animal's brain as an image of the state of affairs that the animal desires to achieve (see SEARCH IMAGE). Others prefer to think of a goal as the natural end-point of behavior, the inevitable outcome of the way behavior is organized. Thus the foraging behavior may cease when food is obtained, without the animal necessarily having a goal-image of the food during its search behavior.

DJM

Bibliography

Weiskrantz, L. ed. 1985: *Animal intelligence.* Oxford: Clarendon.

goal gradient This concept is usually applied to a particular phenomenon of maze learning in animals. When performing in a maze animals often learn not to turn into the blind alleys closest to the goal box long before they learn not to turn into blind alleys further away. This behavior is in conformity with the goal gradient hypothesis which states that blind alleys will be eliminated in reverse order beginning with the one closest to the goal. The hypothesis is based on the idea that in learning experiments prompt reward is more effective than delayed reward. The nature of the last blind alley will be learnt first because it is closest to the goal box. In fact, experiments show that blind alley entry is also affected by factors of maze design, characteristics of the animal and other variables. This may explain the conflicting results which have frequently been reported concerning the goal gradient hypothesis.

RMcH

Bibliography

Hull, C.L. 1943: *Principles of behavior.* New York: Appleton-Century-Crofts.

Mackintosh, N.J. 1974: *The psychology of animal learning.* London: Academic Press.

greeting When two conspecifics meet, their response to one another may be hostile, but if not, and they are positively attracted to each other, they will probably engage in a more or less elaborate series of species characteristic behavior patterns toward each other. These rituals are referred to as greeting displays. Some birds such as nesting kittiwakes have elaborate greeting ceremonies the object of which is to ensure that the new arrival at the nest is indeed the mated partner of the nest-holder and will feed its own genetic offspring. Such greetings are mostly found in pair-bonded species that separate for feeding and then meet up again.

Among social mammals, greetings are extended to other members of the species as well as mates, and involve highly stereotyped behavior patterns such as the side-by-side, head-to-tail, genital sniffing of dogs. Among primates greetings are most marked in chimpanzees, and occur whenever individuals who know each other meet after a temporary spell of separation. Males frequently touch each others' testicles, while both sexes may kiss, touch hands, or hug each other.

In humans greetings are culturally specified, but the fact that they exist, and often involve hand touching, embracing and kissing indicates that their roots may lie in our primate ancestry. (See also BOND.)   VR

Bibliography

Halliday, T.R. and Slater, P.J.B. 1983: *Animal behaviour*, vol. 2. *Communication*. New York: Freeman.

Poole, T. 1985: *Social behaviour in mammals*. Glasgow: Blackie.

gregariousness In ethology, the tendency of individuals to associate in groups. One way of explaining gregariousness relates to its survival value (see NATURAL SELECTION). Two main explanations in these terms have been proposed, relating to advantages accruing to gregarious individuals (or their relatives – see ALTRUISM) in predator avoidance and in food acquisition (Bertram 1978). A quite different type of explanation relates to the causal and developmental basis of gregariousness. In a well known primate study (1932) Zuckerman proposed that sexual BONDS between adult males and females were the primary factor in group cohesion, but it is now clear that this was incorrect. To say instead that groups cohere because individuals are socially attractive to each other is probably true but circular, and it may be more profitable to investigate RELATIONSHIPS AND SOCIAL STRUCTURES in a detailed way than to search for an overall explanation of gregariousness (Chalmers 1979).   RDA

Bibliography

Bertram, B.C.R. 1978: Living in groups: predators and prey. In *Behavioral ecology: an evolutionary approach*, eds. J.R. Krebs and N.B. Davies. Oxford: Blackwell Scientific Publications; Sunderland, Mass.: Sinauer Associates.

Chalmers, N. 1979: *Social behaviour in primates*. London: Edward Arnold; Baltimore: University Park Press.

Krebs, J.R. and Davies, N.B. 1984: *Behavioral ecology*. 2nd edn. Oxford: Blackwell Scientific Publications.

Zuckerman, S. 1932: *The social life of monkeys and apes*. London: Kegan Paul; New York: Harcourt Brace.

group property A property of a collective which is not reducible to the sum of the properties of its parts, e.g. population size.

group selection Differential survival of groups of organisms on the basis of differential group properties (see ALTRUISM; NATURAL SELECTION).

H

habituation A decrease in responsiveness resulting from repeated stimulation. Habituation is normally regarded as a form of learning, although it involves loss of responsiveness rather than the acquisition of new responses. A snail crawling on a table will retract into its shell if the table is tapped. It will emerge after a while and continue crawling. Another tap on the table will cause the snail to retract again, but it will emerge more quickly this time. Repeated taps will have progressively smaller effects until the snail ignores them altogether.

Habituation shows many typical features of learning including GENERALIZATION and EXTINCTION. If the stimulus is withheld for a long time the habituated response reappears.   DJM

Bibliography

Mackintosh, N.J. 1983: *Conditioning and associative learning.* Oxford and New York: Oxford University Press.

Harlow, Harry F. (1905–81) Born in Fairfield, Iowa, Harlow studied at Stanford University, where he took a doctorate in psychology in 1930. He was professor of psychology at the University of Wisconsin where he founded the famous primate laboratory. Harlow's first studies concerned processes of learning and the effects of cortical lesions in monkeys. These investigations led to the concept of learning to learn, a process of rapid acquisition of a problem-solving strategy. This idea is not compatible with the behavioristic models of learning as a chain of associations. Harlow also studied the roles of curiosity and motivation in the learning process.

In the 1950s Harlow and his wife, Margaret, carried on a program of research on attachment and mother-infant socializa-tion. In the laboratory they investigated how very young macaque monkeys behaved towards surrogate-mothers made of wire or covered in terry-cloth. The young preferred contact with the terry-cloth mother even if it was not the source of food like the wire-mother. The Harlows extended their research on the nature of "love" in an attempt to understand the effects that early separation between mother and child has on psychodynamic development and sexual behavior. They also tried to discover how to promote recovery from the behavior disorders, such as depression, which the separation caused. Their study of primate behavior helped to highlight the characteristics of human psychological development and the causes of the onset of psychopathology (Harlow and Mears 1979).   LM

Bibliography

Harlow, H.F. 1950: Learning and satiation of response in intrinsically motivated complex puzzle performance by monkeys. *Journal of comparative and physiological psychology* 43, 289–94.

———— 1958: The nature of love. *American psychologist* 13, 673–85.

———— 1962: The development of affectional patterns in infant monkeys. In *Determinants of infant behavior*, vol 2, ed. B.M. Foss. London: Methuen; New York: Wiley.

———— and Harlow, M.K. 1965: The affectional systems. In *Behavior of nonhuman primates*, vol 2, eds. A.M. Shrier, H.F. Harlow and F. Stollnitz. New York: Academic Press.

———— and Harlow, M.K. 1969: Effects of various mother-infant relationships on rhesus monkey behaviors. In *Determinants of infant behavior*, vol. 4, ed. B.M. Foss. London: Methuen; New York: Wiley.

———— and Mears, C.E. 1979: *The human model: primate perspectives*. Washington, D.C.: Winston and Sons.

hedonic Together with AGONIC this term refers to two extreme mechanisms of social cohesion and to the corresponding modes of mental activity.

Hedonic social cohesion is exhibited by chimpanzee society (and possibly also by groups of gorilla and orang-utan). In these animals, social cohesion is periodically re-established (after periods of dispersion into groups of two, three or more), by excited sessions of mutual display in which food sharing and many forms of body contact occur: hugging, tumble play, slapping, greeting by hand touching, and pseudo sexual behavior as well as mating. In these ways social cohesion is rewarded (in contrast to the agonic form which is based on avoidance of punishment). The display sessions show a build-up of excitement to a peak, which suggests that the initial arousal is usually low and kept so by frequent body contact. Agonistic episodes are frequently followed by appeasement gestures, especially between males, who, thereby, seek reconciliation. The periodic nature of social gatherings and the low state of arousal have two consequences (1) They allow attention to be directed continuously to environmental investigation; and (2) the arousal can fluctuate with the rise and fall of interest in aspects of the physical environment. Exploration is a self-rewarding activity and so generates a positive FEEDBACK. This keeps up the interest in any aspect of the environment for long enough for the ape to become acquainted with all its different features. Hence the power of investigation is generated. As exploration is the essential prerequisite for the operation of intelligence, (see Halstead) so also is the hedonic mode.

The discovery of the two modes was itself the result of the attempt to classify the ATTENTION STRUCTURE of primate societies. Since then it has been possible to see that they rest on an autonomic infrastructure revealed by the work of Gellhorn, who showed that in an egotropic mode, essentially the same as the agonic, the nervous system expends energy through a state of readiness for action in which heart rate increases and cortical excitation also takes place with a rise in muscular tension. In the other, the trophotropic mode, energy stores are built up, heart rate declines and cortical

excitation with its accompanying muscle tension is low, as would be expected in the hedonic mode. Moreover the Laceys have shown that when the heart rate slows ability to take in information is increased and, hence, exploration made possible; thus demonstrating in another way that the hedonic mode is the essential condition for the operation of intelligence.   MRAC

Bibliography

Chance, M.R.A. 1980. The social structure of attention and the operation of intelligence. In *The exercise of intelligence*, ed. Eric Sinderland and Malcolm T. Smith. New York and London: Garland STPM Press.

Gellhorn, E. 1966–7. The tuning of the nervous system: physiological foundations and implications for behavior. *Perspectives in biology and medicine.* 10, 559–91.

Halstead, W.C. 1951: Brain and intelligence. In *Cerebral mechanisms in behavior*, ed. L.A. Jefferies. New York: John Wiley.

Knapp, P.H. ed. 1963: *Expression of the emotions in man.* New York: International Universities Press.

Lacey, J.I. et al. 1963: The visceral level: situational determinants and behavioral correlates of autonomic response patterns. In *Expression of the emotions in man*, ed. P.H. Knapp. New York: International Universities Press.

hierarchy The word has been used in two quite different contexts in ethology. In the field of MOTIVATION various ethologists during the 1940s developed branching (or nested) hierarchical models of the underlying control of behavior. The best known is that of TINBERGEN, often illustrated by the example of the three spined stickleback, *Gasterosteus aculeatus*. Each major behavior system was called an instinct: for instance there was a reproductive instinct and a feeding instinct. Corresponding to each instinct was a "center", a locus in the brain, which was "charged up" over time with drive, or action potential, specific to that instinct. This drive would be released by appropriate external stimuli and discharged, ultimately in overt behavior. But instead of being discharged directly it would activate sub-centers. For example the reproductive instinct of the stickleback was thought to have a nest-building sub-center, a courtship sub-center etc. The hierarchy had many levels. The courtship sub-center in turn discharged into a series of sub-sub-centers, corresponding to various courtship behavior patterns. The hypothetical hierarchy went on sub-dividing until individual muscle units were reached.

The total behavior of the animal could therefore be thought of as being controlled by something like the hierarchical chain of command of an army. This is an obviously efficient system of organization, and there is likely to be some truth underlying the early hierarchical models. The models have been criticized, but usually for reasons only distantly connected with their hierarchical nature. They have been accused of neglecting the important role of FEEDBACK in bringing behavior to an end: in the simplest version of the classical models behavior came to an end when it ran out of action specific energy rather than when feedback signaled that it had achieved its goal. The models have been accused of physiological naiveté, of postulating unitary centers in the brain where the reality may be distributed and diffuse. Some modern ethologists feel that the basic idea of hierarchical organization is too important to throw out just because the classical models can be criticized.

The other context in which the word hierarchy has been used is in social relationships. Animals in groups are often described as forming DOMINANCE hierarchies. The classic example is the "pecking order" of farmyard hens. Each hen learns the identity of the others in her group, learns to defer to individuals that usually beat her in fights, and learns to expect immediate surrender from those that she usually beats. In the simplest cases a linear hierarchy is discerned such that A pecks B, B pecks C, C pecks D etc. Dominance hierarchies are not always simply linear in this way; sometimes nontransitive relationships develop in which A pecks B, B pecks C, but C pecks A. Dominance hierarchies are not always recognized by overt aggression. The ethologist is free to look for a hierarchy expressed by any behavior pattern. For instance primato-logists sometimes count whether particular monkeys get out of the way of other particular monkeys: A is described as dominant to B if B gets out of A's way, but A walks straight on when B is in his path. Other hierarchies have been constructed according to who looks at whom, who is the center of attention (see ATTENTION STRUCTURE; for "dependent rank" see KINSHIP).

True dominance hierarchies depend upon individual recognition. Various kinds of apparent dominance hierarchy can arise when there is no individual recognition. An observer may note that A usually beats B who usually beats C etc. He may conclude that he has seen a dominance hierarchy, but in fact there may be no individual recognition at all. The hierarchy may be based directly on size: A is the largest, B the next largest, etc. Or A may simply be the individual with the most aggressive disposition. True dominance hierarchies with individual recognition have often been interpreted as beneficial for the whole group, because they cut down the amount of overt aggression in the group. Groups of hens that have formed a stable dominance hierarchy produce more eggs than groups that are continually fighting to establish a dominance hierarchy. Nowadays, however, accounts in terms of benefit to the group are not generally thought to have any explanatory power, and the existence of dominance hierarchies has to be explained in terms of benefits and costs to individuals surrendering or not surrendering in particular circumstances.   RD

Bibliography

Chase, I.D. 1985: The sequential analysis of aggressive acts during hierarchy formation: an application of the 'jigsaw puzzle' approach. *Animal behaviour* 33, 86–100.

*Dawkins, R. 1976: Hierarchical organization: a candidate principle for ethology. In *Growing points in ethology*, eds. P.P.G. Bateson and R.A. Hinde. Cambridge and New York: Cambridge University Press.

Seyfarth, R.M. 1981: Do monkeys rank each other? *Behavioral and brain science* 4, 447–8.

*Tinbergen, N. 1951: *The study of instinct*. Oxford: Clarendon Press.

homeostasis Literally "staying the same". Living organisms and some self-regulating machines (such as thermostatically controlled heating systems, or automatic pilots) have the ability to resist change, and to keep certain properties or variables constant, even when factors are present which would tend to change them. This is most commonly done by means of negative FEEDBACK, an arrangement whereby any small fluctuations of the property in question are detected and messages fed back to an earlier point in the causal chain, where compensatory changes are made to cancel out the original fluctuations; hence the name negative feedback.

Homeostatic mechanisms are responsible for many important aspects of automatic self-regulation in animals, from the stabilization of blood chemistry, to the fine control of motor behavior.   DDC

Bibliography

Hogan, J.A. 1980: Homeostasis and behaviour. In *Analysis of motivational processes*, ed. F.M. Toates and T.R. Halliday. London: Academic Press.

Toates, F.M. 1980: *Animal behavior – a systems approach*. Chichester: John Wiley.

home range The area of space in which an animal normally confines its movements. (See TERRITORIALITY.)   MR

homology and analogy In evolutionary biology, both terms refer to similarities between organisms, but they are of contrasting types. Homology refers to similarities between two or more species which are due to shared characteristics inherited from a common evolutionary ancestor; whereas analogy refers to similarities which are due to factors other than common ancestry, such as convergent evolution, where species not closely related develop similar characteristics through subjection to similar natural selection pressures (see Immelmann 1980). Similarities based on homology tend to be close, detailed and structural: similarities based on analogy, however, tend to be general, superficial and functional. Comparative evolutionary arguments have repeatedly revolved around the distinction between homology and analogy, and they have been particularly acute in ethology, as behavioral comparisons across species have often been made, but homology is difficult to demonstrate. LORENZ (1973) has defended the use of an ethological approach that is frankly based on analogy, but while this is undoubtedly preferable to a confusion of the two, there remains a widespread caution about placing undue reliance on either homologies or analogies, especially in relation to behavior (see Barnett 1981).   RDA

Bibliography

Barnett, S.A 1981 *Modern ethology: the science of animal behavior*. New York, Oxford: Oxford University Press.

Immelmann, K. 1980 *Introduction to ethology*. New York, London: Plenum Press.

Lorenz, K. 1973 Analogy as a source of knowledge. *Science* 185, 229–34.

hormones Chemical substances secreted by the endocrine glands and transported in the blood stream to sites of action in various parts of the body. Hormones have profound influences on physiology and behavior and play an important role in the development of certain aspects of behavior.

Hormones are present in the blood in very small quantities and the life of individual molecules is short. To have a sustained effect, therefore, hormones have to be secreted continuously in precisely controlled quantities. In some glands secretion is actuated by the nervous system, in others it is stimulated by other hormones. Control is achieved by FEEDBACK. A high level of circulatory hormone tends to inhibit further secretion, and this inhibition is reduced when the level falls. Hormones are very specific in their actions, affecting only certain parts of the body, called target organs. These may include the adrenal glands and the sex glands, which themselves secrete hormones.

The main endocrine glands of man, showing their products and function

Gland	Hormone	Function or Target
anterior pituitary	growth hormone	growth
	trophic hormones:	
	ACTH	adrenal cortex
	TSH	thyroid
	FSH	gonads
	LH	gonads
	prolactin	mammary glands
posterior pituitary	vasopressin	kidney, blood pressure,
	oxytocin	mammary glands, uterus
thyroid	thyroxine	development, metabolic rate
parathyroid	parathormone	calcium, phosphorus metabolism
adrenal cortex	sex hormones	(see below)
	glucocorticoids	metabolism of carbohydrates, protein, and fat
	mineralocorticoids	electrolyte, water balance
adrenal medulla	norepinephrine	circulatory systems,
	epinephrine	glucose release
pancreas:		
cells	glucagon	glucose release
cells	insulin	glucose transfer, utilization
ovaries:		
Follicles	estrogen	development and
Corpus luteum	progesterone	maintenance of sexual anatomy,
testes	testosterone	physiology, and behavior

ACTH	adrenocorticotrophic hormone
TSH	thyroid stimulating hormone
FSH	follicle stimulating hormone
LH	luteinizing hormone

The brain has a considerable influence upon hormonal activity, and this is exercized primarily through the pituitary gland, which is situated at the base of the brain just below the hypothalamus to which it is neurally connected (see figure opposite). The pituitary gland has an anterior and a posterior part which have different embryonic origins. The anterior pituitary secretes a hormone responsible for growth and a number of trophic hormones, as indicated in the table. The trophic hormones have other endocrine glands as their target organs. The role of the brain in controlling the activity of the anterior pituitary is essentially regulatory.

For example, some trophic hormones are first secreted at puberty and influence the growth and development of the sex glands. Thereafter the level of circulating sex hormones is regulated by feedback via the anterior pituitary.

The brain has a more direct influence upon the posterior pituitary and the adrenal medulla. The posterior pituitary produces two hormones in mammals, vasopressin and oxytocin, which can be released very quickly in response to circumstances. For example when a young animal attempts to suckle, messages from the mammary glands are received by the brain which instructs the posterior pituitary gland to release oxytocin. This hormone is responsible for milk let-down, and the young animal must stimulate this chain of events in order to obtain milk from its mother.

The hormone vasopressin has a similar quick acting role in inducing changes in blood pressure. The adrenal medulla secretes adrenalin hormones which play a role similar to that of the AUTONOMIC NERVOUS SYSTEM and are released during FEAR and in other situations involving emotion.

Hormones affect behavior in a variety of ways. The most important is that they alter the animal's predisposition to indulge in certain types of behavior such as SEXUAL BEHAVIOR and MIGRATION. For example, females of many species have periods of heat during which they are capable of ovulation and are receptive to advances from males, or may actively seek out males. During this period there is a peak in the blood concentrations of estrogen and progesterone, two hormones produced by the ovary under the influence of the pituitary gland. This cycle of hormonal activity, called the estrus cycle, corresponds with the development of eggs in the ovary. The females become receptive when the eggs are ready for fertilization.

In some primates, including humans, all apes and some monkeys, the estrus cycle is replaced by a different type of cycle, called the menstrual cycle. This is characterized by periodic bleeding, called menstruation, from the uterus and vagina of sexually

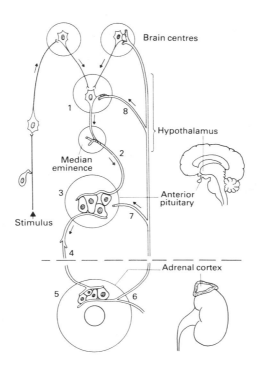

Brain centres

Hypothalamus

Median
eminence

Anterior
pituitary

Stimulus

Adrenal cortex

Pituitary-adrenal system involves nerve cells and hormones in a feedback loop. A stress stimulus reaching neurosecretory cells of the hyopthalamus in the base of the brain (1) stimulates them to release corticotropin-releasing factor (CRF), which moves through short blood vessels (2) to the anterior lobe of the pituitary gland (3). Pituitary cells thereupon release adrenocorticotropic hormone (ACTH) into the circulation (4). The ACTH stimulates cells of the adrenal cortex (5) to secrete glucocorticoid hormones (primarily hydrocortisone in man) into the circulation (6). When glucocorticoids reach neurosecretory cells or other brain cells (it is not clear which), they modulate CRF production (7).

mature females. Menstruation occurs as a result of complex interactions among the circulating hormones. The ovarian follicles (incipient eggs) develop under the influence of follicle stimulating hormone (FSH) released by the anterior pituitary gland. Under the influence of FSH the uterus develops a rich blood supply in readiness for the implantation of the fertilized egg. The ovary also produces estrogen (or estradiol) which has a feedback effect on the pituitary gland, causing it to release more FSH. After about fourteen days the follicle ruptures under the influence of a surge of luteinizing hormone (LH) produced by the anterior pituitary gland. The rupture of the follicle releases the egg and the remaining follicular cells develop into the corpus luteum, which secretes the hormone progesterone. This has a negative feedback effect on the pituitary gland and leads to a reduction in FSH secretion. Fertilization may occur at this stage of the menstrual cycle, in which case the egg becomes implanted in the wall of the uterus and the hormonal changes characteristic of pregnancy are initiated. If fertilization does not occur, the rich blood supply of the uterine wall disintegrates and is shed into the vagina, resulting in the characteristic menstrual flow.

The hormonal balance of female Barbary doves is strongly influenced by participation in COURTSHIP and this form of communication is important in establishing cooperation between the mated pair. In the early stages of courtship the male shows aggression towards the female and this has the effect of inhibiting her reproductive cycle until the male's hormonal condition has time to change. Another aspect of behavior in which social relationships are important is dominance. Males with high levels of testosterone tend to be socially dominant and their aggressiveness towards inferiors may result in hormonal changes due to stress. In this way the reproductive potential of subordinate animals may be suppressed as a result of the action of hormones from the adrenal cortex, secretion of which is characteristic of stress.   DJM

Bibliography

Feder, H.H. 1984: Hormones and sexual behavior. In *Annual review of psychology*, vol. 35, ed. M.R. Rosenzweig and L.W. Porter. Palo Alto: Annual Reviews Inc.

Hutchinson, J.B. ed. 1978: *The biological determinants of sexual behavior*. New York: John Wiley.

Leshner, A.I. 1978: *An introduction to behavioral endocrinology*. New York: Oxford University Press.

hunger and thirst A psychological state that arises primarily as a result of a physiological requirement for nutrients, but may also be due to psychological factors.

Primary hunger is the result of food deprivation and a consequent physiological deficit. The exact nature of the deficit may vary from species to species, depending upon the constitution of the normal diet and upon the animal's physiological tolerance. Small animals which have a high metabolic rate, such as song birds (Passeriformes), quickly suffer an energy shortage when they are unable to obtain food. To maintain its bodyweight and normal activity the great tit (*Parus major*) must feed every few minutes. At night, when feeding is impossible, some birds become torpid, lower their body temperature and conserve energy. Other animals are able to draw upon energy reserves and may live for long periods without food. For example, during the rut a red deer stag may eat little or nothing for six weeks. Incubating jungle fowl do not eat for weeks and eat little even if food is placed next to the nest.

Animals may suffer from a deficiency in one of a number of specific elements of the diet that are essential for good health. These include salt, vitamins and various minerals. Such deficiences are said to lead to *specific hungers*. Failure to satisfy them may result in death. In some cases, and especially with salt and water, the specific hunger results in an increased sensitivity to the missing dietary ingredient, and the animal can readily detect its presence in food. Most minerals and vitamins, on the other hand, cannot be detected in food by taste or smell. Many animals, however, quickly learn to recognize and select those foods which promote recovery from dietary deficiency.

In addition to the physiological aspects of hunger, there are a number of psychological influences. Many animals have distinctive meal patterns which are repeated day after day under constant conditions. Just as humans experience hunger at habitual meal times, so the feeding tendency of animals can be governed by time of day. In conditions in which the environment changes little from day to day animals quickly establish a daily routine of activities and eat at particular times even when food is continuously available.

Physiological processes may become attuned to the routine. In humans, for example, the liver may cease to mobilize glycogen just before a meal is due. This leads to a fall in blood sugar level in anticipation of the increase that will occur when the meal is digested. Experiments have shown that such physiological adjustments can readily undergo conditioning in relation to the time-of-day.

Another important psychological factor in hunger is the increase in appetite that occurs at the beginning of the meal. Once an animal has started to eat there is an apparent increase in hunger, the size of which depends upon the palatability of the food. This positive FEEDBACK effect is short-lived and seems to be part of a mechanism designed to enable animals to exploit feeding opportunities.

Despite a large amount of scientific work the question of which physiological factors initiate eating remains something of a mystery. The influential psychologist Walter Cannon thought (1932) that stomach contractions and other peripheral factors were responsible. However in humans, when the nerves from the stomach are cut, or the stomach is removed for medical reasons, eating is largely unaffected. Several theories have suggested that receptors within the brain are sensitive to the presence of nutrients in the blood. Substances such as glucose, amino acids, or fats, might be used as indices of dietary requirements. The level of glucose in the blood increases during digestion, but it also changes in other circumstances, such as in autonomic arousal and in anticipation of meals. Mayer and Thomas suggested (1967) that the brain responds to the utilization of glucose rather than to its availability. This suggestion is supported by the results of recent research, but the evidence remains inconclusive.

Some scientists doubt whether direct monitoring of the nutrient state of the body is of prime importance in hunger. Although the fact that animals are able to respond to dietary excesses or deficits is suggestive of direct monitoring and regulation, there are alternative possibilities. Animals suffering from a particular deficiency tend to sample a wider range of foods and quickly learn to choose appropriate foods. The evidence suggests that such learning is based upon general sensations of sickness and health, rather than upon detection of specific deficiencies.

The factors that lead animals to cease eating vary considerably. Those which have internal storage organs or which eat bulky food usually finish eating before there have been any significant changes in blood composition as a result of digestion and absorption. For example, a pigeon which eats a meal of about a hundred grains of wheat will still be storing all the food in its crop an hour after the meal has ended. A snake which eats its prey whole, or a lion which eats a large meal every few days is likely to rely on stomach distension as a signal for satisfaction. On the other hand in an animal which nibbles its food like a rat, or an animal with a high throughput of food like a small bird, internal physiological changes occur while the animal is eating and stomach distension is relatively unimportant.

Animals may learn to recalibrate their short-term satiation mechanisms as a result of learning about the physiological consequences of digesting food. Le Magnen (1969) fed two differently flavoured but nutritionally identical diets to rats, and injected them with glucose immediately after they had eaten one diet. The rats associated the flavour of this food with greater absorption of calories, and subsequently ate less food of that particular flavour. There is also evidence that feeding habits may change in association with changes in body weight and fat reserves.

Thirst may have a number of causes. Primary thirst arises from a negative water balance which results in dehydration of the body tissues. Secondary thirst may arise from the intake of dehydrating agents such as food or alcohol, or from changes in environmental temperature.

All animals require water to maintain their metabolic processes, but water is continually lost from the body as a result of excretion, thermoregulation and evaporation from the body surface. Lost water has to be replenished and this is done by drinking in the majority of animals. A few land animals can survive without drinking. Thus the flour moth (*Anagaster kuehuiella*) relies entirely upon the water content of its food. Aquatic animals do not need to drink, and most amphibians absorb water through their skin.

When drinking is not possible the body suffers a negative water balance as a result of a continuing water loss. Some automatic corrective adjustments take place (see HOMEOSTASIS) but these can only serve to cut down on the rate of water loss. Water loss through excretion can be reduced by reabsorption of water in the kidney and small intestine, but some loss remains necessary because the waste products of digestion and metabolism have to be excreted. Many animals eat less when thirsty and this helps to reduce water losses in excretion. Water loss through thermoregulation can sometimes be reduced. By taking less exercise and eating less food animals produce less heat, and by seeking a cool place an animal can conserve some of the water normally lost in keeping cool (see THERMOREGULATION).

Primary thirst results in dehydration of tissue cells. The osmotic pressure of the blood rises and this is monitored by osmoreceptors in the brain, first discovered by Verney (1947). Stimulation of osmoreceptors in the hypothalamus and preoptic areas of the brain leads to the secretion of antidiuretic hormone from the posterior part of the pituitary gland. The presence of antidiuretic hormone in the bloodstream leads to a decrease in the amount and an increase in the concentration of urine excreted by the kidneys. Damage to the pituitary gland or associated area of the hypothalamus results in diabetes insipidus. The symptoms include excessive drinking and urination. Antidiuretic hormone is thus an important factor in water conservation.

Another important hormone is angiotensin, produced from a precursor in the kidney. Angiotensin in the bloodstream leads to an increase in blood pressure. It is also monitored by the brain, where it acts as a primary thirst stimulus. There are thus two bodily states that elicit primary drinking. (1) Water loss from cells due to a high concentration of salts in the body fluids resulting from food intake or water loss. This is monitored by the osmoreceptors. (2) Low fluid volume in the bloodstream as a result of haemorrhage, etc. This is monitored by the kidney, which stimulates angiotensin production, which in turn raises blood pressure as a short-term means of compensating for the fluid loss, and induces thirst. Angiotensin also suppresses feeding, which also helps to conserve water.

Secondary thirst is purely psychological and arises in situations in which the behavior of the animal is likely to induce a future primary thirst. For example, many animals drink in response to an increase in environmental temperature. Andersson (1964) showed that goats could be induced to drink by warming the anterior part of the hypothalamus. By drinking in direct response to a temperature increase the animal is making water available for thermoregulation. If the animal did not drink at this stage, its thermoregulatory water losses would induce a primary thirst. Similarly, many animals drink in association with meals. This type of secondary drinking anticipates the primary thirst-inducing consequences of food intake.

Species vary greatly in their requirements for water. Some such as the budgerigar (*Melospittacus*) and the kangaroo rat (*Dipodomys*) have such efficient water conservation mechanisms that they can survive without drinking. They obtain a little water from their food, which usually consists of seeds, and they will drink if water becomes available. Camels can manage for long periods without water, but when given a chance to drink they take in a large amount: a male camel weighing 325 kg. can drink over 100 litres of water. A very thirsty man can drink about two litres.

Some animals can make use of sources of water that are denied to others. The pack rat (*Neotoma*) can metabolize oxalic acid which is toxic for most other animals. This enables it to use water from cacti which would otherwise be poisonous. A number of reptiles and birds have special salt glands which excrete salt in a highly concentrated solution. They can therefore drink water with a salt concentration that would be lethal for other animals. Salt glands are found not only in marine animals such as the marine iguana (*Amblyrhynchus*) and many sea birds, but also in desert reptiles and in birds such as sand partridges (*Ammoperdix*) and road-runners (*Geococcyx*). Some fresh water birds, such as ducks and flamingos, also have salt glands which enable them to exploit salt marshes and other marginal habitats.

Similarly they can learn to avoid foods which make them sick (see FOOD SELECTION). DJM

Bibliography

Andersson, B. 1964: Aspects of the interrelations between central regulation of body temperature and food and water intake. In *Brain and behavior* II, ed. M. Brazier. Washington, D.C.: American Institute of Biological Sciences.

Cannon, W.B. 1932: *The wisdom of the body*. London: Kegan Paul.

Hogan, J.A. 1980: Homeostasis and behaviour. In *Analysis of motivational processes*, eds. F.M. Toates and T.R. Halliday. London: Academic Press.

Le Magnen, J. 1969: Peripheral and systemic actions of food in the caloric regulation of intake. *Annals of the New York Academy of Science* 157, 1126–57.

——— 1985: *Hunger*. Cambridge: Cambridge University Press.

Mayer, J. and Thomas, D.W. 1967: Regulations of food intake and obesity. *Science* 156, 328–37.

*Milner, P.M. 1970: *Physiological psychology*. New York and London: Holt, Rinehart and Winston.

Rolls, B.J. and Rolls, E.T. 1982: *Thirst*. Cambridge: Cambridge University Press.

Toates, F.M. 1980: *Animal behavior – a systems approach*. Chichester: John Wiley.

Verney, E.B. 1947: The antidiuretic hormone and the factors which determine its release. *Proceedings of the Royal Society of London* 135, 25–106.

Huxley, Sir Julian (1887 – 1975)

Educated and later a lecturer in zoology at Oxford University, Huxley spent three years in the USA, returned to Oxford and was later professor of zoology at King's College, London. He was Secretary of the Zoological Society of London from 1935 to 1942, and Director-General of UNESCO from 1946 to 1948. Lorenz has referred to Huxley as one of the founding fathers of ethology. His 1914 publication on the courtship habits of the great crested grebe was a landmark of objective naturalistic study of "instinctive" behavior patterns. Fifty years later he organized a Royal Society symposium entitled *A discussion on ritualization of behaviour in animals and man* (1965). His interest in evolutionary theory was profound; and his 1942 book is a classic. He was also instrumental in furthering the ideas of scientific humanism, and eugenics. PKS

Bibliography

Huxley, J.S. 1942 (1974): *Evolution: the modern synthesis*. 3rd edn. London: Allen and Unwin; New York: Hafner.

hypothetical constructs and intervening variables

Terms in scientific propositions which respectively refer to unobserved entities and processes; or else serve only as calculational conveniences, to link observed events and quantities but without any reference or surplus meaning beyond their mode of use, and their definition in terms of observables.

For a realist, hypothetical constructs are legitimate conjectures about the world beyond the set of observation statements, which are necessary but not sufficient for the support of a theory (hence the claim by Popper that scientific generalizations are empirically falsifiable, but not verifiable). For an instrumentalist, only intervening variables are legitimate, and their value or meaning is confined to the instrumental one of organizing and inter-relating observables, and the stating of empirical laws whose truth is necessary and sufficient for the more limited claims made by the concept of intervening variable.

In marginal cases it can be open to debate as to whether a concept is to be read as an intervening variable or a hypothetical construct. For the latter interpretation the general principle of scientific realism must be acceptable, and the construct must be compatible with other related forms of knowledge.   DDC

Bibliography

MacCorquodale, K. and Meehl, P. 1948: On a distinction between hypothetical constructs and intervening variables. *Psychological review* 55, 95–107.

I

imitation and observational learning Learning achieved not by practice or by direct experience on the learner's part of the consequences of performing a particular action, but solely by observation of another agent.

Thorndike (1911) was one of the first psychologists to study imitation as a species of observational learning in animals – with uniformly negative results. Having taught a cat to escape from a puzzle box by pressing a catch, he wanted to see if a second cat could be taught the solution simply by observing the trained cat performing the correct response. Finding no evidence of any such learning he concluded that in animals other than man, at least, all learning was by direct trial and error.

It remains unclear why Thorndike's experiments were so unsuccessful. Later experimenters, at any rate, have had little difficulty in demonstrating that animals can learn the solution to a problem by observing the performance of another, trained animal. It is important, however, to distinguish several ways in which observation of another animal may affect behavior.

1. The simplest possibility is sometimes called "social facilitation". A domestic chick given the opportunity to feed from a pile of food will eventually stop, apparently satiated. But if it now sees other chicks feeding, it will start again (Turner 1965). There is a sense in which the chick is imitating the others, but it is not clear that it has learned anything very important from observation of them – for it already knows how to eat and that food is available. It would be more parsimonious to conclude that among the stimuli that can elicit feeding is the sight (or sound) of conspecifics feeding.

2. A demonstration of true observa-

tional learning requires, at the least, that the observer would have been unlikely to respond the way he does, had he not learned something relatively specific from observing the model. But even where this condition is satisfied, it is not always easy to show just what it is that the observer has learned. An untrained rat may observe a trained rat pressing a lever and obtaining food, and may then show an increased tendency to press the lever itself when given the opportunity. But it is possible that all the observer has learned is that some parts of the apparatus are more interesting than others.

There are, fortunately, studies which have established more precise conclusions than this. In one (Darby and Riopelle 1959), two monkeys took it in turns to act as observer and demonstrator in solving a series of two-choice discrimination problems. The observer would watch the other monkey receive a single trial on which he was given the opportunity to choose between two novel objects, one of which was "correct" (i.e. choice of it was rewarded with food) and the other incorrect. On the next trial the observer was allowed to choose between the same pair of objects, and was rewarded for choice of the correct object. The role of demonstrator and observer changed for the next problem, when two new objects were presented. The demonstrator, being confronted with two entirely novel objects, had no way of knowing which was correct and chose at random. But the observer, when it came to his turn, showed that he had benefited from watching the demonstrator's trial, and scored well above chance.

This experiment provides clear evidence of observational learning. But it is important to notice that the observer was not simply imitating the demonstrator's actions. If he had been, he would have copied the demonstrator's choice even when it was wrong. In fact, the observer was rather *more* likely to choose correctly when the demonstrator had been wrong than when he had, by chance, been right. So here is a case where the observer is learning something about the consequences of another animal's actions, but does not necessarily choose to imitate those actions.

3. True imitation requires the observer to copy the demonstrator's or model's actions – perhaps even regardless of the consequences of those actions. This last condition is not easily satisfied in animal studies, but there are experiments establishing imitation of a model's actions. Dawson and Foss (1965) trained several demonstrator budgerigars to obtain food from a covered receptacle; one learned, for example, by tearing the cover off with its beak, another by clawing it off with one foot. Observers were permitted to watch one of these demonstrators in action, and, when presented with the covered box themselves, obtained food in the same way (either with beak or with claw) as the particular demonstrator they had watched. They were clearly imitating a particular action, rather than learning that food was to be found in the box.

There is thus good analytic evidence from experimental studies of imitation and observational learning in a variety of animals. More naturalistic studies suggest that this is indeed an important form of learning. Young birds of many species learn to sing their species typical song by being exposed to it at an early age: in the absence of exposure at a CRITICAL PERIOD, a normal repertoire of song may fail to develop (Hinde 1969), but under normal circumstances the year-old bird will start singing the song it was exposed to during the critical period. A celebrated example of imitation is provided by the behavior of a troop of Japanese monkeys who, although living in the wild, obtained much of their food from scientists who lured them out into the open, the better to study their behavior, by leaving piles of sweet potatoes and wheat on the sea shore

(Tsumori 1967). Although the monkeys were happy to eat these provisions they had to put up with sand in their food until one enterprising juvenile female discovered that sand could be washed off sweet potatoes by rubbing them in the hands under water, and that if a handful of wheat plus sand were thrown into a pool of water, the sand would sink leaving the wheat floating on the surface. In due course these novel solutions spread through the entire troop, and since it was the family and immediate companions of the original inventor who first started copying her and the conservative adult males who were the last to acquire the new practice, one may be reasonably confident that this was a case of imitation or observational learning rather than an independent series of chance discoveries.

NJM

Bibliography

Bonner, J.T. 1980: *The evolution of culture in animals.* Princeton: Princeton University Press.

Darby, C.L. and Riopelle, A.J 1959: Observational learning in the rhesus monkey. *Journal of comparative and physiological psychology* 52, 94–8.

Dawson, B.V. and Foss, B.M. 1965: Observational learning in budgerigars. *Animal behaviour* 13, 470–4.

Hinde, R.A. 1969: *Bird vocalizations.* Cambridge: Cambridge University Press.

Thorndike, E.L. 1911: *Animal intelligence.* New York: Macmillan.

Tsumori, A. 1967: Newly acquired behavior and social interactions of Japanese monkeys. In *Social communication among primates,* ed. S.A. Altmann. Chicago: University of Chicago Press.

Turner, E.R.A. 1965: Social feeding in birds. *Behaviour* 24, 1–46.

imprinting Originally the name given to the process by which a young animal forms a lasting attachment to and preference for some object, usually its parent. The concept has now been extended to encompass many kinds of preference. It was first studied in detail by LORENZ (1935) who discovered that young presocial birds, which are active and leave the nest shortly after hatching, would treat almost any conspicuous moving object as they normally treat their mother. Imprinting objects have ranged from a matchbox to a large canvas hide and many inappropriate living objects, including people. Indeed, the sight of a gaggle of goslings following the youthful Lorenz is one of the seminal images of ethology.

Two types of imprinting were distinguished in the early days, full imprinting, for the attachment of young bird to parent, and sexual imprinting, for the more broadly based attachment to the species of the imprinting object, later used as the basis for selection of a mating partner. Lorenz used the word *prägung* to denote the rapidity and irreversibility of the process, likening it to die-stamping. He noted properties of imprinting that seemed to set it apart from other forms of behavior: it took place only during a brief critical period early in the life of the organism; its effects were irreversible, and might be manifested only after a long delay. Each of these has been investigated in some detail, but the modern consensus is that imprinting is not a unique process but is a form of perceptual learning.

The CRITICAL PERIOD can be demonstrated by exposing chicks of various ages to an imprinting object for a brief period and measuring their preference for that object some time later. Ramsay and Hess (1954), using mallard ducklings (*Anas platyrhynchos*), found a very sharp peak of imprintability about fifteen hours after hatching. Boyd and Fabricius (1965) exposed ducklings to a moving object at different ages and found a gradual decline in the readiness of the bird to follow the model over the first ten days of life. The criticality of Lorenz's critical period thus depends on exactly how it is measured. Nevertheless it is clear that imprinting takes place very much more readily at certain times than at others and indeed may be impossible outside the limits of a sensitive, rather than a critical, period.

The factors that control the timing of the sensitive period are poorly understood (see Bateson 1979). It seems to begin as soon as the neuro-muscular coordination of the bird is sufficiently advanced to permit it to follow a moving object, although following per se is not necessary for the bird to imprint. Developmental age and time since hatching both play a part in the onset of the sensitive period. The end of the period is more of a problem. Young birds do not avoid novel objects, but as they mature they begin to respond to novelty with fear and flight, and this prevents approach and imprinting. The very process of imprinting, forming an attachment to some object in the environment, may bring sensitivity to an end. Birds reared without an imprinting stimulus in an impoverished environment remain sensitive longer than birds raised in social groups. And if a bird is imprinted very early in the sensitive period it becomes difficult to imprint it on another object even within the normal sensitive period (see Boakes and Panter 1985).

The irreversibility of imprinting has also come under scrutiny. Lorenz took this to mean that an attachment, once formed, could not be transferred to a different object, probably because the critical period had passed, but imprinting is normally self-limiting in that the attachment formed serves to prevent the bird from coming into close and prolonged contact with another object to which its attachment could be transferred. The experimental evidence is confusing. Filial imprinting can be reversed if the young bird is confined with a novel stimulus and prevented from fleeing. Sexual imprinting seems more permanent, but is less absolute. Turkeys (*Meleagris gallopavo*) imprinted on humans will court turkeys, but given a choice between a turkey and a person they prefer the person. The same is true for zebra finch (*Taenopygia guttata*) males cross-fostered by Bengalese finches (*Lonchura striata*); they will court female zebra finches if forced to, but given a choice prefer the unreceptive and uncooperative Bengalese finch female to the encouraging zebra finch. It appears that there is a bias to imprint upon members of the same species, but that experience of a different species will lead to a permanent preference for that species as a mating partner.

The long delay between learning and performance apparently sets sexual imprinting apart from other forms of discrimination, although song learning in birds can also include a delay of similar length. A year or more may elapse between exposure to an imprinting stimulus and subsequent selection of that stimulus as a partner for reproduction.

Imprinting occupies a curious place in the pantheon of learning. No reward is needed to obtain the response, although in the natural world the mother is a source of heat, food, and protection. The response itself is not necessary for the discriminative ability to be learned. Once an animal has formed an attachment to an object, that object can be used as a reinforcer to modify behavior. Chicks and ducklings will perform an operant behavior to present themselves with the object they are imprinted on. The process of imprinting itself also acts as a reinforcer. Bateson placed naive chicks in a modified Skinner box, where the weight of the chick on a pedal switched on an imprinting stimulus. Even before the chick had formed an attachment to the stimulus or learned its characteristics it would stand on the pedal and make the stimulus appear. Chicks will also work to present themselves with novel views of the imprinting object, and as they learn more about the stimulus so the amount of discrepancy they will work for decreases. The young animal thus plays an active role in becoming imprinted; it seeks out objects on which to imprint, and its preference for slight novelty during imprinting has been interpreted as a mechanism to ensure that it sees, and learns about, all visual aspects of the parent. Different views – front, back, side and so on – are then integrated to form a perceptual model of the parent.

The ease with which birds can be imprinted and the strength of their learning measured (as a preference for one object over another) have made imprinting a key part in studies of the biochemistry of learning. Horn and his colleagues have shown that there are specific biochemical changes in localized areas of the brain, notably the hyperstriatum ventrale, and that these changes are consequent upon the specific experience of imprinting. Destruction of these areas after exposure to an imprinting stimulus prevents the bird from showing any preference.

The biological functions of imprinting must be considered separately for filial and sexual imprinting. Filial imprinting serves to identify the parent and keep the young close to it. In this way the young learn about food and shelter and gain protection against predators. Sexual imprinting is more problematical. It seems to provide the animal with a model for the sexual partner; in monomorphic animals, where both sexes have similar coloration, both imprint, but in dimorphic species it is often only the male that shows sexual imprinting. Once thought to identify the species for the animal, sexual imprinting is now thought to proscribe certain members of the species. Bateson has shown that quail avoid as sexual partners the animals they were raised with, while nevertheless preferring that type over others. Brown quail raised with albinos avoid the albinos they were raised with but prefer novel albinos over novel brown quail. Bateson interprets this in terms of "optimal outbreeding", and argues that sexual imprinting provides a mechanism whereby animals can avoid incest, as the imprinting objects will generally be close kin.

Imprinting has also been applied to other phenomena in which a lasting preference is formed relatively quickly. Thus a mother (human and goat) is said to imprint upon her young shortly after birth, young animals to imprint upon the odor of their nest and the flavor of the mother's milk, and so on. JJCh

Bibliography

Bateson, P.P.G. 1966: The characteristics and context of imprinting. *Biological reviews* 41, 177–220.

Boakes, R. and Panter, D. 1985: Secondary imprinting in the domestic chick blocked by previous exposure to a live hen. *Animal behaviour* 33, 353–65.

Boyd, H. and Fabricius, 1965: Observations on the incidence of following of visual and auditory stimuli in naive mallard ducklings (*Anas platyrhynchos*). *Behaviour* 25, 1–15.

————— 1979: How do sensitive periods arise and what are they for? *Animal behaviour* 27, 470–86.

————— 1981: Optimal outbreeding and the development of sexual preferences in Japanese quail. *Zeitschrift für Tierpsychologie* 53, 231–44.

————— 1982: Preferences for cousins in Japanese quail. *Nature* 295, 236–37.

Hinde, Robert A. 1982: *Ethology*. London: Fontana; New York and Oxford: Oxford University Press.

Horn, G. 1981: Neural mechanisms of learning: an analysis of imprinting in the domestic chick. *Proceedings of the Royal Society of London*, Series B, 213, 101–37.

Lorenz, Konrad 1935: Der Kumpan in der Umwelt des Vogels. Reprinted as: Companions as factors in the bird's environment. In *Studies on animal and human behaviour*. London: Methuen; Cambridge, Mass.: Harvard University Press.

Ramsay, A.O. and Hess, E.H. 1954: A laboratory approach to the study of imprinting. *Wilson bulletin* 66, 196–206.

inbreeding Breeding with a genetically related individual. Brother-sister mating is the most extreme form of inbreeding but the term also refers to breeding among more distant relatives.

Some kinds of animals typically avoid inbreeding; others do not. In order to avoid inbreeding an animal must be able to recognize its relatives. Two questions are raised: how is this achieved, and what is the advantage of avoiding inbreeding for the species that do avoid it? Inbreeding avoidance may be achieved by direct recognition of genetic relatives, or as a consequence of some other habit. In the former case an animal might recognize its relatives either with or without learning. We have no direct evidence that animals learn the appearance of relatives in order to avoid mating with them, but in many vertebrate species individuals do learn the appearance of relatives (for instance, by "imprinting") and they also avoid inbreeding. It is therefore likely that they apply the former in effecting the latter but it is not proved.

In recent years evidence has shown that animals can recognize their relatives even if they have had no opportunity for learning.

For instance, mice can distinguish the genotype of another mouse at a set of genetic loci called the H-2 system (which functions in the immune response); they make the distinction by smell and do not need to have encountered the mouse before. Mice preferentially mate with other mice that differ from themselves in H-2 genotype, a preference that necessarily results in their avoidance of inbreeding. Comparable unlearned abilities to distinguish relatives have been discovered in bees, quails, and some primates.

Group living primates and other mammals (such as lions) avoid inbreeding as a consequence of sex-specific group transfer. At a certain age, usually as a young adult, individuals of one sex leave their natal groups and try to transfer to another group. In baboons, macaques and langurs the males transfer; in gorillas and chimpanzees the females do. It is difficult to see what function group transfer could serve other than to prevent inbreeding.

Why should animals avoid inbreeding? The answer favored by biologists is recessive lethal or deleterious genes. Every individual carries a few recessive deleterious genes in single copy; these genes are not expressed and do not affect their bearers' well-being. Different unrelated individuals carry recessive lethals at different loci; they can therefore breed together successfully, producing offspring with a mixture of the parents' recessive lethals, all in a single copy. Related individuals are more likely to carry recessive lethals at the same locus. If they inbreed they will probably produce offspring with two copies of some recessive deleterious genes; the genes will then be expressed and the offspring will be unfit. Such is the explanation of the phenomenon called "inbreeding depression"; because of it, natural selection acts to prevent inbreeding.

But some animals characteristically do inbreed. Small pyemotid mites are an extreme example. In these viviparous mites, brothers mate with their sisters even while they are still living within their mother.

Although natural selection initially acts to prevent the evolution of inbreeding, the force would be transitory. If animals persisted in inbreeding the recessive deleterious genes would eventually be "bred out" as the inbred possessors of double copies of those genes would die. So, in a normally outbreeding population recessive lethals can accumulate because they are rarely expressed, being held in single copy; but in an inbred population they are expressed and eliminated. If in evolutionary time a population could cross, the deleterious intermediate stage from outbreeding to inbreeding, then inbreeding could stably persist. The argument leads to the prediction (which is untested) that inbreeding species should have lower frequencies of deleterious recessive genes than outbreeding species such as ourselves.   MR

Bibliography

Foltz, D.W. and Hoogland, J.L. 1983: Genetic evidence of outbreeding in the black-tailed prairie dog (*Cynomys ludovicianus*). *Evolution* 37, 273–81.

Moore, J. and Ali, R. 1984: Are dispersal and inbreeding avoidance related? *Animal behaviour* 32, 94–112.

Müller-Schwarze, D. and Mozell, M.M. 1977: *Chemical signals in vertebrates*. New York: Plenum.

Partridge, L. 1983: Non-random mating and offspring fitness. In *Mate choice*, ed. P. Bateson. Cambridge: Cambridge University Press.

incentive An aspect of MOTIVATION that results from expectation of reward or punishment. The concept was first introduced into behavior theory by Hull (1931) and it has since developed into a variety of formulations (Bolles 1975). Basically, incentive is a learned form of motivation in which certain external stimuli acquire motivating properties because the animal associates them with REINFORCEMENT. If a rat is rewarded with food for pressing a bar (see CONDITIONING) presentation of the bar on a future occasion may increase the animal's motivation to obtain food. On the other hand if the rat receives an electric shock for pressing the bar subsequent presentation of the bar will probably have a negative incentive effect.   DJM

Bibliography

Bolles, Robert C. 1975: *Theory of motivation*. 2nd edn. New York and London: Harper and Row.

Hull, C.L. 1931: Goal attraction and directing ideas conceived as habit phenomena. *Psychology review* 38, 487–506.

incest *See* inbreeding.

inhibition A demonstrable nervous activity or a hypothetical process which holds in abeyance some neural and/or behavioral activity which might otherwise occur. At the interneuronal level in the central nervous system inhibition as an accompaniment to excitation clearly expands the logical possibilities of neural functioning in "computer circuit" terms, and some of its roles, e.g. in sharpening sensory input (Hartline and Ratliff 1957) and in feedback control of muscles, have been elegantly analyzed (Eccles 1969).

It has long been clear (Sherrington 1906) that the contractions of particular sets of muscles must entail the suppression of activity in other muscles for coordinated individual movements to emerge, and the same notion has been applied to the motivational problem of how a specific sequence of action is selected by an animal at any one time from its total behavioral repertoire. The ethological concept of CONFLICT entails inhibitory relations between behavior tendencies, and Andrew (1956) and van Iersel and Bol (1958) postulated that it was the balanced mutual inhibition between powerful drives such as flight, fight or sexual attraction (e.g. in courtship or agonistic situations) which cleared the stage for the occurrence of the more mundane displacement activities (the "disinhibition hypothesis"). Incomplete inhibition might result in alternation between one behavior and another ambivalent behavior, or the truncated intention movements.

From Sherrington, the term was also introduced into psychology by PAVLOV, who referred to inhibition as the process responsible for the suppression of conditioned reflexes. After a conditioned response of salivation had been established to a stimulus paired with food, the response could be made to disappear either by repeatedly presenting the stimulus alone without food (internal inhibition) or by presenting another, novel stimulus along with the conditioned stimulus (external inhibition). Pavlov attributed the loss of responding in the former case to an active process of inhibition rather than to a loss of conditioning, because the conditioned response would reappear after an interval of time, or could be "disinhibited" by presentation of another novel stimulus.

With qualifiers such as "internal", "external" or "conditioned" inhibition, and inhibition "of delay" "reactive" inhibition and "latent" inhibition (Lubow and Moore 1959), learning theorists and comparative psychologists have subsequently used the term inhibition in a plethora of ways (see e.g. Boakes and Halliday 1972). Indeed, several kinds of "neuropsychological" (Hebb 1949) inhibition had been postulated on largely behavioral grounds before the demonstration by physiologists of inhibitory synapses and presynaptic inhibition in the brain. Although clear links may sometimes be demonstrable, it is important not to assume that there is necessarily any direct correspondence between inhibitory processes at synaptic or ganglionic levels and those postulated at behavioral levels of explanation.   DWD

Bibliography

Andrew, R.J. 1956: Some remarks on behavior in conflict situations, with special reference to *Emberiza* spp. *British journal of animal behaviour* 4, 41–5.

*Boakes, Robert A. and Halliday, Michael S. eds., 1972: *Inhibition and learning*. New York: Academic Press.

Eccles, John C. 1969: *The inhibitory pathways of the central nervous system*. Sherrington Lectures. Liverpool: Liverpool University Press; Springfield, Ill.: Thomas.

Hartline, H.K. and Ratliff, S. 1957: Inhibitory interaction of receptor units in the eye of limulus. *Journal of general physiology* 40, 357–76.

Hebb, D.O. 1949: *The organization of behavior*. New York: Wiley.

Iersel, J.J. van and Bol, A.C.A. 1958: Preening of two tern species. A study on displacement activities. *Behaviour* 13, 1–88.

Lubow, R.E. and Moore, A.U. 1959: Latent inhibitions: the effect of non-reinforced preexposure to the conditioned stimulus. *Journal of comparative and physiological psychology* 52, 415–19.

Roeder, K.D. 1967: *Nerve cells and insect behavior*. 2nd edn. Cambridge, Mass.: Harvard University Press.

Sherrington, C.S. 1906: *Integrative action of the nervous system*. Cambridge: Cambridge University Press.

Woody, C.D. 1986: Understanding the cellular basis of memory and learning. In *Annual review of psychology*, vol. 37, eds. M.R. Rosenzweig and L.W. Porter. Palo Alto: Annual Reviews Inc.

innate releasing mechanism (IRM) and releaser

In classical ethological motivation theory there were two distinct roles for external stimuli. They could contribute, as "priming" stimuli, to the buildup of action specific energy or drive. But, with or without priming stimuli, action specific energy to perform a particular behavior pattern was thought to build up spontaneously with time since that behavior pattern was last performed, in the same way as water pressure builds up behind a dam. The major role of external stimuli was to open the sluice gates. The innate releasing mechanism was a block, a gate holding back the specific drive. Each gate was unlocked by a specific key from the outside world, an appropriate stimulus or releaser perceived by the senses. The word releaser has been used in different senses. Some authors use it for any stimulus that releases behavior, including, for example a stone that elicits pecking in a bird. Others insist on reserving it for a stimulus specifically designed by natural selection to release behavior in another individual. According to this definition a stone would not qualify but the red spot on the bill of a herring gull, which releases food begging in chicks, would qualify. The releasing function has sometimes been sharply distinguished from "directing": one stimulus, the releaser, was thought to unlock the sluice gates and allow the behavior to occur. Once the behavior pattern had been released it would usually not be directed randomly with respect to the environment, but would be orientated.

Stimuli perceived via the sense organs would be used to orientate the behavior, but these stimuli would not necessarily be releasers. The behavior had, by now, already been released. Sometimes, as in the case of the red spot on the herring gull's bill, the same stimulus might serve both a releasing and a directing function.　　RD

Bibliography

Manning, A. 1979: *An introduction to animal behaviour*. 3rd edn. London: Edward Arnold; Reading, Mass.: Addison Wesley.

Tinbergen, N. 1969: *The study of instinct*. 2nd edn. Oxford: Oxford University Press.

insight A term used by the gestalt psychologist Wolfgang Köhler (1925) to denote a form of intelligent problem solving. Köhler set adult chimpanzees tasks that required solution by indirect means, for example, retrieval of bananas out of reach by means of a stick or by stacking boxes to form a step ladder. The chimpanzees succeeded only when all the constituent elements of the problem had first been seen within the same field of view. They behaved as though their perception of the problem had undergone a sudden radical restructuring and they would then rapidly arrive at an appropriate solution. When the elements were widely separated in space, "insightful" learning did not occur and the chimpanzees continued to attempt ineffective "trial and error" strategies. GEB

Bibliography

Köhler, Wolfgang 1925: *The mentality of apes*. New York: Kegan Paul.

McFarland, D. ed. 1981: *Oxford companion to animal behaviour*. Oxford: Oxford University Press.

instinct A set of behavior patterns which contribute to a common function (reproduction, feeding), which are shared by all members of a species, and which develop in the absence of conventional learning or practice. TINBERGEN saw instincts as based upon hierarchically arranged neural systems sharing a common source of motivation (see HIERARCHY). Instinct was com-

monly understood to imply that the whole behavioral system was inherited, and there was a tendency to ignore the role of the developing animal's environment. For this reason the term is now less used. It is more common to refer to the various elements of a functionally related set, e.g. reproductive behavior as examples of "instinctive behavior". The different elements may develop at different rates and be affected by distinct factors during development. Thus certain elements of male sexual behavior can develop in the absence of testosterone, while other elements require this hormone, and still others may require social experience for their full development.　　AWGM

Bibliography

Bolles, R.C. 1975: *Theory of motivation*. 2nd edn. New York and London: Harper and Row.

Tinbergen, N. 1969: *Theory of instinct*. 2nd edn. Oxford: Oxford University Press.

Toates, F.M. 1983: Models of motivation. In *Animal behaviour*, vol. 1. *Causes and effects*, eds. T.R. Halliday and P.J.B. Slater. Oxford: Blackwell Scientific Publications.

intelligence An index of ability in tasks requiring cognition. There is no generally agreed measure of animal intelligence. There are numerous examples and demonstrations of intelligent behavior, but the validity of tests of intelligence is open to criticism on the grounds that it is not possible to devise a PROBLEM SOLVING test that is not biased in respect of one species or another. Some birds can provide good imitation of sounds but not of actions; tool using is found in some species and not in others, but there are no obvious differences in intelligence between animals that use tools and those that do not.　　DJM

Bibliography

Harlow, H.F. 1949: The formation of learning sets. *Psychological review* 56, 51–65.

MacPhail, E.M. 1982: *Brain and intelligence in vertebrates*. Oxford: Clarendon Press.

Weiskrantz, L. 1985: *Animal intelligence*. Oxford and New York: Oxford University Press.

intention movement A somewhat unfortunate technical term, because it seems to have subjective connotations. When the term was fashionable in ethology this was no difficulty because objectivism was so dominant in the thinking of ethologists. An intention movement is simply an incomplete movement. An animal is said to perform an intention movement when it starts to perform an action pattern recognizable from the species repertoire, but then breaks off before the action is completed. For example the sequence of movements leading to take-off and flight in a bird typically begins with a stretching of the neck. Birds on the ground, particularly when a little frightened, sometimes stretch the neck as though about to take off, but then do not do so. This might be called an "intention flight movement".

Intention movements play an important role in ethological theories of the evolution of animal signals. Neck stretching in a bird is, statistically speaking, likely to be followed by flight. Tooth-baring in a dog is statistically likely to be followed by biting.

NATURAL SELECTION therefore is supposed to favor the evolution of what looks like anticipatory behavior in animals after they have perceived an intention movement in another individual. A dog whose rival bares its teeth may flee as if in anticipation of being bitten. Selection thereupon, according to the theory, favored the ritualization of tooth-baring as a threat display. In the same way, many other ritualized signals have been supposed to evolve from intention movements. RD

Bibliography

Krebs, J.R. and Dawkins, R. 1984: *Behavioural ecology: an evolutionary approach*. 2nd edn. Oxford: Blackwell Scientific Publications.

Manning, A. 1979: *An introduction to animal behaviour*. 3rd edn. London: Edward Arnold; Reading, Mass.: Addison Wesley.

intervening variable *See* hypothetical constructs and intervening variables.

K

kinesis A form of orientation in which the animal's speed of locomotion depends upon the intensity of stimulation. For example, flatworms (*Platyhelminthes*) tend to aggregate in dark places because they move or turn more quickly under high illumination and consequently slow down, or even stop when they happen to reach a dark place. Kinesis is regarded as a fundamental type of ORIENTATION (Fraenkel and Gunn 1940), although it is not a very common one.   DJM

Bibliography

Fraenkel, Gottfried S. and Gunn, Donald L. 1940: *The orientation of animals*. Oxford: Clarendon Press. New edn. 1961. New York: Dover.

Hinde, R.A. 1970: *Animal behavior*. 2nd edn. New York: McGraw-Hill.

kinship In ethological terms a relationship determined by genealogical descent. This is a narrower definition than is found in social anthropology etc. in which affinal kin (through marriage), and fictional kin are also included. Kinship is of interest to ethologists primarily because of the existence of kin selection, a form of natural selection in which genetically transmitted behavior that increases the chance of close relatives surviving or reproducing is selected. Thus Bertram (1976) has argued that kin selection in lions could be responsible for communal suckling, males' tolerance toward cubs, and the lack of competition for estrous females. The existence of close kinship links was demonstrated in the 1950s in Japanese macaques, with the discovery by Japanese anthropologists of ranked matrilineages. In the society of these monkeys, all the offspring of a particular grandmother, through the female line, share a higher rank than all the offspring of a second grandmother who is of lower rank than the first. This phenomenon results from "dependent rank", by which monkeys achieve their social status during childhood through the intervention of their parents in competitive situations.   VR

Bibliography

Bertram, B.C.R. 1976: Kin selection in lions and in evolution. In *Growing points in ethology*, eds. Paul P.G. Bateson and Robert A. Hinde. Cambridge and New York: Cambridge University Press.

Grafen, A. 1984: Natural selection, kin selection and group selection. In *Behavioural ecology*, 2nd edn. eds. J.R. Krebs and N.B. Davies. Oxford: Blackwell Scientific Publications.

Maynard-Smith, J. 1964: Group selection and kin selection. *Nature* 201.

L

language: anthropoid ape Ape communication, whether acquired naturally or through training, can be termed linguistic if it shares essential features with human language or if it utilizes psychological or biological mechanisms that underlie language in man. Attempts have been made to teach apes both referential symbols equivalent to words and rules for combining symbols into longer combinations. However, since apes apparently have little ability to modulate voiced sounds (Lieberman 1975), experiments on ape language have used visual instead of auditory symbols to test usage. Two kinds of visual symbols have been used: manual gestures similar to those used in the sign languages of deaf humans (see, e.g., Klima and Bellugi 1979), and written symbols or objects analogous to the graphemes of a non-alphabetic writing system such as Chinese, where each distinct visual shape denotes a concept not a sound in the language (Fouts 1975; Gardner and Gardner 1975; Premack 1976; Neago, personal communication; Patterson 1979; Patterson and Linden 1981; Rumbaugh 1977; Terrace 1979; Terrace et al. 1979). In addition, research using keyboard control of machine-synthesized speech is also under way (Patterson and Linden 1981).

In all of these studies, the animal is first taught a set of names for familiar objects, body parts, persons and common activities by pairing the symbol with examples of its referent. After the association is learned, the researcher notes the ape's ability to use the symbol in a spontaneous and appropriate manner and tests its ability to select the correct referent when presented only with the symbol. Whether taught with gestures, plastic tokens or computer-controlled displays, all three genera of existing anthropoid apes (gorilla, chimpanzee and orangutan) can reliably learn a set of symbols for a set of conceptual classes and can use them on their own initiative to request services from humans or other apes. Since the criteria for judging sign acquisition can be very strict (for example, spontaneous and appropriate use on half the days of a given month), the published vocabularies of about 150 signs probably underestimate apes' abilities. The gorilla Koko's unofficial vocabulary is now over 700 signs. Also, ape sign acquisition shows parallels to human vocabulary learning, both spoken and signed, in the generalization and over-extension of words (Gardner and Gardner 1975; Patterson 1979). Home-reared apes also have some understanding of spoken English words (Fouts, Chown and Goodin 1976; Patterson 1979), but it is not known whether apes discriminate spoken words phonemically, in terms of the acoustic cues for articulatory differences among speech sound, or by gross differences in the acoustic waveforms of different words, as human would discriminate a fog horn from a fire siren.

Students of ape language have tried to show that apes have syntactic as well as lexical (vocabulary) knowledge. Premack and Rumbaugh required their chimpanzees to learn rules for sequences of symbols. The apes were able to present symbols in certain prescribed orders, to fit the missing symbol in a blank space in a sequence, and to use different sequences for different meanings. However, critics have argued that the apes learned only complex conditional discrimination tasks, not syntax *per se*, because they did not understand the meaning of the manipulations they learned to perform. Another strategy has been to examine the spontaneous sign combinations of apes for evidence of syntax. Apes commonly produce combinations of two or three signs, with occasional longer, more repetitive sequences. In all cases in which the sequential order of signs was specifically recorded, there were statistically significant differences in the serial positions of different signs. Thus, in Terrace's chimpanzee, Nim, verb + *me*, verb + *Nim*, *more* + *X* (where *X* is a sign), and *give* + *X* combinations are more frequent than their opposites (Terrace et al. 1979). The gorilla Koko (Patterson 1979) used various orderings in action + object constructions such as *open bottle*; action + object for feeding verbs such as *eat* and the reverse order for social verbs such as *tickle*. In addition to order constraints, modifications of signs have been observed that are reminiscent of the puns and innovative constructions of human sign language (Fouts 1975; Patterson 1979). Several observers have also noted that a number of different semantic relations or functions appear to be implicit in the sign combinations of apes when considered in context (Gardner and Gardner 1975; Patterson 1979). These relations include nomination (*that bird*), recurrence (*more cereal*), non-existence (*me can't*), affected state (*me good*), attributive (*hot potato*), possessive (*hat mine*), direction toward a goal (*go bed*), dative (*give me drink*), and the agent, action and object relations already noted above. These semantic relations are similar to the relationships implicit in early child speech, which must also be interpreted to a large extent by the context. However, in the case of apes, where the speech does not develop into adult grammar, critics have argued that such inferred relations are conjectural (Terrace et al. 1979). However, since apes are capable of using such relationships in the observational learning of tool use and social behavior (Premack 1976), it is likely they function in communication as well. Nonetheless the range of semantic and syntactic relations that must be postulated in order to account for ape utterance types is far smaller than for children, and apes show a slower acquisition rate and a far lower level of achievement in both vocabulary and syntax. The mean number of signs in multi-sign combinations is much lower in apes, and grammatical function words, such as *Wh*-questions (*what, who*, etc.), are only rudimentary.

Critics have also recently challenged the inference of ape grammar on methodological grounds by claiming that ape sign combinations are prompted by human tutors, lack spontaneity and are highly imitative (Terrace et al. 1979). It is also claimed that apes, unlike humans, do not take turns in conversation but interrupt their tutors. However, these conclusions are based on the analysis of film and videotape materials that are unlikely to represent the animals' true abilities. Turn-taking cues are subtle; and they develop, like all language, in intimate social contexts. Such behavior is unlikely to develop under impoverished rearing conditions or to be exhibited in disruptive filming sessions. The tutorial methods commonly used may also inflate the number of prompted signs. Similarly, the criticism that ape signing can be explained by unconscious social cueing, analogous to the "counting" horse Clever Hans (Umiker-Sebeok and Sebeok 1980), is not only contradicted by successful double-blind experiments of vocabularly comprehension, but the behavior is too complex to be explained in this way. Nonetheless, these criticisms make it clear that the traditional verbal methods of recording ape sign language are too inaccurate to sustain the precise comparisons needed to assess apes' syntactic abilities, and systematic video records of the development of ape signing, such as Patterson's 250 hours of videotape, will be needed to resolve the question of ape grammar. Also, since the definitions of grammar that have been used in discussions of ape sign language were not derived from the analysis of film records of normal human conversational speech, and are not completely compatible with human signing, there is reason to question their psychological adequacy. By defining as language only those utterances that depart most from face-to-face conversational gatherings where most human language occurs, the theory underlying most studies of ape syntax forces us categorically to deny language to animals if they fail to meet the most stringent formalistic criteria and to ignore the similarities that otherwise exist.

A psychological definition of language should not focus exclusively on the features that are found only in man but should evaluate a species' linguistic competence in the light of its other cognitive and behavioral capacities. For example, the claim by Terrace et al. (1979) that apes are little inclined to comment on conversation topics introduced by others is congruent with other aspects of simian psychology. Apes, as shown by their tool using, are also deficient compared to man in exchange of both artifacts and techniques and in the coordination of the actions of many individuals to produce a common product (Reynolds 1981). Consequently, it would not be surprising if their sign language proved to lack these features also. However, such discrepancies do not prove that apes "lack language". If human language is taken to be communication from which propositional relationships can be inferred, then linguistic ability, far from being an absolute, will vary with the capacity for intentional action on one hand and with the capacity for conceptual inference on the other.   PCR

Bibliography

Fouts, Roger S. 1975: Capacities for language in great apes. In *Socioecology and psychology of primates*, ed. R. Tuttle. The Hague: Mouton.

——— , Chown, B. and Goodin, L. 1976: Transfer of signed responses in American Sign Language from vocal English stimuli to physical object stimuli by a chimpanze (*Pan*). *Learning and motivation* 7, 458–75.

Gardner, R.A., and Gardner, B.T. 1975: Early signs of language in child and chimpanze. *Science* 187, 752–3.

Klima, Edward, and Bellugi, Ursula 1979: *The signs of language*. Cambridge, Mass. and London: Harvard University Press.

Lieberman, P. 1975: *On the origins of language*. New York: Macmillan.

Menzel, E.W. 1979: Communication of object locations in a group of young chimpanzees. In *The great apes*, eds. D.A. Hamburg and E.R. McGown. Merlo Park, California: Benjamin/ Cummings.

Patterson, Francine 1978: The gestures of a gorilla: sign language acquisition in another pongid species. *Brain and language* 5, 72–97.

——— 1979: *Linguistic capabilities of a lowland gorilla*. Ann Arbor, Michigan: University Microfilms International.

——— and Linden, Eugene 1981: *The education of Koko*. New York: Holt, Rinehart and Winston.

Premack, David 1971: Language in chimpanzees? *Science* 172, 808–22.

*——— 1976: *Intelligence in ape and man*. Hillsdale, N.J.: Erlbaum.

Reynolds, Peter C. 1981: *On the evolution of human behavior*. Berkeley and Los Angeles: University of California Press.

Rumbaugh, Duane M. ed. 1977: *Language learning by a chimpanzee: the LANA project*. New York: Academic Press.

Seyforth, R.M., Cheney, D.L. and Marler, P. 1980: Monkey responses to three different alarm calls: evidence of predator classification and semantic communication. *Science* 210, 801–3.

Sutton, D. 1979: Mechanisms underlying vocal control in nonhuman primates. In *Neurobiology of social communication*, eds. H.D. Steklin and M.J. Raleigh. New York: Academic Press, pp. 45–67.

Terrace, H.S. 1979: *Nim*. New York: Knopf.

——— et al. 1979: Can an ape create a sentence? *Science* 206, 891–902.

*Umiker-Sebeok, J. and Sebeok, T.A. eds. 1980: *Speaking of apes: a critical anthology of two-way communication with man*. New York and London: Plenum Press.

Weiskrantz, L. ed. 1985: *Animal intelligence*. Oxford and New York: Oxford University Press.

latent learning Learning which is not manifest in overt behavior at the time learning takes place, but may become evident in a later transfer test. For example animals may learn that one neutral event follows another (sensory preconditioning) or learn the layout of a maze through exploration without any incentive to follow a particular route. Generally, they may learn what stimuli occur in a given context even though those stimuli are not currently reinforcing; latent learning may be revealed by subsequently rendering some of these stimuli reinforcing, whereupon appropriate behavior is evinced (or acquired more rapidly than by inexperienced control subjects). Latent learning provides crucial support for cognitive learning theories such as Tolman's which characterize learning as the acquisition of knowledge or expectancy, to which changes in behavior are merely secondary.   EAG

Bibliography
Mackintosh, N.J. 1974: *The psychology of animal learning*. London: Academic Press.

───── 1983: *Conditioning and associative learning*. Oxford and New York: Oxford University Press.

learning A change of an animal's behavior in a particular situation attributable to its previous experience of the situation, and excluding changes due to sensory adaptation, muscular fatigue, injury or maturation.

Many behavioral phenomena are usually included under the general heading of learning, without it being necessarily assumed that they are caused either by common or by entirely distinctive underlying mechanisms: the most studied instances include HABITUATION and sensitization (Groves and Thompson 1970); CLASSICAL CONDITIONING (PAVLOV); OPERANT CONDITIONING (SKINNER) or instrumental learning (THORNDIKE); other kinds of associative learning intermediate between classical and operant conditioning like sign-tracking (Hearst and Jenkins 1974) and observational learning; learning seemingly restricted to critical or sensitive periods in ontogeny like IMPRINTING (LORENZ) and song learning (Catchpole 1979); and performance on more complex tasks such as learning sets (Harlow 1959), delayed matching to sample (Roberts and Grant 1976), serial pattern learning (Hulse 1978), and the manipulation of symbols (Premack 1978) which many feel justify the descriptive if not the explanatory use of "cognitive" terminology (Hulse, Fowler and Honig 1978) without infringing the law of parsimony (Lloyd Morgan's canon). The extent to which maturational factors (envisaged as the execution of a genetic program) can be disentangled from experiential (learned) factors in the ontogeny of behavior probably depends mainly upon how research has been done into the behavior concerned: in intensively researched areas, such as song learning in passerine birds, interactions between genetic and experiential factors of fascinating diversity and varying from species to species are being found.

For most of the twentieth-century experimental psychologists, especially the so called "learning theorists" (Bower and Hilgard 1981), have endeavored to establish general laws of learning perhaps common to all animal species. So far as they exist, these could reflect (i) homologous or evolutionarily convergent mechanisms perhaps delimited by fundamental neuronal mechanisms; (ii) commonalities in what is required of information systems for the selection of predictive correlations caused by the logical constancies of the universe; (iii) limitations in the conceptual and technical ingenuity of contemporary experimenters.

Recently, under the influence of ethology the degree of generality of such laws has been questioned (Seligman 1970) and the notion of constraints on learning (Shettleworth 1972) – i.e. that a particular species may have a considerable facility to learn certain things but little or none to learn others, or that specific kinds of association may be governed by specific kinds of laws – has stimulated much empirical research (such as the great volume of work on conditioned food aversion, reviewed, e.g. by Goudie 1980).

Also ethology's historic emphasis on functional explanations of behavior has recently begun to interact with both psychological and zoological studies of animal learning in a potentially fruitful way: efforts are being made both in laboratory and field to assess the way in which the learning abilities of higher vertebrates may actually be put to use and contribute to Darwinian FITNESS in an ecological setting such as in FORAGING (e.g. review by Lea 1981). Yet another field of interdisciplinary endeavor covering the whole breadth of the neurosciences is the long quest to understand the neural bases of learning and memory (the search for the "engram") and here the study of relatively short-term changes in behavior and of animals with very simple nervous systems such as the mollusc *Aplysia* (Kandel 1976) is every bit as exciting as the much more voluminous literature on brain mechanisms underlying associative and instrumental learning in birds and mammals whose brains in both their anatomy and their functioning would seem to be amongst the most complex systems in the known universe. DWD

Bibliography

Bower, Gordon H. and Hilgard, Ernest R. 1981: *Theories of learning.* 5th edn. Englewood Cliffs, N.J. and London: Prentice Hall.

Catchpole, C.K. 1979: *Vocal communication in birds.* Studies in biology, 115. London: Edward Arnold.

*Fantino, E. and Logan, C.A. 1979: *The experimental analysis of behavior: a biological perspective.* San Francisco: W.H. Freeman.

Goudie, A.J. 1980. Conditioned food aversion: an adaptive specialisation of learning? *International research communication system journal of medical science* 8, 591–4.

Groves, P. and Thompson, R. 1970: Habituation: a dual-process theory. *Psychological review* 77, 419–50.

Harlow, H.F. 1959: In *Psychology: a study of a science.* Study 1, vol. 2, ed. S. Koch. New York: McGraw-Hill.

Hearst, Eliot and Jenkins, H.M. 1974: *Sign tracking: the stimulus-reinforcer relation and directed action.* Monograph of the Psychonomic Society. Austin, Texas: Psychonomic Society.

Hulse, S.H. 1978: In Hulse, Fowler and Honig.

Hulse, Stewart H., Fowler, Harry and Honig, Werner K. eds. 1978: *Cognitive processes in animal behavior.* Hillsdale, N.J.: Lawrence Erlbaum Associates.

Kandel, Eric R. 1976: *Cellular basis of behavior: an introduction to behavioral neurobiology.* San Francisco: W.H. Freeman.

Lea, S.E.G. 1981: In *Advances in analysis of behavior,* vol. 2. *Predictability, correlation and contiguity,* eds. Peter Harzem and Michael D. Zeiler. Chichester and New York: Wiley.

Premack, D. 1978: In Hulse, Fowler and Honig.

Roberts, W.A. and Grant, D.S. 1976: Studies of short-term memory in the pigeon using the delayed matching-to-sample procedure. In *Processes of animal memory,* eds. Douglas L. Medin, William A. Roberts and Roper T. Davis. Hillsdale, N.J.: Lawrence Erlbaum Associates.

Seligman, M.E.P. 1970: On the generality of the laws of learning. *Psychological review 77,* 406–18.

Shettleworth, S.J. 1972: Constraints on learning. In *Advances in the study of behavior,* eds. Daniel S. Lehrman, Robert A. Hinde and Evelyn Shaw. New York and London: Academic Press.

Zeiler, M.D. and Harzem, P. eds. 1983: *Biological factors in learning.* New York: Wiley.

learning; state-dependent Learning in which the degree of recall depends on the degree of similarity of the physiological state of the animal at the time of training to the animal's physiological state at the time of retention testing. In studies of state-dependent learning an animal is trained under the influence of a drug or some other agent and then tested at a later time either under drug or no-drug conditions. Animals demonstrating state-dependent learning show better retention when tested under the drug condition than the no-drug condition. In other words, habits learned while an animal is in one physiological state do not transfer well when the animal is tested in a different physiological state. This phenomenon is sometimes referred to as drug-induced dissociation. RAJ

learning: synaptic structure and intracellular chemical theories These theories postulate that the changes in nervous tissue underlying learning and the formation of memory involve either the growth of new synapses or the alteration of the properties of existing synapses. (Pictures of a synapse and a nerve cell, or neuron, appear in the entry on DRUGS.) A synapse is the area of communication between one nerve cell and another. The communication usually occurs when a signal (action potential) in one neuron leads to the release of a chemical transmitter from its terminals. The transmitter diffuses across the synaptic gap and combines with a receptor molecule in the membrane of the postsynaptic cell. This combination then leads either to activation (excitation) or depression (inhibition) of activity in the postsynaptic cell. Synapses may occur on the cell body (soma and dendrites) or on the initial segment of the axon of a neuron, in which case they can either excite or inhibit the generation of the action potential. Synapses may also be present on the axon terminals, in which case their action is to modulate the release of transmitter from the terminals when a nerve action potential arrives down the axon.

Before much was known about the nature of synaptic transmission Hebb

(1949) suggested that the formation of long-term memories could occur via the development of new synaptic knobs which would thus increase the area of contact between the axon of one neuron and the cell body of another. As more information became available, he also included the possibility that an existing synapse might become more effective perhaps through an increase in the amount of transmitter in the presynaptic terminal. There is some evidence that large changes in environmental conditions (such as a change from dark to light in previously dark-reared young animals (Rose 1980)) lead to changes in the number of synapses detectable by anatomical methods. However, the majority of present theories of the physical basis of learning and memory propose modification of existing synapses. The types of changes which have been proposed include: altering the width of the synaptic gap (Hyden 1974); altering the effectiveness of the presynaptic action potential in activating transmitter release (Kandel 1978; Mark 1979); altering the affinity or number of postsynaptic receptors for the neurotransmitter (Rose 1980). Such modification could lead to either an increase or a decrease in the efficacy of transmission at a synapse. Any particular memory would presumably involve modification of a large number of synapses. The memory would then be coded in terms of which synapses were modified and in each case whether the modification involved depression or activation. This point of view concerning how a memory is coded need, in principle, require only one species of synaptic molecule, which would be either increased or decreased in number or activity. There might be a number of ways in which the modification of this molecule could be brought about, but the hypothesis does not require a vast range of different molecules to code for different memories.

In the late 1950s and 1960s the climate of scientific opinion was different and there was a surprisingly wide acceptance of the idea that memories should be coded molecularly – one memory, one molecule. This led to the search for such memory molecules. The major strategy in this search was to train animals on a task and then kill them and administer homogenates or extracts of their brain (or even of their whole bodies in the case of planaria) to naive animals and see whether the memory was transferred. A number of positive results were reported. However, they were difficult or impossible to replicate, and in the case of the transfer of information between planaria by cannibalism it was found that the animals had not learnt the task but had merely been pseudo-conditioned (Jensen 1965). Another problem with the early transfer experiments was that they purported to show transfer of an RNA code from one animal to another via oral ingestion or by injection, and yet the RNA would have been most unlikely to have remained intact or if it had to have been able to gain access to brain cells. For these reasons, the idea of memories being coded individually by RNA has fallen into disrepute.

However, one sort of transfer experiment has been replicated in some laboratories. This is the ability of a peptide (named scotaphobin) apparently formed in the brain of rats during training in a one-trial dark avoidance situation to cause dark avoidance in mice injected with it (Ungar, Desiderio and Parr 1972). While the significance of this finding is not understood it is probably related to the finding that a number of other peptides which are found in the brain and elsewhere, which are whole or are parts of neurohormones (viz. vasopressin, oxytocin, the 4–10 part of ACTH, encephalins, etc.) can have profound and fairly specific effects on behavior including learning and memory (de Wied and Jolles 1982). It is perfectly possible that the synthesis, release and action of these and other peptides is involved in the modulation of synaptic activity underlying learning and memory.

Research into the biochemical basis of learning and memory has involved experiments both on complex animals learning complex tasks and also on simpler "models of learning". In both cases two main approaches have been used: the interventional and the correlational. In the first the strategy is to look for drugs which have a well-defined action at the molecular level and see whether they interfere with learning and memory storage and/or retrieval. In the second approach, animals are taught a task and then a search is made for biochemical/physiological changes in the nervous system correlated with the acquisition of the memory. A major problem in this latter sort of experiment is what controls should be used since even "rested" controls may be learning something and "yoked" controls (which for example receive matched non-contingent shocks every time an experimental animal receives a contingent shock) undoubtedly learn something (e.g. "whatever I do I can't get away from the shock").

Simple models of learning include single synapses such as the neuromuscular junction of vertebrates. Here it is well known that synaptic efficacy can be increased for periods as long as an hour if the nerve is stimulated tetanically, that is by a rapid repetition of the stimulus, (say 30 shocks/second for 60 seconds) – post-tetanic potentiation. The molecular basis of this process is not fully understood, but it is likely to involve increased effectiveness of an action potential in the presynaptic terminal in opening the calcium channels of the presynaptic membrane. (These channels allow calcium to enter and activate, by an as yet unknown mechanism, the release of transmitters from presynaptic vesicles probably by exocytosis).

Changes in the presynaptic release mechanism have been postulated to occur in another model of learning, that is long-term facilitation of synaptically-generated field potentials in the mammalian hippocampus (Bliss 1979). The hippocampus is an area of the brain which is widely believed to have a role in learning and memory in man and other mammals. It has been shown that infrequent repetition of tetanic stimulation of inputs such as the perforant path (which runs from the entorhinal cortex to the granule cells of the dentate gyrus) leads to potentiation of the granule cells' responses to single stimuli to the perforant path. This potentiation can last for many weeks and may well be a component of memory systems.

Another example of presynaptic changes underlying long-term alteration of synaptic efficacy has been elegantly demonstrated by Kandel (1978) in the marine snail, *Aplysia*. The gill withdrawal reflex of this animal in response to stimulation of the siphon or the mantle has been shown to habituate or under different circumstances to become sensitized. Such habituation and sensitization while not falling within a classical definition of learning has been used as a simple model of learning (and more recently, associative learning has also been demonstrated in this animal). Long-term habituation, lasting days or even weeks, is produced if four training sessions, of ten stimuli each, are given on consecutive days. The habituation of responses has been postulated to involve a decrease in the number of calcium channels in the axon terminals of the sensory nerve cell in consequence of its own prolonged activity. Such a change could be brought about via presynaptic autoreceptors for the transmitter being released, or via changes in intraterminal ion content or might be more directly related to the presynaptic action potential. Similarly, the contrasting sensitization to noxious stimuli can also last for periods of weeks if the pattern of training is suitably chosen. In this case the mechanism is heterosynaptic, involving facilitation of the synaptic release of transmitter from the sensory nerve terminal by the terminal of an axon originating in the head of the animal, which synapses upon the sensory presynaptic terminal. It appears that the transmitter released from this presynaptically facilitating neuron may be 5-hydroxytryptamine (5HT) and there is some evidence that its effect may be exerted via an increase in the intracellular level of cyclic AMP which somehow increases the effectiveness of the voltage-dependent calcium channels in the sensory neuron terminal. Such an effect means that each nerve impulse in the sensitized sensory neuron would release more transmitter than before sensitization. This work of Kandel and his associates is the nearest that research has got to a molecular and physiological understanding of any learning process. Such work has become increasingly relevant to learning in "higher" animals as it has been extended into the study of associative learning (Kandel and Schwarz 1982).

It is of importance to emphasize that in all those cases where changes in synaptic efficacy have been demonstrated as an integral part of a model learning system, the changes have occurred presynaptically. It is also of considerable interest that the changes observed were qualitatively similar in *Aplysia* for both short-lived (up to a day) and long-lasting (weeks) habituation and sensitization.

These hypotheses which propose that modulation of presynaptic efficacy underlies learning and memory do not in themselves explain the long-lasting nature of the changes. Any theory of the biochemical basis of memory must take into account the remarkable durability of some memories – for example, childhood memories can persist into extreme old age in humans. The synaptic growth theory of course would appear to account for this durability of memory.

If, however, memory involves near-permanent activation or inactivation of specific existing synapses, then we need to assume that there are new molecules synthesized as a correlate of learning which are involved in this modification. For example, if we consider the long-term sensitization of the *Aplysia* reflex, activation of a 5 HT-mediated synapse leads to activation of the enzyme adenylate cyclase which leads to an increase in cyclic AMP which acts via activation of another enzyme (probably a protein kinase) to depress activity in a membrane potassium channel. (Potassium current in this channel is required in the repolarization of the presynaptic membrane and hence in closing the calcium channels.)

Long-term changes in the effectiveness of transmitter release could involve long-term changes in the properties of the protein kinase or the potassium channel itself. Such long-term effects would probably require a change in the nature of the protein synthesized (perhaps production of different subunits). For this to occur, a signal must pass from the nerve terminals back to the cell body of the sensory neuron. This signal would then (say) switch on,

either at the level of transcription of DNA in the nucleus, or at the level of translation in the cytoplasm, the synthesis of the new protein. The new protein would then be transported down the axon to be incorporated into the nerve terminal membrane. (Kandel and Schwarz, 1982, have hypothesized that the signal is cyclic AMP and that the new protein is a high affinity regulatory subunit of a protein kinase which is activated by cyclic AMP and interacts with the potassium channel. This theory would explain the permanence of long-term sensitization in *Aplysia* and proposes that cyclic AMP has the role both of the short-term sensitizing agent and the long-term signal.)

It has often been suggested that memory involves the synthesis of new proteins. As mentioned earlier, these proteins do not need to be specific to any particular memory. There is ample evidence from correlational experiments that both learning of tasks such as a Y-maze discrimination task in rats, and models for learning including imprinting in chicks, are associated with increased incorporation of radioactive precursor into RNA, simple proteins and glycoproteins (Matthies 1979; Rose 1980; Routtenberg 1979). Furthermore, interventional studies, using drugs which inhibit protein synthesis have shown that it is possible to block either long term storage or long term retrieval processes by massively blocking protein synthesis (e.g. Squire and Barondes 1973). Such inhibition does not necessarily interfere with learning, although it can do where the learning procedure involves many trials.

Time-dependent changes in the susceptibility of memories to disruption are well known and have been built into a number of theories of memory formation. Mark (1979) studying one-trial aversion learning in the chick (they learnt not to peck an attractive object painted with nasty-tasting methyl-anthranilate) used ouabain to block the sodium pump (which normally pumps potassium ions into and sodium ions out of cells, and is responsible for keeping intracellular concentration of these ions constant). If the ouabain was given at the time of exposure to the aversive situation it blocked subsequent memory, but ouabain had no effect if administered after learning. In contrast, inhibition of protein synthesis with cycloheximide at the time of learning left memory unaffected for about half an hour, but later caused amnesia. Mark interpreted these findings by suggesting that activity at the "learning" synapses led to a small increase in intracellular sodium which activates the sodium-pump. He suggested that the increased flow of sodium out of the cell is an essential component of the memory formation and is coupled to an increase in the rate of entry of amino acids which would then stimulate protein synthesis (presumably at the cell body). This protein synthesis is necessary for the formation of the long-term memory. While there is no evidence either for or against such a suggestion, the protein concerned could of course be involved in the calcium channel as was proposed for the *Aplysia* synapse.

Another hypothesis which incorporates time-dependent changes in memory is the cholinergic theory of Deutsch (1973, ch. 3, pp. 59–76). There is a wealth of information, including clinical data, that cholinergic systems are involved in memory. Deutsch apparently showed that the susceptibility of memory (for a light-discrimination task) in rats to drugs which interact with cholinergic synapses, varied in a time-dependent way. He suggested that the formation of memory (and/or its retrieval system) involved a gradual increase in the efficacy of the nerve action potential in causing acetylcholine release in the hippocampus. He further proposed that forgetting involved a decrease in this efficacy. While not all Deutsch's findings are readily reproducible (see George and Mellanby 1974) the theory has been of value in providing readily testable predictions and in the discussion of clinical findings, including the memory deterioration found in old age and more dramatically in Alzheimer's disease.

In conclusion, it appears likely that the long-term changes underlying learning and memory involve presynaptic transmitter release mechanisms modulated via changes in the amounts or activity of membrane proteins.   JHM

Bibliography

Bliss, T.V.P. 1979: Synaptic plasticity in the hippocampus. *Trends in neuroscience* 2, 42–5.

Deutsch, J.A. 1973: *The physiological basis of memory*. New York and London: Academic Press.

de Wied, D. and Jolles, J. 1982: Neuropeptides derived from pro-opiocortin: behavioral, physiological, and neurochemical effects. *Physiological review* 62, 976–1043.

Farley, J. and Alkon, D.L. 1985: Cellular mechanisms of learning, memory and information storage. In *Annual review of psychology*, vol. 36, eds. M.R. Rosenzweig and L.W. Porter. Palo Alto: Annual Reviews Inc.

George, G. and Mellanby, J. 1974: A further study of the effect of physostigmine on memory in rats. *Brain research* 81, 133–44.

Hebb, D.O. 1949: *The organization of behavior*. New York: John Wiley and Son; London: Chapman and Hall.

Horn, G. 1985: *Memory, imprinting and the brain*. Oxford and New York: Oxford University Press.

Hyden, H. 1974: A calcium-dependent mechanism for synapse and nerve cell membrane modulation. *Proceedings of the National Academy of Sciences*, New York 71, 2965–8.

Jensen, D.D. 1965: Paramecium, planaria and pseudolearning. *Animal behaviour* Supplement 1, 9–20.

Kandel, F.R. 1978: *A cell-biological approach to learning*. Grass Lecture Monograph 1. Bethesda, Maryland: Society for Neuroscience.

—— and Schwarz, J.H. 1982: Molecular biology of learning: Modulation of transmitter release. *Science* 218, 433–43.

Mark, R. 1979: Sequential biochemical steps in memory formation: evidence from the use of metabolic inhibitors. In *Brain mechanisms in memory and learning*, ed. M.A.B. Brazier. New York: Raven Press.

Matthies, H. 1979: Biochemical, electrophysiological and morphological correlates of brightness discrimination in rats. In *Brain mechanisms in memory and learning*, ed. M.A.B. Brazier. New York: Raven Press.

Rose, S.P.R. 1980: Neurochemical correlates of early learning in the chick. In *Neurobiological basis of learning and memory*. eds. Y. Tsukada and B.W. Agranoff. New York: John Wiley and Sons.

Routtenberg, A. 1979: Anatomical localization of phosphoprotein and glycoprotein substrates of memory. *Progress in neurobiology* 12, 85–113.

Squire, L.R. and Barondes, B.H. 1973: Memory impairment during prolonged training in mice given inhibitors of cerebral protein synthesis. *Brain research* 56, 215.

Ungar, G., Desiderio, D. and Parr, W. 1972: Scotophobia. *Nature* 238, 198.

learning: theories of Theories usually derived from conditioning experiments with animals designed to describe the most general features of learning and how behavior changes with learning. The heyday of learning theory was in the thirty years between 1930 and 1960, when a number of rival, global theories or systems were proposed, associated with the names of THORNDIKE (1911), Hull (1943), Tolman (1932), Guthrie (1935) and SKINNER (1938). Although these theories were based almost exclusively on work with animals in restricted and no doubt artificial experimental situations, the theories were freely extrapolated to man. As Tolman wrote:

I believe that everything important in psychology (except such matters as the building up of a superego, that is everything save such matters as involve society and words) can be investigated in essence through the continued experimental and theoretical analysis of the determiners of rat behavior at a choice point in a maze. Herein I believe I agree with Professor Hull and also with Professor Thorndike (1938, p.34).

Theories of learning were developed to answer at least three separate, but not altogether unrelated questions. First, *what* does an organism learn; secondly, what are the sufficient and necessary conditions producing learning; and thirdly, how does learning affect behavior? To these questions, they tended to give different answers and, because the questions are linked, differences in answers to one question implied differences in answers to another. There was a fourth question, often not explicitly asked, but often implicitly answered: how far can the results of conditioning experiments in rats and dogs be applied to other animals, including man, solving other kinds of problem? On this point, as the quotation from Tolman suggests, there was rather general agreement.

There was also a measure of agreement in their answers to the second question: what are the conditions under which learning occurs? Here an associationist bias suggested to all theorists that learning is a matter of association, and that temporal contiguity between the events to be associated is the single most important determinant of successful learning. An important point at issue was whether temporal contiguity was sufficient to produce learning or whether some additional process was necessary. This amounts to asking whether Pavlov's or Thorndike's account of reinforcement is correct, and one plausible answer is that both are correct for different varieties of conditioning, PAVLOV for classical and Thorndike for instrumental (see CONDITIONING).

The main points at issue revolved round the answers to the first question, what is learned, and the associated answers the theorists gave to the third question, how is learning translated into performance. The answers proposed by Thorndike, Hull and Guthrie were that learning consists of the establishment or strengthening of stimulus-response connections, and that such learning is seen as a change in behavior rather directly, for a stimulus which did not elicit a particular response before will now do so as a consequence of learning. Stimulus-response analyses of behavior have been popular with psychologists since WATSON (1913) announced the dawn of BEHAVIORISM. But their origin antedates that event by many years. Classical reflex theory attempted to analyze behavior into stimulus-response units: the reflex arc provided the direct connection between stimulus input and response output. Reflexes are, of course, relatively fixed, inborn patterns of behavior: the same stimulus always elicits the same response. It is obvious that learning causes behavior to change, but it might be possible to explain learning as the formation of new stimulus-response connections.

Thorndike developed such an account of the behavior of animals in his puzzle boxes. Where at first the animal struggled ineffectually and eventually hit upon the correct response which gained its release purely by chance, with continued training it would efficiently perform the required response as soon as it was placed in the apparatus. The set of stimuli produced by being placed in the apparatus now immediately elicited a response which they had only slowly and haphazardly elicited at the outset of training: a new stimulus-response connection had been formed.

Learning is undoubtedly quite often evidenced by an increase in the probability of the learner performing some particular response. But it does not follow even here that such learning can be understood as the establishment or strengthening of a stimulus-response connection. At the very least, this conclusion requires that successful solution of the sort of problem set by Thorndike should depend on the animal having had the opportunity to perform the required response in this situation and that an association between situation and response should then have been strengthened (presumably because the response was followed by some consequence). Thorndike himself thought he had provided such evidence: he spent much fruitless time and energy seeing whether animals could learn the way to escape from one of his puzzle boxes simply by observing the correct solution being performed by someone else. Finding no sign of successful IMITATION or OBSERVATIONAL LEARNING, he concluded that learning did indeed depend on the strengthening of a stimulus-response connection. But in fact there is now ample evidence that animals can learn by observation, without the opportunity to practice.

There are other reasons for questioning whether learning can always be understood as the establishment of stimulus-response connections. Learning frequently leads to no immediate or obvious change in behavior at all. The young white-crowned sparrow will not fully develop its typical species' song unless exposed to that song in the first two months of its life. During this period it must be supposed that the young sparrow learns to identify the critical features of white-crowned sparrow song. But so far as anyone can tell, there is no evidence in the bird's behavior that it has learned anything at all until the following spring when it starts practicing what it learned six months earlier (Marler 1970). Tolman and his colleagues reported numerous experiments on what they called LATENT LEARNING which implied much the same conclusion: a satiated rat given the opportunity to run through a maze which contained food at the end of one path but not others might show no tendency to choose the path that led to food until it was made hungry, at which point it would show that it had profited from its past experience by choosing that path immediately and consistently.

Learning is probably not, therefore, always a matter of strengthening responses: it is more usefully regarded as the acquisition of knowledge which may or may not produce an immediate change in behavior, just as Tolman had argued (Dickinson 1980). The connection between learning and performance is much less close than stimulus-response theories imply. But there are also reasons for questioning not only the gross oversimplification of learning implicit in a stimulus-response analysis, but also the assumption common to most of the classic learning theorists that experiments on conditioning in rats were sufficient to reveal all the important laws of learning. This assumption has been attacked by some psychologists ever since Köhler's celebrated study of problem solving by chimpanzees (1925) (see INSIGHT). Köhler tested the ability of his chimpanzees to obtain food that lay out of their reach by improvising rakes to draw the food through the bars of their cage or by piling boxes on top of one another so that they could climb up and reach the banana hanging from the ceiling. He found no evidence of trial and error attempts at solutions in the behavior of his chimpanzees and concluded that they must have relied on insight into the nature of the problem. As a matter of fact, Köhler was probably wrong, for subsequent investigation has suggested that chimpanzees need experience with related problems, gained if need be during the course of play, in order to solve the sort of problem he set them (Schiller 1952).

But the issue raised by Köhler's critique

remains. Theories of learning have typically been based on extrapolation from some very simple experimental procedures. Is it really plausible to suppose that all forms of learning can be understood by appeal to the same simple processes that are sufficient to explain conditioning? Although advanced explicitly or implicitly by most classic learning theorists, and still advanced by Skinner, it is doubtful whether many psychologists today would accept such a claim. Indeed, so far has the tide of opinion flowed in the opposite direction that conditioning experiments are now often derided as trivial and irrelevant to any understanding of human behavior. This is probably an over-reaction. Skinner and his followers have done some service by pointing to numerous examples from everyday life of behavior that can easily be analysed in terms of a simple theory of learning. The fond parents who hasten to pick up their crying baby may well be rewarding the baby for crying and thus increasing the chances that it will do so again whenever it is bored or alone. And when they subsequently refuse to respond immediately the baby starts crying, but still give in eventually if it goes on long enough, they are probably instituting a schedule of partial and delayed reinforcement which, as many animal experiments have established, is nicely calculated to prolong rather than put a stop to the baby's new-found habit.

Theories of learning based on simple conditioning experiments are surely insufficient to explain the learning capacities of the chimpanzee. Just how far chimpanzees have progressed in learning anything approximating to language is a matter of some dispute. Yet although some aspects of language learning may be relatively simple (the meanings of concrete nouns, for example, can probably be learned by a rather simple associative process), some chimpanzees have clearly progressed beyond this stage (see LANGUAGE: ANTHROPOID APE). Premack (1976) has shown that the chimpanzee Sarah is capable of understanding and using symbols meaning "is the color of" (as in "red is the color of apple") or "is the shape of" or "is the name of" (as in "apple is the name of apple"). She is also, as

Gillan, Woodruff and Premack (1981) have shown, capable of solving quite complex analogical reasoning problems of the kind popular in IQ tests ("shoe is to foot as glove is to . . . "). A theory of learning based on conditioning experiments with rats or pigeons (there is good reason to believe that pigeons would be unable to solve these problems) does not take us very far in understanding the cognitive processes involved in this sort of behavior.   NJM

Bibliography

*Bower, G.H. and Hilgard, E.R. 1981: *Theories of learning*. 5th edn. Englewood Cliffs, N.J.: Prentice Hall.

*Dickinson, A. 1980: *Contemporary animal learning theory*. Cambridge: Cambridge University Press.

Gillan, D.J. Woodruff, G. and Premack, D. 1981: Reasoning in the chimpanzee: I. Analogical reasoning. *Journal of experimental psychology, animal behavior processes* 7, 1–17.

Guthrie, E.R. 1935: *The psychology of learning*. New York: Harper.

Hull, Clark L. 1943: *Principles of behavior*. New York and London: Appleton-Century.

Köhler, Wolfgang 1925 (1973): *The mentality of apes*. London and Boston: Routledge and Kegan Paul.

Marler, P. 1970: A comparative approach to vocal learning: song-development in white-crowned sparrow. *Journal of comparative and physiological psychology* Monograph 71, No. 2. Part 2.

*Premack, D. 1976: *Intelligence in ape and man*. Hillsdale, N.J.: Erlbaum.

Roitblat, H.L., Bever, T.G. and Terrace, H.S. 1984: *Animal cognition*. Hillsdale, N.J.: Erlbaum.

Schiller, P.H. 1952: Innate constituents of complex responses in primates. *Psychological review* 59, 177–91.

Skinner, B.F. 1938: *The behavior of organisms*. New York and London: Appleton-Century.

Thorndike, Edward L. 1911: *Animal intelligence*. New York: Macmillan.

Tolman, E.C. 1932: *Purposive behavior in animals and men*. New York: Century.

———— 1938: The determiners of behavior at a choice point. *Psychological review* 45, 1–41.

Watson, J.B. 1913: Psychology as the behaviorist views it. *Psychological review* 20, 158–77.

learning: Thorndike's laws The law of effect and the law of exercise. The law of effect states that a response followed by a satisfying or pleasant consequence (i.e. a response that is rewarded) tends to be repeated, while one followed by an annoying or unpleasant consequence (i.e. one that is punished) tends not to be repeated. To explain these empirical generalizations (sometimes referred to as the empirical law of effect) Thorndike assumed that satisfying consequences strengthen stimulus-response connections, while annoying consequences weaken them. The law of exercise states that, other things being equal, the more often a response is performed in a given situation, the more likely it is to be repeated.

Thorndike had no doubt that the law of effect was the more important of the two: only if two responses had similar effects would the law of exercise come into play to increase the probability of the more frequently performed response. And in both theoretical and empirical forms the law of effect has had much the greater impact on later psychologists. Hull attempted to explain all learning in terms of Thorndike's theoretical law of effect; while SKINNER defined instrumental or operant CONDITIONING as the establishment of responses by their consequences in accordance with the empirical law of effect. NJM

Bibliography

Thorndike, Edward L. 1911: *Animal intelligence.* New York: Macmillan.

learning: two factor/single factor theories Single factor theories of conditioning assume that classical and instrumental conditioning differ only in the experimental operations used to study them, not in any underlying process, while two factor theories assume that the two forms of conditioning are fundamentally distinct.

Two factor theorists insist that different theories are needed to account for classical conditioning, where a response initially elicited by one stimulus comes to be elicited by another solely as a consequence of the association between the two stimuli, and for instrumental conditioning where a response is modified because of its consequences. Single factor theorists attempt to reduce one type of conditioning to the other: historically the most important version of such a theory was that of Hull, who argued that all responses were modified by their consequences.

Two factor theorists assume that any such reduction of one type of conditioning to the other is impossible, but they have assumed that both processes usually occur together in any experiment. In particular they have assumed that classical conditioning to stimuli occurring at the same time as the reinforcer in an instrumental experiment endow those stimuli with classically conditioned motivational states which influence the performance of the instrumental response. (See CONDITIONING.) NJM

learning and motivation There are two related questions here: (i) to what extent are motivational factors necessary for learning to take place and (ii) how are motivational factors involved in the initiation and regulation of conditioned behavior?

Experiments investigating the first question have involved LATENT LEARNING and sensory preconditioning procedures. In the latter, subjects initially receive paired presentations of two motivationally neutral stimuli, such as a light and tone, which will not produce any overt evidence of learning. One of these stimuli is then paired with a motivationally significant event, such as shock, and as a consequence the other will be capable of eliciting a conditioned response. Such a result could only be possible if subjects had learned about the light-tone relationship during the first stage of the experiment. This has led to the view that motivation may not be necessary for learning to occur but it is essential if the effects of that learning are to be demonstrated.

In answer to the second question theorists have subdivided motivational factors into those determined by biological needs, e.g. hunger, and those determined by the reinforcer for the conditioned response. According to Hull's formal account of the relationship between learning and motivation (1952), biological needs are related to a central state, Drive (D), and the properties of reward influence incentive motivation (K). Hull maintained that the repeated pairing of a response with reward resulted in the gradual strengthening of the response as a habit. Whether or not a habit would be executed and its resultant intensity (E) is given by Equation 1, where H represents the conditioned strength of the habit.

$$E = H \times D \times K \qquad (1)$$

Once a response has acquired some habit strength, the likelihood of its being performed depends upon there being a measure of drive and incentive motivation present.

As far as manipulations of drive are concerned Equation 1 is reasonably accurate when only one motivational state is involved. The hungrier an animal is the more vigorously it will perform an instrumental response to obtain food. Alternatively, the stronger an electric shock the more rapidly will an animal run to escape it. A more controversial feature of Hull's theory is the claim that drive is general, that is, that different biological needs combine to determine the resultant level of activity of this central state and that this state can energize all types of behavior. The consequent prediction that the energizing influence of drive should be independent of the need(s) responsible for its arousal has met with conflicting evidence. In support it has been found that giving a rat a mild shock before it runs in an alley for food increases the speed of this response. In contrast attempts to enhance drive by increasing food deprivation have failed to show a corresponding increase in the speed at which animals will run to escape shock. This type of result has led some theorists to accept the unparsimonious view that each need state is associated with its own drive condition (e.g. Estes 1969).

In view of its assumed general properties Hull's drive was theoretically incapable of exerting a guiding influence on behavior.

The selection of responses that led to a goal appropriate to a subject's needs was left to drive stimuli. A drive stimulus was hypothesized to be a pattern of stimulation that was unique to a particular deprivation state and could serve as an eliciting stimulus for any habit strengthened in its presence. Somewhat surprisingly it has proved rather difficult to demonstrate the existence of these stimuli (see Bolles 1975, pp. 270 ff. for a review). Recent research has shown that animals can associate a drive stimulus with reward (Capaldi and Davidson 1979), but it remains to be shown unequivocally that such stimuli can elicit habits.

Hull's initial proposal that drive was the only motivational influence on instrumental responding was rejected on the basis of an experiment by Crespi (1942). This study demonstrated for rats that rapid changes in the speed of running down an alley for food could be produced by manipulating the size of reward. Hull regarded these changes as being too rapid to be explained by variations in habit strength. Accordingly, he proposed that stimuli which precede the consumption of reward, such as those encountered in the alley, elicit anticipatory goal responses (r_g) that in turn arouse incentive motivation. Since a change in goal magnitude should produce a corresponding change in r_g and hence incentive motivation. Equation 1 can explain Crespi's results.

This incentive feature of Hull's theorizing has been developed in a variety of ways. Some theorists (e.g. Mowrer 1960; Bindra 1972) extended his views to such an extent that habit learning was not considered to play any role in guiding behavior. Very broadly, they proposed that stimuli preceding reward aroused positive incentive motivation while stimuli associated with aversive events excited negative incentive motivation (Bindra's terminology). By approaching stimuli that increase positive incentive and avoiding those that arouse negative incentive, animals should behave adaptively by being guided towards reward and away from aversive events. The postulation of two incentive systems has been accompanied by the proposal that they are interconnected by inhibitory links, so that increases in negative incentive will suppress appetitive responding and vice versa (see Dickinson and Pearce 1977 for a review). This feature enables incentive theories to explain many of the interactions obtained when appetitive and aversive conditioning procedures are intermixed.

If, as Hull maintained, incentive motivation is aroused by r_g then changes in the frequency of these responses should be correlated with changes in the intensity of instrumental responding. Unfortunately a considerable number of experiments have failed to reveal any support for this prediction. In reviewing these data Rescorla and Solomon (1967) concluded that stimuli that reliably precede reward will excite a central nervous state (incentive motivation) as well as eliciting overt $r_g s$. The consequent implication that the occurrence of r_g will not provide a behavioral index of incentive motivation has led to two reactions. Trapold and Overmier (1972), for example, warn against invoking central states that are unobservable as mediators of performance. They, propose, therefore, that $r_g s$ should be regarded, in a manner similar to that initially intended by Hull, as events with response cueing but not incentive properties. Whereas theorists such as Bolles (1975) have used this opportunity to regard the central state as being cognitive rather than motivational, replacing the term "incentive" with "expectancy". Whether the properties of the goal for responding influence performance by response cueing, incentive motivational or cognitive processes remains a matter of continuing debate. At present this issue is decided more by theoretical predilection than by experimental evidence.　　　JMP

Bibliography

Bindra, D. 1972: A unified account of classical conditioning and operant training. In *Classical conditioning*, eds. A.H. Black and W.F. Prokasy. New York: Appleton.

*Bolles, R.C. 1975: *Theory of motivation*. New York: Harper and Row.

Capaldi, E.D. and Davidson, T.L. 1979: Control of instrumental behavior by deprivation stimuli. *Journal of experimental psychology: animal behavior processes* 4, 355–67.

Crespi, L.P. 1942: Quantitative variation of incentive and performance in the white rat. *American journal of psychology* 55, 467–517.

Dickinson, A. and Pearce, J.M. 1977: Inhibitory interactions between appetitive and aversive stimuli. *Psychological bulletin* 84, 690–711.

Estes, W.K. 1969: New perspectives on some old issues in association theory. In *Fundamental issues in associative learning*, eds. N.J. Mackintosh and W.K. Honig. Halifax: Dalhousie University Press.

Hull, C.L. 1952: *A behavior system*. New Haven: Yale University Press.

McFarland, D.J. and Houston, A. 1981: *Quantitative ethology*. Boston and London: Pitman.

Mowrer, O.H. 1960: *Learning theory and behavior*. New York: Wiley.

Rescorla, R.A. and Solomon, R.L. 1967: Two process learning theory: relationships between Pavlovian conditioning and instrumental learning. *Psychological review* 74, 151–82.

Trapold, M.A. and Overmier, J.B. 1972: The second learning process in instrumental learning. In *Classical conditioning*, eds. A.H. Black and W.F. Prokasy. New York: Appleton.

learning sets Or "sets to learn" (Harlow 1949) refer to the acquisition by an individual of the ability to learn a particular kind of task, or solve a particular kind of problem, progressively more efficiently as a result of experiencing a variety of examples of such tasks or problems. For example rhesus monkeys required to discriminate between pairs of objects for food reward learn the first few pairs slowly, but after learning several hundred different pairs are able to learn any new pair very rapidly – an object-discrimination learning set. A simpler task where a learning set may also develop in many species is serial reversal; a single pair of discriminanda is used (e.g. left and right sides of a maze, a black and a white object) and first one and then the other must be chosen to obtain food reward, the rewarded member being switched (reversed) whenever the subject is consistently choosing the currently correct one. Early reversals are learned slowly, later ones more rapidly. In general, any class of problem where there is a common rule or CONCEPT to guide solution – e.g. choose pictures showing people, choose left and right in double-alternating sequence – it may give rise to a learning set. It is recognized that learning set formation reflects the abandonment of inappropriate strategies or "error factors", including the forgetting of irrelevant preferences derived from previous problems. In addition it may reflect acquisition of the underlying rule or concept; or it may be that the concept was already present but masked by error factors.

In many cases subjects may show some degree of learning set formation, i.e. some improvement in problem-solving rate, without attaining the maximum speed or generality indicative of having learnt the precise rule. The rate and completeness with which various learning sets are acquired has often been proposed as a test of comparative intelligence across animal species, but recent work suggests little consistency within orders or even within single species; learning set capacity seems to depend more on procedural or ecological variables than on any "general intelligence" factor supposedly characteristic of a phyletic grouping. Nonetheless, insofar as they demonstrate an ability for abstraction and wide transfer of learning, learning sets illustrate an important aspect of cognitive capacity in animals. EAG

Bibliography

Bessemer, D.W. and Stollnitz, F. 1971: Retention of discriminations and an analysis of learning set. In Schrier and Stollnitz.

Harlow, H.F. 1949: The formation of learning sets. *Psychological review* 56, 51–65.

*Warren, J.M. 1973: Learning in vertebrates. In *Comparative psychology*, eds. D.A. Dewsbury and D.A. Rethlingshafer. New York: McGraw-Hill.

Schrier, A.M. and Stollnitz, F. eds. 1971: *Behaviour of nonhuman primates*, vol 4. New York: Academic Press.

Weiskrantz, L. ed. 1985: *Animal intelligence.* New York and Oxford: Oxford University Press.

locomotion The coordinated muscular movements which displace the whole body of an animal. Many very small animals float freely in air or in water, but these movements are entirely passive and do not count as locomotion. A great variety of means of locomotion is found among animals.

The techniques used for locomotion in water include undulating swimming such as that of eels, water snakes and some marine worms (polychaetes); rowing as in ducks, water beetles and ciliated protozoa; hydrofoil swimming which is found in tunnies and other fast-swimming fish, marine turtles, penguins and auks; and the jet propulsion of squid, octopus and dragon-fly larvae. The physical principles involved in aquatic locomotion have received considerable study and are well understood.

Flight has evolved in few groups of animals, probably because it requires extreme anatomical specialization which can be achieved only by animals which are already adapted for an agile life on land. Insects were the first animals to develop flight and there were numerous types of flying insects 300 million years ago. Flying reptiles appeared about 170 million years ago and were abundant up to about 70 million years ago. Birds evolved during the same period, the early forms being similar to flying reptiles. Flying mammals (bats) appeared about 40 million years ago. Even today there are some incipient flying animals, including flying marsupials, such as the gliding possums (*Petaurus*) and flying squirrels (*Glaucomys*). There are also flying lizards, snakes and fish. All these animals have a short-range primitive type of gliding flight. Nevertheless, the potential for evolution to more sophisticated forms is present.

Modern birds and insects are able to exploit many principles of aerodynamics and exhibit many forms of flight, including gliding, napping flight and hovering flight. Aerodynamic principles dictate that larger animals fly faster and require less frequent wing beats. Only very small birds, such as humming birds, and insects can perform hovering flight in which there is no forward locomotion. Very large birds have to run to attain sufficient speed to become airborne. This requirement is reduced if they take off into the wind. Large birds have proportionally larger wings and their flapping flight requires considerable energy expenditure compared to that of small birds. For this reason most large birds prefer gliding flight and tend to exploit conditions where this is possible. Natural up-currents occur where the wind strikes a hill or sea cliff. Seagulls can often glide along a cliff when there is a sea breeze. Over land, up-currents called thermals may occur where there are features, such as rocky areas, which induce differential heating. Large birds, such as vultures, may save more than 90 per cent of the energy required for flapping flight, by exploiting thermals as they search for prey.

Locomotion on land occurs in a number of forms in animals without legs. Amoeboid movement is found in some single-celled animals and various types of crawling occur in worms, leeches, etc. Waves of muscular contraction pass down the body of an earthworm producing a form of concertina crawling. The serpentine crawling used by snakes exploits irregularities on the ground, such as stones and tufts of grass. Lateral pressure against these enables the snake to glide forward.

Locomotion on legs occurs mainly in the arthropods and vertebrates. Among two-legged animals there are three basic types of gait, the walk, the run and the hop. During walking there is always one foot on the ground, whereas both feet may be momentarily off the ground during running. Hopping on two legs, as in kangaroos and many birds, involves simultaneous propulsion from the two legs.

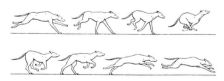

Whippet running (from Gray 1968)

Animals have numerous possible gaits, depending upon the order in which the feet touch the ground, as illustrated. In four-legged animals the main propulsion comes from the hind feet, but in many mammals the stride is lengthened by bending the back so that the hind feet may touch the ground in front of the fore feet during galloping.

Jumping from a running or standing start occurs in many mammals but few can jump much more than their own height. Some insects have a special catapult mechanism which enables them to jump many times their own height from a standing start.

Moving in trees occurs in a variety of animals and many different methods are employed. On vertical tree trunks, birds grip the bark with their claws and use their tail to brace the body. Squirrels brace their fore and hind limbs against each other. When descending vertically they rotate their hind feet so that the toes point backwards and the bark can be gripped by the claws. Cats cannot rotate their feet in this way and so cannot walk down vertical surfaces. Horizontal movement in trees may be similar to locomotion on the ground, as in small birds and mammals which run along branches. Primates swing from branch to branch with their arms and tail, a form of locomotion called brachiation.

The mechanics of locomotion have received considerable study and it has been discovered that animals use a wide variety of devices including the lever, spring, aerofoil, etc. Animals are remarkably well engineered and adapted to achieve maximum economy of movement.

DJM

Bibliography

Alexander, R., McNeill and Goldspink, G. 1977; *Mechanics and energetics of animal locomotion.* London: Chapman and Hall.

Bush, B.M.H. and Clarac, F. 1985: *Coordination of motor behaviour.* Cambridge: Cambridge University Press.

Carlsöo, Sven 1972: *How man moves: kinesiological studies and methods.* London: Heinemann.

Gewecke, M. and Wendler, G. 1985: *Insect locomotion.* Berlin and Hamburg: Paul Parey.

Gray, J. 1968: *Animal locomotion.* London: Weidenfeld and Nicolson: New York: Norton.

Trueman, E.R. 1975: *The locomotion of soft bodied animals.* London: Edward Arnold.

Wickstrom, Ralph L. 1970: *Fundamental motor patterns.* Philadelphia: Lea and Febiger.

Lorenz, Konrad Born in Vienna in 1901, the son of a prosperous orthopaedic surgeon. His childhood was spent in the family home in the village of Altenberg where he was able to maintain a collection of animals and birds. It was there that he built up the colony of jackdaws which provided the material for his first scientific paper. He was a student in the Vienna Medical School, going on to become an assistant in anatomy. It was there that he met Oskar Heinroth from whom he picked up the germs of many of his major ideas. During the war years he was head of the psychology department at the University of Königsburg, and then an army doctor on the Eastern Front. He spent some years in Russian captivity. After the war Lorenz became involved with the development of a research institution specifically devoted to ethology. From 1961 he was director of the Max Planck Institute for the Physiology of Behavior which had been set up partly with private funds.

During the 1930s and 1940s Lorenz published a series of influential papers, mainly based on observations of bird behavior. Among many remarkable discoveries the phenomenon of IMPRINTING was amongst the most important. Goslings do not possess an innate capacity to recognize their conspecifics. This ability is acquired during a short and particularly sensitive period, after which the "imprint" of the salient individual is more or less permanent. Perhaps the most startling of Lorenz's demonstrations was his imprinting of goslings on himself.

In the background was the general Darwinian idea of the natural selection of behavioral routines as a contribution to the inclusive FITNESS of the animal. Lorenz's work refined this basic hypothesis, clearly distinguishing the learnt routines of which only a capacity for their acquisition was inherited, from those where the routine itself was genetically based.

Lorenz's theoretical contributions amounted to a comprehensive theory of instinctive behavior. Instincts were seen as inherited, stereotyped behavior patterns which were released by specific stimuli, or even without them if the reaction-specific energy had accumulated sufficiently in the organism. Later subject to heavy criticism (e.g. Lehrman 1953), the theory was instrumental in providing a framework for the systematic growth of ETHOLOGY. Lorenz's writings have continued to be controversial, as for instance in his approach to human behavior in books such as *On aggression* (1966) and *Behind the mirror* (1977). He shared the Nobel Prize for physiology and medicine in 1973 with VON FRISCH and TINBERGEN. PKS/RHa

Bibliography

Dewsbury, D.A. ed. 1985: *Leaders in the study of animal behavior: autobiographical perspectives.* Cranbury, N.J.: Associated Universities Press.

Lehrman, D.S. 1953: A critique of Konrad Lorenz's theory of instinctive behavior. *Quarterly review of biology* 28, 337–63.

Lorenz, Konrad Zacharias 1966: *On aggression.* New York: Harcourt, Brace and World; London: Methuen.

—— 1977: *Behind the mirror.* New York: Harcourt Brace; London: Methuen.

Thorpe, W.H. 1979: *The origins and rise of ethology.* London: Heinemann.

M

meme A term introduced by Dawkins (1976) in his proposed analogy between biological and cultural evolution, to refer to the hypothetical cultural counterpart of the gene – a "unit" of cultural inheritance. Suggestions that socio-cultural change has some of the properties of biological evolution have been made repeatedly, and early ones have long been discredited (see EVOLUTION). Recently, however, a number of subtler models have been proposed and debated (see Plotkin and Odling-Smee 1981). Some schemes suggest that cultural traits change in frequency according to their effects on the biological fitness of their bearer, but Dawkins's idea differs in suggesting that memes change frequency simply according to their capacity for cultural transmission from one individual to another. Dawkins (1982) also distinguishes between memes (units of information residing in the brain) and meme products (their outward and perceptible manifestations). This speculative scheme has stimulated a continuing debate (see Dawkins 1982, Staddon 1981, Harré 1979). RDA

Bibliography

Dawkins, R. 1976: *The selfish gene.* Oxford: Oxford University Press.

—— 1982: *The extended phenotype: the gene as the unit of selection.* Oxford and San Francisco: W.H. Freeman.

Harré, Rom 1979: *Social being.* Part 4. Oxford: Basil Blackwell; Totowa, N.J.: Littlefield Adams.

Plotkin, H.C. and Odling-Smee, F.J. 1981: A multiple-level model of evolution and its implications for sociobiology. *Behavioral and brain science* 4, 225–68.

Staddon, J.E.R. 1981: On a possible relation between cultural transmission and genetical evolution. In *Perspectives in ethology 4: advantages of diversity,* eds. P.P.G. Bateson and P.H. Klopfer. New York and London: Plenum Press.

memory The retention of novel behavior or perception. In animal behavior we know about perception only through the behavior of the animal. By analogy with our own experience, however, we can distinguish between the recognition memory of sensory stimuli and the memory of how to perform certain activities.

An animal's repertoire of behavior is made up of innate patterns and of activities acquired through experience. We can distinguish between behavior due to instinct and that due to learning. The term memory is normally reserved for the retention of behavior acquired by the animal during its lifetime. It is not normally used for the retention of innate behavior.

Memory involves learning, storage and retention of information. In experiments with animals, however, tests that these processes have occurred must involve some form of recall, recognition, or relearning. An animal may be required to recall a particular type of operant behavior to obtain food. It may be required to choose between an array of stimuli, a task requiring recognition of stimuli previously encountered. Or it may be given a previously encountered learning task, the aim being to see whether the animal learns more quickly the second time. Memory is measured by the savings that the animal shows in relearning the task.

Animal learning is not perfect and animals do not retain all that they learn. Two basic theories try to account for this phenomenon: the decay theory, which maintains that memories simply fade with time if the behavior is not rehearsed, and the interference theory, which maintains that the maintenance or recall of an existing memory is interfered with by the establishment of new memories and may be obliterated.

Psychologists also recognize three basic types of memory: immediate, short-term and long-term. Immediate memories last fractions of a second and have been recognized in research on humans as an aspect of the initial encoding part of the memory process. It is very difficult to study this aspect of memory in animals not capable of verbal responses.

Short-term memory lasts a number of minutes and research on humans has shown that the amount of information that can be held in short-term memory is limited. Experiments on short-term memory in animals often employ CONDITIONING procedures. In the delayed response test an animal is required to make a response a certain time after a signal indicating which response is to be made. For example a pigeon may be trained to peck one of three disks to obtain a reward. On a given trial one of the disks is briefly illuminated and then there is a delay before the pigeon is allowed to peck. A refinement of this technique is the delayed match-to-sample test. The animal is presented with a particular stimulus (the sample) and after a delay it is shown an array of stimuli including the sample stimulus. The correct response is to choose the sample stimulus. With considerable practice pigeons can perform correctly with delays of up to 60 seconds. Monkeys can manage delays of up to 120 seconds as can the bottle-nosed dolphin when trained in an auditory version of the problem.

Animals may appear to have poor short-term memory when tested in one way, but a good memory when tested in another. For example rats and dogs perform poorly in delayed response tasks unless they are able to rely on the orientation of parts of the body during the delay period. Rats are particularly good at spatial memory problems and dogs are adept at finding bones hidden in a field, but perform poorly when tested in an analogous way in the laboratory. A dog can be restrained for a considerable time after seeing a bone placed in one of several places, and can then retrieve it.

Once an animal has mastered a laboratory problem it may remember it for many months. Such long-term memory and its counterpart, forgetting, have been the subject of considerable scientific research. It has been discovered that fear-based behavior is particularly resistant to forgetting, though interestingly, this type of memory is less marked in young animals.

Study of the age-retention effect shows that memory for aversive stimuli is very poor during the early stages of development. Rats conditioned to an aversive flavor at ten days old quickly lost their avoidance behavior but rats conditioned at eighteen days old retained their response to the aversive flavor for at least fifty-six days. It seems likely that it is adaptive for young animals to forget aversive experiences which seldom recur. Repeated occurrence of aversive stimuli, however, leads to reinstatement of the memory. Some psychologists believe that the young forget more easily because they are more exposed to novel stimuli by virtue of their relative inexperience. The succession of novel stimuli interferes with the memory process in young animals, but this effect is not so marked in adults. An alternative view is that the age-retention effect is a specially adaptive type of memory decay.

DJM

Bibliography

Hulse, Stewart H., Fowler, Harry and Honig, Werner K., eds. 1978: *Cognitive processes in animal behavior.* Hillsdale, N.J.: Erlbaum.

Tarpy, Roger M. and Mayer, Richard F. 1978: *Foundations of learning and memory.* Glenview, Ill. and London: Scott, Foresman.

meta-communication Communication about communication. For instance, a signal may be given by an animal to a conspecific, and this signal has a particular "meaning" or effect in the communicative system of the species. However, a second signal, or set of signals, may accompany the first, changing its basic significance. This second signal is the meta-communicative one. Meta-communication has not been described outside mammals. Among mammals it is found, for instance as a characteristic of PLAY in macaques, baboons and chimpanzees. Such play is not necessarily juvenile. The playful animal may bite, chase or perform some other aggressive action, which is then modified by particular facial expressions, vocalizations or body postures to indicate that the hostility is not "real". Similar activity is prevalent among humans who laugh or smile to indicate that harsh words or aggressive actions are not to be taken at face value.   VR

Bibliography
Poole, T. 1985: *Social behaviour in mammals.* Glasgow: Blackie.

migration Has been defined by Baker (1978) as the "act of moving from one spatial unit to another". If, within this definition, we set aside first of all *species migration*, which covers changes in the geographical range of a species over a number of years, secondly the *accidental migration* of individuals, and thirdly the common but not universal tendencies of individual animals towards *exploration and dispersal* from their birthplace, we have passed through a number of acceptable definitions of migration leaving only the most familiar (and emphasizing the possibility of evolutionary continua between it and the others): that of significant journeys between two spatial units, eventually involving return to units previously visited. Long-term migrations of the latter type include *ontogenetic returns*, as in those of some fish returning after several years and over thousands of miles to breed near their birthplace and *annual returns* as shown by some birds between breeding and wintering grounds. Much research has concentrated upon the guidance mechanisms involved in the latter (see NAVIGATION).   AW

Bibliography
Baker, Reginald R. 1978: *The evolutionary ecology of animal migration.* London: Hodder and Stoughton; New York: Holmes and Meier.
*Davies, C. 1981: Migration. In *The Oxford companion to animal behaviour*, ed. D. McFarland. Oxford and New York: Oxford University Press.

mimicry In evolutionary biology, a close resemblance between two organisms, or parts of organisms, evolved by natural selection as a result of the advantage accruing to one or both from the resemblance. Classically, mimicry is an adaptation of prey species: a harmless species (the mimic) may resemble a dangerous or unpalatable one (the model), or a number of dangerous or unpalatable species may resemble each other, presumably because these result in decreased predation. Predators themselves, however, exhibit mimicry on occasion too, presumably because resemblance to a harmless species aids predatory success. It has also been suggested that mimicry occurs within species, and may constitute an evolutionary origin of social communication. Many examples of mimicry are based on form and colour, visually detected, but mimicry may relate to other senses too, and may also be behavioral. (See Wickler 1968).   RDA

Bibliography
Krebs, J.R. and Davies, N.B. eds. 1984: *Behavioural ecology: an evolutionary approach.* 2nd ed. Oxford: Blackwell Scientific Publications.
Wickler, W. 1968: *Mimicry in plants and animals.* London: Weidenfeld and Nicolson; New York: McGraw-Hill.

models: role in theories Analogical (and idealized) representations of things, processes, etc. and more recently of formal systems. A specialized use for the term has appeared in psychology, as a synonym for "theory". In most scientific contexts a model is distinguished from a theory, in that a theory is taken to be a discourse about a model.

In engineering and the physical sciences models play a very large part both in the design of experiments and in the construction of theories. The uses of models can best be understood through the distinctions between a model, its subjects and its source. A doll is both a model *of* a human infant (subject) and modeled *on* a human infant (source). Source and subject are identical. Such models are homoeomorphs. Natural selection is modeled *on* domestic selection but it is a model *of* the unobservable real process of speciation. Source and subject are different. These are paramorphs.

Homoeomorphic models are used to bring out features of systems we already know about. For example, a hydraulic network can be used as a model of an electric circuit, suggesting certain otherwise unnoticed features of the circuit. Models are also used creatively when the behavior of a class of physical objects or substances is known but the process that produces that behavior is unobservable. Paramorphic models are used to represent the unknown productive mechanisms. Such models must be functionally equivalent to the unobservable productive process, that is the imagined model must behave like the real process. For example, a machine computational process which produces results like those produced by animals which are subjected to certain stimuli may be used as a paramorphic model of the unknown process by which the real creature solves a problem. The success of a paramorphic model in modeling the behavior of the real system it represents is not enough to guarantee that it is a true representation of that system, but it will be seen as a probable representation if it continues successfully to simulate the thinker's cognitive processes and has no equally plausible rival.

If explanations were merely formal discourses, deductively related to that which they purported to explain, there would be indefinitely many explanations for any given set of phenomena. The use of a paramorphic model not only allows for a plausible interpretation of the theoretical terms in a favored formal theory, but serves to eliminate all those others which are incompatible with it. There is no known formal criterion which will serve the same purpose. Models, then, are indispensable for developing theoretical explanations to the point at which their plausibility as representations of the real processes productive of the phenomena of interest can be tested.

Models are analogues of whatever they represent. The principles by which models are used in scientific reasoning are part of the "logic of analogy". An analogue has three comparative relations with its subject, a positive analogy (likenesses), a negative analogy (differences), and a neutral analogy (those properties of the model and its subject which have not been tested for likeness or difference one with another). The assessment of the plausibility of a model can be made fairly rigorous in terms of the balance between positive, negative and neutral analogies. For instance, if there are many likenesses, few differences and not much unexplored, a model is likely to be found acceptable by its users as a true representation of the process it simulates.

Discussion of the use of models in the sciences has centered on two issues. (1) Under what conditions are models to be taken as good guides to hypotheses about unobserved processes and structures? Commentators who have concentrated only on examples of homoeomorphic or heuristic models have tended to argue that models are dispensable and should be treated as part of the psychology of scientific thinking. Those who have studied the creative uses of paramorphic models have tended to argue that novel representations of previously unknown processes could not have been achieved without the use of a model. (2) A corresponding argument has developed around the issue of the role of metaphor and simile in scientific discourse. The two issues are closely related since a system of metaphors (say the homeostatic theory in animal psychology) may be introduced into a scientific discourse on the basis of a model-source. On the basis of the analogy the unobservable determinants of regularities in behavior are likened to feedback loops, and the process of the regulation of behavior to system maintenance.   RHa

Bibliography

Black, M. 1962: *Models and metaphors: studies in language and philosophy*. Ithaca, N.Y.: Cornell University Press.

Bunge, M. 1973: *Model, matter and method*. Dordrecht: Reidel.

Harré, R. 1972: *The principles of scientific thinking*. London: Macmillan; Chicago: Chicago University Press (1973).

Hesse, M.B. 1963: *Models and analogies in science*. London and New York: Sheed and Ward.

motivation The state of an animal that is immediately responsible for the control of its behavior. Motivational changes are usually temporary and reversible in contrast to the more permanent changes in behavior that are brought about by learning, maturation, or injury.

In everyday language the term motivation is used to describe the urges, desires or reasons that are thought to account for behavior. In the early days of behavioral science motivation was envisaged in terms of the DRIVE that was necessary for the manifestation of behavior: sexual behavior was due to the sex drive, eating to the hunger drive, etc. This is no longer a prevalent view and it is generally recognized that it is not necessary to account for behavior in terms of motive forces, rather that a particular activity is the result of an animal being in a particular motivational state.

It is important to distinguish between an animal's motivational potential for behavior and the motivational state that characterizes its behavior at a particular time. These are sometimes called the primary and secondary aspects of motivation. Primary thirst results from the brain's measurements of the physiological state of the body. This provides a motivational potential for drinking, which may or may not be realized according to the circumstances. A thirsty animal may not drink because there is no water available, or because some other activity is more important. Secondary thirst is an aspect of motivation that is closely related to the situation at the time of drinking. An animal might drink more than the amount required by its primary thirst because it had just eaten, or because the environmental temperature was high. Similarly, primary hunger depends upon the animal's nutritional state, whereas secondary hunger is determined by such factors as the palatability of the food or the time of day.

Within the repertoire of any given species certain activities will be incompatible with other activities in the sense that the animal cannot do them simultaneously. In other words animals can do only one thing at a time. For example an animal engaged in territorial defense may have the motivational potential for foraging, sleep, etc. The primary motivation for many activities may be simultaneously strong, but the secondary motivation associated with the performance of the relevant behavior will exist for only one of the potential activities.

The behavior observed at a particular time is usually that which has the strongest primary motivation, but this is not always the case. Sometimes there is conflict between equally strong tendencies to perform different activities. This may result in a compromise in which the animal takes up a posture intermediate between the two activities. The most common type of compromise occurs in APPROACH/AVOIDANCE situations in which the animal is simultaneously motivated to approach an object, such as a food source or a rival, and to avoid it on account of fear of an unfamiliar situation, or of attack. Such behavior has frequently been the subject of ritualization during evolution, resulting in a characteristic DISPLAY. For example the male three-spined stickleback (*Gasterosteus aculeatus*) is aggressive towards intruders into its territory. Near the boundary of the territory the aggression is mixed with fear and the stickleback typically adopts a head-down threat display. This display is thought to be a ritualized form of the sand-digging that occurs at the beginning of nest-building (Tinbergen 1952).

It is a common observation that animals perform seemingly irrelevant activities in moments of conflict. For example fighting cockerels may suddenly peck at the ground as if feeding. Such activities are called DISPLACEMENT ACTIVITIES and they are thought to be an example of behavior which does not correspond to the animal's strongest primary motivation or behavioral tendency. Displacement activities are thought to occur when the tendency for a motivationally dominant activity is suddenly reduced, thus removing its inhibition on other aspects of motivation with the potential for overt activity.

This type of disinhibition process can occur as a result of conflict, frustration, or as a part of time-sharing strategy (see DECISION MAKING). An activity is said to be disinhibited when the inhibition from a stronger motivational tendency is removed. An example is provided by the courtship of the male smooth newt (*Triturus vulgaris*). This animal breathes air but carries out its courtship under water. During courtship there is a build-up of motivation to visit the surface of the water to breathe, but this is usually suppressed by the stronger courtship tendency. If however the courtship founders owing to the uncooperative behavior of the female, there is disinhibition and the male makes a rapid ascent to breathe (Halliday and Sweatman 1976).

Observation of behavior often indicates that certain activities tend to occur in temporal association. We might see a bird flying to some bushes, scratching at the ground, and apparently searching for something. We might then see it fly off to its nest with a twig in its bill. If we saw the bird inserting the twig into its nest we would probably conclude that it was involved in nest-building. On the basis of its temporal organization, the behavior can be divided into a searching, appetitive phase and a more stereotyped consummatory phase. (See APPETITIVE BEHAVIOR; CONSUMMATORY BEHAVIOR.) Some consummatory patterns are so inflexible as to be called fixed-action patterns. These are usually of a reflex nature, though they may involve fairly complex routines.

Close temporal association among activities suggests that they share common causal factors, such as a common influence from hormones, a common goal, etc. Such suggestions can often be investigated by means of laboratory experiments.

The fully controlled laboratory experiment involves careful procedures to ensure that all sources of variation are kept constant, or their effects monitored, apart from those that the experimenter intends to manipulate. In investigating primary motivational states the animals must be maintained on a regime involving controlled laboratory climatic conditions and a strict daily routine. Changes in known aspects of the maintenance conditions can then be introduced and their effects noted. For example the animals may be subjected to changes in environmental temperature, changes in diet, or injected with a substance with a known physiological effect, such as a HORMONE. Standardized tests are then given to assess the effects of different treatments, and the experimental animals are compared with control animals which had no change in their maintenance conditions.

In investigating secondary motivational changes similar standardized procedures are used, but all animals are usually given the same treatment up to the time of testing, and they are then tested in different ways. For example, in investigating the effects of frustration the animals will be deprived of food for a particular period and then provided with food in an experimental test. Some may have food freely available, others may have to work for it, while others may only be allowed to see the food through a glass partition. All these animals will have the same primary hunger, but their secondary motivational states will differ.

The maintenance of a stable internal physiological environment is an important aspect of motivation (see HOMEOSTASIS), and many animals are able to compensate for physiological malfunction by means of appropriate behavior. Some animals can learn to compensate for dietary deficiencies, or poisoning, by altering their feeding habits (see FOOD SELECTION). They can learn to avoid unfavourable environments (see THERMOREGULATION) and to exploit new resources.

In addition to the maintenance of the internal *status quo*, changes in primary motivation are often programmed on a seasonal basis. This is often controlled by an internal biological clock which exerts its effects through the medium of hormones (see CLOCK-DRIVEN BEHAVIOR). For example the seasonal reproductive activity of some birds is directly dependent upon their hormonal state, which changes throughout the year under the combined influences of hours of daylight and the circannual clock (Pengelley 1974). Migration and hibernation are annual activities that are controlled in a similar manner.

The more psychological secondary aspects of motivation are less well understood than the principles underlying primary motivation. The minute-to-minute behavior of animals is influenced by many factors including the behavior that has just been performed, the current external stimulus, and the consequences of current behavior. If the consequences are favorable, there is often a positive FEEDBACK effect such that the motivation to continue with the current activity is increased. This is particularly noticeable when an animal eats a favorite highly palatable food. When the consequences are unfavorable and the animal does not obtain the expected feedback, a number of things may happen. Initially an animal will often try harder to obtain the desired consequences of its behavior. If unsuccessful it will usually switch attention to other aspects of the environment and this may result in a temporary change in behavior. If luck of success is prolonged the behavior will be subject to extinction as the animal learns that the behavior is not profitable. In psychological terms success is associated with incentive motivation and failure with frustration and eventual EXTINCTION of the response. The situation is complicated, however, by motivational competition from other potential activities. While an animal is foraging successfully its secondary motivation may be raised sufficiently to postpone a change to some other activity, such as territorial defense. If the foraging is unsuccessful the animal may switch earlier to an alternative activity, but if it remains hungry it will soon return to foraging. At any time the foraging may be interrupted by the powerful stimulus of a territorial intruder which has to be chased away. At other times the motivational priorities will change because the animal has become satiated.

Thus changes in behavior that appear to be the same to the outside observer may have very different motivational causes.

DJM

Bibliography

*Bolles, R.C. 1975: *Theory of motivation*. New York: Harper and Row.

Halliday, T.R. and Sweatman, H.P.A. 1976: To breathe or not to breathe: the newt's problem. *Animal behaviour* 24, 551–61.

Pengelley, E.T., ed. 1974: *Circannual clocks*. New York: Academic Press.

Tinbergen, N. 1952: Derived activities: their causation, biological significance, origin and emancipation during evolution. *Quarterly review of biology* 27, 1–32.

Toates, F.M. 1980: *Animal behavior – a systems approach*. Chichester: John Wiley.

Toates, F.M. 1983: Models of motivation. In *Animal behaviour*, vol. 1. *Causes and effects*, eds. T.R. Halliday and P.J.B. Slater. Oxford: Blackwell Scientific Publications.

N

natural selection Natural selection is the biological process whereby some members of an animal (or plant) population survive and reproduce more successfully than others, and transmit to their offspring the inherited basis of the characteristics which enabled them to do so. In any environment, individual animals live for differing lengths of time, and produce differing numbers of offspring. They also differ in their physical and behavioral characteristics, and such differences sometimes have a genetic basis. Where these patterns of variation are related, so that possessors of one genetically inherited characteristic regularly survive and reproduce more successfully than possessors of an alternative one, natural processes are in effect selecting one characteristic in the animal population at the expense of another. Acting over many generations, selection of this kind will generally result in the retention and spread through the population of those characteristics which confer the greatest advantages on their possessors, given the survival problems posed by their particular environment. Sometimes selection may act directionally, so bringing about biological changes in a population; at other times it may simply act against departures from the common form of a characteristic, thus having a stabilizing effect. Through natural selection, members of an animal population come to have characteristics which render them well adapted for living and breeding in the environment where the selection has taken place. This concept of ADAPTA-TION by natural selection, combined with modern understanding of the origins and inheritance of genetic variation, forms a powerful theory of the working of biological evolution – the neo-Darwinian theory.

The idea of natural selection was prop-osed by DARWIN and Wallace (1859). In their account of how the differential survival and reproduction of individuals with different biological characteristics lead to changes in the overall frequencies of those characteristics in a natural population, the process was summed up as "natural selection", by analogy with the artificial selection practiced by breeders of domestic animals and plants, and the term has been used ever since. The force of their proposal lay in the suggestion that the effects of natural selection, even if imperceptibly small in any particular generation, have no definite limits and so may cumulatively be very large over long periods of time. This theory, entailing biological evolution and the emergence of new species, appeared against the background of a belief in the fixity of species, and although it was by no means the first theory to challenge that doctrine, it was more cogent than earlier evolutionary theories, and it soon became embroiled in a now famous controversy. As the nineteenth century proceeded, the idea of natural selection became very influential in biology, and in the twentieth century, with the rise of classical and population genetics, Darwin and Wallace's proposal has been developed in a number of ways but not fundamentally revised. Today virtually all biologists probably consider natural selection to be a well-established phenomenon, and many would also consider it the main process underlying biological evolution (though other processes are also considered – see EVOLUTION).

Darwin also proposed a theory of sexual selection, whereby characteristics were favored which enhanced REPRODUCTIVE SUCCESS via advantages in sexual competition rather than in survival: and he suggested that this occurred in two main ways, competition between males and mate choice by females. This theory has been less consistently upheld by subsequent evolutionary biologists than the main natural selection theory, and for some time it was in partial eclipse. More recently, however, it has been widely reinstated in a developed form (see O'Donald 1980, Short 1977). Scope for the action of sexual selection is probably greatest in polygynous species, but it may nonetheless be responsible for some biological differences between the sexes in other species also. Nowadays many biologists probably consider sexual selection an aspect of natural selection rather than a distinct process.

Darwin himself envisaged that behavior (habits, instincts) would in principle be subject to natural selection in the same way as any other characteristic of an animal species; and, although it took some time to be widely accepted, this recognition became an important feature of the behavioral disciplines of ETHOLOGY and SOCIOBIOLOGY. Evidently, however, natural selection is expected to operate on behavioral characteristics only where those characteristics are genetically influenced, and where they have an impact on an animal's survival and reproduction. The genetic inheritance of behavior patterns has been precisely analysed only in a few cases: but there are undoubtedly numerous other cases where genes play an important role, including many where both genetic and environmental factors have a substantial effect on behavior (see BEHAVIOR GENETICS). The most striking indications of the influence of genes on behavior, and also of the presumed impact of natural selection on behavioral characteristics, are to be seen in the numerous behavioral differences between animal species, and these provided an important line of evidence for the founders of ethology.

In the most widely accepted form of the theory, frequently invoked in ethology, natural selection operates, as described above, on the biological and behavioral characteristics of individuals, and predominantly within species. Evolutionary ideas are in a state of considerable fer-ment, however, and there are less ortho-dox versions of natural selection theory in currency, some of which are relevant to behavioral questions. One suggestion repeatedly made in recent years is that natural selection may operate on groups (i.e. via differential extinction and fission of groups) and result in increased adaptation of groups themselves rather than the constituent individuals. Wynne-Edwards was interested in how animal populations avoid over-exploitation of resources, and he proposed that the ecologically successful groups were those whose members abstained from reproducing in response to certain social signals (see CONVENTIONAL AND EPIDEICTIC BEHAVIOR) – a system which, he proposed, was maintained by group selection, to the benefit of the group. Various other authors have proposed versions and mathematical models of group selection theory (e.g. Wilson 1980). Despite considerable debate in recent years, however, the theory has not gained general acceptance: it appears that, even though group selection may be a viable mechanism in principle, the conditions under which it is expected to outweigh individual selection are limited, and may occur rarely if at all in nature. Another large scale unit of selection is proposed in species selection theory, where it is argued that evolutionary pressures are acting between species, rather than being concentrated within them (Stanley 1979) – a proposition still under considerable debate.

A contrasting elaboration of Darwinian natural selection theory is that involved in kin selection. Hamilton was interested in the special case of the social insects, where many individuals are non-reproductive, and he argued, by an extension of the ordinary explanation of parental care, that ALTRUISM directed toward any related individual would be favored in natural selection (subject to certain specified constraints). This evolutionary explanation of altruism between kin (referred to by the terms kin selection and inclusive fitness) has gained more general acceptance among biologists than the group selection theory of altruism, at least as an explanation of the extreme altruism found among social insects and possibly for other cases too (see KINSHIP). To some authors (especially Dawkins 1982), the logical conclusion from kin selection theory is to propose the gene rather than the individual as the unit of natural selection: others, while accepting the principle of kin selection, argue for the continuing importance of the individual as an entity on which natural selection acts, or suggest that it may not be fruitful to insist on a single unit or level of selection.

Natural selection may, according to one hypothesis, operate in different ways under different ecological conditions: in particular there may be a continuum of modes whose opposite poles are termed r-selection and K-selection (Pianka 1970). K-selection, it is proposed, is the mode characteristic of relatively constant or predictable ecological conditions, and r-selection of relatively variable or unpredictable ones. The evolutionary consequences of these contrasting selective regimes are considered to be contrasting sets of characteristics in the organisms affected -in the case of K-selection, slow development, large size, late reproduction, intensive parental care, and high learning capacity; and in the case of r-selection, the opposites of those characteristics. Distinctions along the r-K continuum are sometimes drawn on a large scale (e.g. between terrestrial vertebrates and terrestrial invertebrates) and sometimes in the smaller scale comparison of closely related species (Richardson 1975). A number of authors have found this r-K distinction a useful one, but like many in this area, it has its limitations also.

(See also SOCIOBIOLOGY.)　　　RDA

Bibliography

Bateson, P. ed. 1983: *Mate choice*. Cambridge and New York: Cambridge University Press.

Darwin, C. 1859: *The origin of species by means of natural selection*. London: John Murray (Penguin edition 1968).

——— and Wallace, A. 1859: On the tendency of species to form varieties: and on the perpetuation of varieties and species by natural means of selection. *Journal of the proceedings of the Linnean society (Zoology)* 3, 45–62.

Dawkins, R. 1982: *The extended phenotype: the gene as the unit of selection*. Oxford and San Francisco: W.H. Freeman.

Greenwood, P.J., Harvey, P.H. and Slatkin, M. eds. 1985: *Evolution: essays in honour of John Maynard Smith*. Cambridge and New York: Cambridge University Press.

Hinde, R.A. 1982: *Ethology: its nature and relations with other sciences*. Oxford and New York: Oxford University Press.

Maynard Smith, J. 1975: *The theory of evolution*. 3rd edn. Harmondsworth and New York: Penguin.

O'Donald, P. 1980: *Genetic models of sexual selection*. Cambridge, New York and Melbourne: Cambridge University Press.

Pianka, E.R. 1970: On r- and K-selection. *American naturalist* 104, 592–7.

Richardson, B.J. 1975: r and K selection in kangaroos. *Nature* 255, 323–4.

Ridley, M. 1985: *The problems of evolution*. Oxford and New York: Oxford University Press.

Short, R.V. 1977: Sexual selection and the descent of man. In *Reproduction and evolution*. International Symposium on Comparative Biology of Reproduction, eds. J.H. Calaby and C.H. Tyndale-Biscoe. Canberra: Australian Academy of Science.

Stanley, S.M. 1979: *Macroevolution: pattern and process*. San Francisco: W.H. Freeman.

Williams, G.C. 1966: *Adaptation and natural selection: a critique of some current evolutionary thought*. Princeton: Princeton University Press.

Wilson, D.S. 1980: *The natural selection of populations and communities*. Menlo Park (California), London and Sydney: Benjamin Cummings.

navigation In the broad sense includes all non-random movement, but is usually distinguished from mere orientation in the following way. ORIENTATION refers to movement which has direction relative to some physical entity, but which is not guided by information about the location of a goal: this latter ability is what distinguishes navigation.

Some birds migrating for the first time use the sun or stars as a compass to maintain orientation, coping with the relative movements of the sun by means of an internal biological clock or of the stars through the patterning of constellations.

Following a fixed compass orientation for a specific distance normally delivers them to the ' species wintering grounds but experimental displacements of these birds at right angles to their migratory route produces a corresponding displacement in final destination. That experienced adult birds may return to habitual areas despite such displacement is evidence for navigation.

Navigation in this sense is often divided into pilotage, which involves homing to a destination by known landmarks, and true navigation involving homing by other means. Release experiments in novel areas have shown that pigeons are capable of true navigation, and, in addition to using a sun compass, appear to use a magnetic compass in overcast conditions. However a compass, although sufficient for orientation, is insufficient for navigation: information which is equivalent to a map must supplement it. The nature of the bird's map remains unknown, despite vigorous current research into such possibilities as the use of smells and atmospheric cues, and unsuspected abilities to sense polarized light, ultrasound and barometric pressure. (See also MIGRATION; CLOCK-DRIVEN BEHAVIOR). AW

Bibliography

Keeton, W.T. 1981: Navigation. In *The Oxford companion to animal behaviour*, ed. D. McFarland. Oxford and New York: Oxford University Press.

Wiltschko, R. and Wiltschko, W. 1985: Pigeon homing: change in navigational strategy during ontogeny. *Animal behaviour* 33, 583–90.

neuroethology The experimental analysis of the causal mechanisms which underlie behavior. It could be argued, though, that all physiology fits this description: what then distinguishes neuroethology as a discipline in its own right? The answer lies in a matter of priorities. Whilst the physiologist studies the mechanisms as an end in themselves, the neuroethologist investigates them in the context of the natural behavior of the animal. In order to study how nerves and muscles are integrated to produce behavior the neuroethologist must usually restrain, anesthetize and dissect his subject. An animal treated in this way obviously cannot behave normally. It is therefore vital that the physiological work has been directed by detailed studies of behavior. The results obtained from the physiology can then, in turn, be used to direct further ethological studies.

Neuroethology had its beginnings in the late nineteenth century with crude lesion and stimulation studies of the vertebrate brain, including that of man. However the advent of ethology and the rapid advances in neuroanatomical and neurophysiological techniques have led to its establishment during the past 30 years. Problems which have been investigated neuroethologically are many and varied. They include the detection, localization, discrimination and integration of sensory signals; decision making in the central nervous system; the neural and hormonal basis of motivation, learning, orientation; the coordination of behavioral sequences and the development and genetic basis of behavior. The animals used in these studies vary from nematodes to molluscs to insects to monkeys. Much of the work has been done on invertebrates since these animals offer the advantage of a simpler and more experimentally amenable nervous system than vertebrates as well as a relatively simple repertoire of behaviors.

One study which exemplifies the neuroethological approach is that of J.P. Ewert on the prey catching behavior in the common toad, *Bufo bufo*. In the early evening a toad can be observed sitting motionless by its hiding place. It shows no behavioral response to static objects in its visual field but if an object moves the toad responds in one of two ways. It either orientates towards the object, leans forwards and binocularly fixates it, then snaps it up, swallows and wipes its mouth; or alternatively, the toad ducks away from the object, stands up and inflates itself or runs away. Ewert termed these behaviors "prey catching" and "enemy avoidance". The first question Ewert asked was which parameters of the moving stimulus are important in evoking these behaviors? In order to answer this he treated the toad as a black box and investigated its input-output relations: a classical ethological approach. He developed a behavioral assay which allowed him to alter parameters of the stimulus and measure the behavioral responses of the toad. It turned out that the color of the object was not important but that its size, contrast with the background and its movement were. The crucial feature which determined whether an object was treated as a prey or an enemy was discovered to be its direction of movement relative to its long axis. If a small, black, elongated rectangle moves in the direction of its long axis it is treated as prey, but if it moves perpendicularly to its long axis it evokes enemy avoidance. Ewert speaks of "worms" and "antiworms".

Having elucidated the key parameters of the stimulus, Ewert then asked how the nervous system recognizes these features and how the visual information is converted into behavior. Firstly he used gross physiological techniques to localize areas in the brain which were involved in the two behaviors. By a combination of lesion and electrical stimulation studies he demonstrated that the optic tectum is the site where prey catching is initiated, with different areas of the tectum being responsible for triggering particular components of the prey catching sequence. Similarly, a region of the thalamic-pretectal area was found to initiate enemy avoidance. Ewert then recorded from individual neurones in these regions of the brain while the toad was actually behaving. He found that the neurones in the prey catching area respond only to objects moving in the direction of their long axis while nerves in the enemy avoidance areas only respond to objects moving perpendicularly to their long axis. In addition he showed that nerves in the retina could not distinguish prey from enemy objects. Neither did they respond to color nor to static objects.

Ewert's study is so elegant and has proved so productive because he has integrated detailed ethology with physiology. He has also approached the physiology from the top down, using lesion and stimulation studies to indicate where he should probe with his electrodes. When you consider that a vertebrate has some ten thousand million nerve cells and even an insect has about a million, then the hierarchical approach of the neuroethologist is a powerful one indeed.   SJS

Bibliography

Camhi, J.M. 1984: *Neuroethology. Nerve cells and the natural behavior of animals.* Sunderland, Mass.: Sinauer Associates Inc.

Ewert, J.P. 1976: *Neuroethology. An introduction to the neurophysiological fundamentals of behavior.* Berlin: Springer-Verlag.

—— 1985: Concepts in vertebrate neuroethology. *Animal behaviour* 33, 1–29.

Guthrie, D.M. 1980: *Neuroethology. An introduction.* Oxford: Blackwell Scientific Publications.

O

observational learning *See* imitation and observational learning.

observational methods A distinctive feature of ETHOLOGY from its origins, and one which has proved more durable to the present day than some of its specific theories, has been its insistence on the importance of observation (see Tinbergen 1963, Thorpe 1979). This does not imply avoidance of experimentation or of laboratories: rather it reflects a stress on meticulously detailed observational descriptions of animal behavior, whatever the context. Ethologists also try to ensure that the categories used for describing observed behavior are objective – that is, that they refer to its observable form and consequences, and are capable of consistent use over time and between observers. Ethologists do recognize, however, that objectivity in this sense is not perfectible, and also that the actual designation of behavior categories studied is invariably selective (see Reynolds 1976). Errors which ethologists hope to avoid in their descriptions include choosing behavior categories that are too crude to be useful, describing behavior in ways that do not distinguish clearly between observation and interpretation, and ANTHROPOMORPHISM.

For much of ethology's development, observational methods have largely been based on prolonged immersion in observation and becoming a "good observer", compiling a behavior catalog or ETHOGRAM, extended recording of observations, and analysis in predominantly verbal terms. In recent decades, however, the emphasis has shifted towards quantification and the use of computer and other technology in both the recording and analysis of observed behavior (see e.g. Bramblett 1976).   RDA

Bibliography

Bramblett, C.A. 1976: *Patterns of primate behavior*. Palo Alto, California: Mayfield.

McFarland, D.N. and Houston, A. 1981: *Quantitative ethology: the state space approach*. London: Pitman.

Reynolds, V. 1976: The origins of a behavioural vocabulary: the case of the rhesus monkey. *Journal of the theory of social behaviour* 6, 105–42.

Thorpe, W.H. 1979: *The origins and rise of ethology: the science of the natural behaviour of animals*. London, Melbourne: Heinemann; New York: Praeger.

Tinbergen, N. 1963: On aims and methods of ethology. *Zeitschrift für Tierpsychologie* 20, 410–433.

ontogeny Development from egg to adult.

operant conditioning *See* conditioning.

orientation The maintenance of position and posture in relation to the external environment. Two aspects of orientation are usually distinguished: primary or positional orientation and secondary or goal orientation. Positional orientations guide the animal to its normal stance and maintain it in physical equilibrium. Included in this category are position with respect to gravity, postures associated with balance, etc. Goal orientations have to do with position and locomotion in relation to external goals, such as a source of food, or a social companion.

Positional orientation is closely tied to the preference positions that are characteristic of each species. Thus schooling fish maintain a particular position not only with respect to gravity, but also with respect to the surface of the water, the substratum, and to each other.

Positional orientation is an important aspect of camouflage and the positional preferences of many species are related to their body coloration. Thus the bark-like underwing moth *Catocala* is normally active at night and spends the day resting on tree trunks. Experiments with blue jays (*Cyanocitta cristata*) show that the moths are much less subject to predation when resting in the vertical preferred position compared with other orientations. In the preferred position the moth's bark-like markings most closely conform with the background.

Positional orientation is attained by FEEDBACK from sense organs, usually mechanical or visual. For example the orientation of fish with respect to gravity is attained by feedback from the statocysts, but many fish also show a dorsal light reaction. This involves positioning the body in such a way that light always falls on the dorsal surface. Experiments using a centrifuge combined with controlled light directionality show that the contributions of the various sense organs involved in maintaining a vertical body position are summed algebraically in the central nervous system. However the weighting given to the different components may vary with the state of arousal of the fish. Thus sleeping fish rely entirely upon the statocysts, whereas active fish respond more to visual cues.

Goal orientation involves a spatially distant target or end-point, which may be proximate or distal. Proximate orientation implies direct sensory contact with the goal, whereas distal orientation may include NAVIGATION and MIGRATION, where there is no such contact. Goal orientation may involve a very simple form of response to environmental stimuli, as in KINESIS. This is a form of orientation in which the animal's response is proportional to the intensity of the stimulation. Woodlice (*Porcellio scaber*) for instance, are active at low humidity levels and less active at high humidities. Their rapid locomotion in dry places increases the chances of discovering damper conditions. Conse-

quently woodlice tend to aggregate in damp places, such as beneath fallen logs, etc.

Taxes involve movement directly toward or away from a source of stimulation. The negative photo-taxis of the maggot larva of the house fly (*Musca domestica*) provides an example. The maggot has a simple eye on its head, capable of registering light intensity but not of forming images. As the maggot crawls along it moves its head from side to side, measuring the light intensity on each side of its body. If a turn results in an increase in perceived brightness it tends not to be repeated and the maggot changes its course and moves away from the light source. Such successive comparison of stimulus intensity, called klino-taxis, is found in a number of species.

However, simultaneous comparison is more common. This is called tropo-taxis and is characterized by a straight course toward or away from the source of stimulation. To achieve this type of orientation it is necessary to have more than one sense organ. The pill woodlouse (*Armadillidium*), for example, has a pair of compound eyes on its head and can move directly toward a light source. When one eye is blacked out the animal describes a circle, showing that simultaneous comparison is a necessary component of the orientation.

Those animals which have eyes which can provide information about the direction of light by virtue of their structure are capable of telo-taxis, which does not require simultaneous comparison from two sense organs. The image-forming eye, for example, provides the necessary directional information.

Distal orientation generally involves navigation, for which it is necessary to have some form of compass. Ants and bees use the sun as a compass and are able to compensate for the movement of the sun throughout the day. Compass orientation is essentially a form of telo-taxis in which the animal maintains a particular angle between its body axis and the direction of the sun. By means of an internal clock ants and bees can progressively alter this angle to match the changing direction of the sun. Clock-compensation is also found in bird navigation and in various species of fishes.

Flying animals face additional problems of orientation and navigation, because of the influence of the wind. The course of a flying animal is its locomotory direction with respect to the surrounding air, and its track is its path with respect to the ground. An animal heading in a particular compass direction may have to compensate for differences between its intended course and its actual track over the ground. The angle between the track and the animal's course direction, called the drift angle, depends upon the strength and direction of the wind. The navigating animal has to compensate for changes in wind speed and direction by changing its flight speed and drift angle. This is done with respect to visual landmarks or with reference to a compass. The compensation thus involves a comparison between the intended track and the feedback that the animal obtains about the consequences of its locomotory behavior.

The sun compass is not the only form of compass used in distal orientation. Bees and pigeons can detect the plane of polarization of sunlight and thus obtain compass bearings in overcast conditions. A number of species, including bacteria, bees, snails and birds, are sensitive to the earth's magnetic field and can use this information for orientation purposes. The electromagnetic sense is not completely understood but seems to be based upon the presence of iron-rich molecules within certain cells. The direction of migration of European robins (*Erittacus rubecula*) can be experimentally altered by superimposing an artificial magnetic field. Homing pigeons fitted with magnets become disoriented when the sky is overcast and they are not able to use the sun as a compass.

Orientation reactions are not entirely REFLEX responses, but may also involve changes in the goal of the orientation. Although an animal may normally respond to movement in its visual field, this may not occur when the movement is a consequence of the animal's own behavior. The most widely accepted explanation of this phenomenon is the reafference theory of von Holst and Mittelstaedt. In essence the reafference principle suggests that when an animal intends to change direction the brain produces a representation of the expected consequences of the change. If the actual consequences match the expected consequences the two cancel and no movement is perceived. So if an animal moved its direction of vision 10° to the right, the visual field as first registered by the brain would move 10° to the left. This, however, would be canceled by the representation of the intended movement (10° to the right) and no movement would actually be perceived.

Reafference theory applies not only to vision but to many aspects of orientation and locomotion. Any movement made by an animal produces consequences which must be distinguished from independent changes in the external environment, whether perceived visually, proprioceptively, or electrically. Reafference is thus an integral aspect of perception.   DJM

Bibliography

Fraenkel, G.S. and Gunn, D.L. 1961: *The orientation of animals.* New York: Dover Publications.

Howard, I.P. and Templeton, W.B. 1966: *Human spatial orientation.* London and New York: John Wiley and Sons.

Schmidt-Koenig, K. 1979: *Avian orientation and navigation.* London and New York: Academic Press.

von Holst, E. 1954: Relations between the CNS and the peripheral organs. *British journal of animal behaviour* 2, 89–94.

orienting response A reflex response in which the animal focusses attention upon a suddenly presented stimulus. For example, a strange noise may cause a cat to turn its head, prick its ears and look towards the source of the sound. When the disturbance is very marked the orienting response is usually preceded by a startle response in which the animal jumps and experiences a marked increase in heart beat rate. Repeated presentation of a stimulus leads to HABITUATION of the orienting response, but there is usually very little GENERALIZATION of the habituation. When repeated presentation of a particular stimulus leads to a decline in the orienting response, presentation of a slightly different stimulus will cause the orienting response to reappear.   DJM

Bibliography
Gray, J.A. 1975: *Elements of a two-process theory of learning.* London: Academic Press.

P

pain An aspect of emotion which is entirely subjective. Although human pain is often associated with cries for help, this is not always the case with other animals. It is impossible to know to what extent animals feel pain, right to assume that, during stress, they suffer in the same way as we do (Dawkins 1980). Pain gives warning of tissue damage, both internal and external to the body. Pain due to noxious stimuli on the body surface is usually easy to locate compared with internal pain. Internal disorders sometimes induce peripheral pain, known as *referred* pain. Pain receptors exist in all tissues except the brain and the non-living parts of bone, nail, teeth and hair. The receptors cannot be identified anatomically and may simply be undifferentiated nerve endings. All pain nerves enter the spinal cord and their messages are thence relayed to the brain.   DJM

Bibliography

Dawkins, Marion 1980: *Animal suffering: the science of animal welfare.* London: Chapman and Hall.

Griffin, D.R. 1981: *The question of animal awareness.* 2nd edn. New York: Rockefeller University Press.

—— 1982: *Animal mind – human mind.* Berlin: Springer-Verlag.

parasitism In its normal meaning parasitism is a way of making a living by feeding on the tissues of another organism without first killing it. A mosquito sucks blood from a living human. An aphid sucks sap from a living oak tree. Parasites are distinguished from predators who first kill their prey then eat it, but the distinction is not always clear cut: parasites often eventually kill their hosts; predators such as hyenas start eating their prey before it is dead; digger wasps paralyse prey by stinging them, so that their larvae can eat them alive; grazing animals take leaves and stems from grass plants without necessarily killing the plants themselves.

The concept of parasitism is often generalized to include cases other than direct feeding on the living tissues of the host. A tapeworm resides in the gut of a pig and diverts to its own use food that the pig has worked to procure and digest. In the domain of overt behavior, the name kleptoparasitism is sometimes given to the habit, shown by some seabirds for instance, of systematically robbing other individuals of prey. One of the most interesting special cases of parasitism is brood-parasitism or cuckooism, which has arisen not just in cuckoos but in several families of birds, bees, wasps, ants, fish and probably many other animal groups. Brood parasites typically lay their eggs in the nest of another species, and the host parents are duped into feeding the young brood parasite. In the case of ants it is not the host parents that are duped but host workers. The parasite queen invades a host nest, typically kills the host queen and is then adopted as queen by the host workers who tend her eggs and unwittingly rear a new generation of parasite queens and males. Most ant nests are parasitized by beetles, crustaceans and a mixed crew of other animals, who feed on the food gathered by the ants, or on the ant brood. They are tolerated by the ants often because they secrete chemical substances that mimic the natural communication chemicals of the ants, or even that appear to work as addictive drugs on the ants. There is scarcely any way of life that cannot in some senses, be regarded as parasitic on other organisms.   RD

Bibliography

Barnard, C.J. ed. 1984: *Producers and scroungers: strategies of exploitation and parasitism.* London and Sydney: Croom Helm; New York: Chapman and Hall.

Rothschild, M. and Clay, T. 1952: *Fleas, flukes and cuckoos.* London: Collins; New York: Philosophical Library.

Wilson, E.O. 1975: *Sociobiology: the new synthesis.* Cambridge, Mass.: The Belknap Press of Harvard University Press.

parent-offspring conflict Conflict between a parent and its offspring over the extent of PARENTAL INVESTMENT (PI). Formerly it was generally expected that selection would always favor the strategy (see EVOLUTIONARILY STABLE STRATEGY) that results in the maximum number of surviving offspring, and that PI would be apportioned to each offspring in accordance with this principle. However, Trivers (1974) argued that this will be true only with a sexually reproducing species. He suggested that in sexually reproducing diploids, selection will be opposed on the parent and on the offspring. It will be to the advantage of genes acting in the parent to allocate PI so as to produce the maximum number of surviving offspring. However, it will be to the advantage of genes acting in the offspring to take more than this parental optimum PI. The extent of parent-offspring conflict will depend on the mating system, and on how an offspring can affect the behavior of its parent. In a series of evolutionarily stable strategy models, Parker and Macnair (1979) deduced that parent-offspring conflict would generally resolve as a compromise between the interests of the parent and those of the offspring; parents would give more PI than their optimum, but not so much as is optimal for the offspring, who would nevertheless continue to solicit further attention. GAP

Bibliography

Parker, G.A. 1985: Models of parent-offspring conflict. V. Effects of the behaviour of the two parents. *Animal behaviour* 33, 519–33.

—— and Macnair, M.R. 1979: Models of parent-offspring conflict. IV. Suppression: evolutionary retaliation by the parent. *Animal behaviour* 27, 1210–35.

Trivers, R.L. 1974: Parent-offspring conflict. *American zoologist* 14, 249–64.

parental investment (PI) Any investment or expenditure on a given offspring that reduces a parent's capacity to produce future offspring. This concept probably dates back to the "parental expenditure" of Fisher (1930), but was developed extensively in an important paper by Trivers (1972). The notion conveyed by PI is that if a parent invests care and provisioning in a particular offspring this improves the viability and REPRODUCTIVE SUCCESS of the offspring, but reduces the number of future offspring that can be generated because the parent has a limited total REPRODUCTIVE EFFORT.

The relative PI of each sex in a given species is important in determining the intensity of intrasexual competition (a component of sexual selection). Males of most species show less PI than females; often male PI is virtually zero (the sperm itself). Thus the theoretical maximum reproductive potential of a male is far higher than that of a female, and intense competition is likely to occur between males over females. Another aspect of PI is that parents may be in conflict with their offspring (PARENT-OFFSPRING CONFLICT) over the amount of PI given to each offspring (Trivers 1974). GAP

Bibliography

Fisher, R.A. 1930: *The genetical theory of natural selection.* Oxford: Clarendon Press.

Townshend, T.J. and Wootton, R.J. 1985: Adjusting parental investment to changing environmental conditions. *Animal behaviour* 33, 494–501.

Trivers, R.L. 1972. Parental investment and sexual selection. In: *Sexual selection and the descent of man, 1871–1971*, ed. B. Campbell. Chicago: Aldine Atherton.

—— 1974: Parent-offspring conflict. *American zoologist* 14, 249–64.

partial reinforcement effect The increase in persistence, or resistance to

EXTINCTION, produced by scheduling reinforcement on only some conditioning trials. If two groups of rats are trained to run down a runway for food in the goal box, with one group finding food on every trial and the other on only a random 50 per cent of trials, the former, consistently reinforced group will stop running very much sooner than the latter, partially reinforced group, when the food is omitted on all trials in extinction.

The partial reinforcement effect poses a problem if it is supposed that consistent reinforcement should produce stronger CONDITIONING and that persistence in extinction directly reflects the strength of conditioning. The most generally accepted explanation is that partially reinforced animals, unlike consistently reinforced ones, have been reinforced for responding in the presence of stimuli associated with the absence of reinforcement and will therefore continue to respond in the presence of such stimuli in extinction. NJM

Bibliography

Mackintosh, N.J. 1974: *The psychology of animal learning*. London: Academic Press.

———— 1983: *Conditioning and associative learning*. Oxford: Clarendon Press.

Pavlov, Ivan Petrovich (1849–1936) Physiologist and pioneer of the study of CONDITIONING. Pavlov was born in Ryazan, Russia and entered the University of St Petersburg in 1870. He graduated in natural science in 1875 and entered the Military Medical Academy. He obtained his doctorate in 1883 and then spent a few years in Germany, studying with Carl Ludwig in Leipzig. He became professor of pharmacology at the Military Medical Academy in 1890 and professor of physiology in 1895. He received the Nobel Prize for Medicine in 1904 for his work on the physiology of digestion.

An opponent of simplistic experimentation in physiology, Pavlov developed a range of new methods for the empirical study of processes in the normal, living animals. His earliest work was on the physiology of the circulation of the blood. By an ingenious surgical technique he was able to isolate different parts of the digestive system to study the relationship between digestive processes and venous and arterial activity. Out of this came his theory of specific irritability, that is the idea that particular organic systems are sensitive to specific stimulants and represents.

During the course of his digestive studies Pavlov noticed that dogs sometimes salivated in anticipation of receiving food. This led him to the discovery of the conditioned reflex, now regarded as a fundamental aspect of learning. He distinguished between unconditioned reflexes, internally stimulated and inbuilt so to speak, and conditioned reflexes, the effect of environmental and external agencies, or built up to continue the metaphor. It is the conditioned reflex that makes possible the fine adaptation of individual systems to their particular environments. From 1902 until his death Pavlov more or less concentrated his researches on this phenomenon of conditioning, and he is responsible for many of the basic concepts current in this field of study today. In particular he extended his researches to the creation and dissipation of artificial neuroses. The connection with human psychology did not escape him, and many of his later studies had a human slant, for instance his attempt to find a physiological basis for the traditional classifications of the human temperament. Pavlov died in 1936. DJM/RHa

Bibliography

Pavlov, I.R. 1927: *Conditioned reflexes*. London: Oxford University Press.

perception The appreciation of the world through the senses depends upon the information received by the brain. All perception is initiated by stimulation of specialized nerve cells called receptors, which are sensitive to specific chemical or physical events. The receptors, together with ancillary structures, make up the sense organs.

Sense organs are adapted for the reception of events or stimuli from outside the nervous system. The stimuli may be internal such as temperature within blood vessels (see THERMOREGULATION) or external such as auditory or visual stimuli. Each receptor is associated with some kind of transducer mechanism which converts energy into an electrical potential by which the receptor cell can influence other nerve cells. The receptors within a sense organ connect to other cells of the nervous system.

Sensory quality depends on which nerve is stimulated, not on how it is stimulated. This doctrine of specific nerve energies was first suggested by Johannes Muller in 1834. It is not the stimuli that determine sensory quality but the nerves activated by the stimuli. For example auditory sensations in man can be generated by sound waves reaching the ear, or by mechanical or electrical stimulation of the auditory sense organs. Any kind of activation of the auditory nerves will produce auditory sensations, because the nerve goes to the auditory system of the brain. Similarly activation of the optic nerve produces visual sensations because the optic nerve transmits information to the visual system of the brain. As a rule different receptors provide information about different aspects of sensory quality and variations in the message transmitted along a nerve provide information about the intensity of the stimulation.

Animals are responsive only to certain sets of stimuli and these differ considerably from species to species. Humans respond to a restricted range of visual stimuli. People cannot detect ultraviolet radiation, whereas some bees can do this. Humans are insensitive to infra-red radiation, whereas some rattlesnakes (*Crotalus*) are directionally sensitive to infra-red radiation and use this information in attacking warm-blooded prey. The human eye cannot detect the polarization of light, but pigeons and bees can do this and use it as a navigational aid.

This diversity arises from the fact that different species occupy different ecological niches and consequently have differ-

ent sensory requirements. Because of this diversity it is not possible to provide a useful answer to the often asked question – how many senses are there? Those usually regarded as being the most important are the chemical senses, including taste and smell; the electromagnetic senses including the ability of some animals to detect magnetic fields; the mechanical senses including hearing and the sense of balance; and vision. In addition there are sensations arising from specialized receptors within the brain itself which provide information concerning hunger, thirst and thermoregulation.

A certain amount of perceptual selectivity is imposed by the sense organs themselves. In the mammalian ear each receptor responds in a proportional manner to the bending of an associated hair-like projection within the cochlea situated within the inner ear. Each hair cell is stimulated only by tones of a certain pitch, and it transduces the sound energy associated with that pitch. The auditory range of a mammal is therefore associated with the structure of the sense organs themselves. Similarly, the ability to discriminate colors is associated with pigments in the retina of the eye which are differentially sensitive to the wavelength of the light entering the eye (see COLOR VISION). In some animals considerable visual processing occurs at the retinal level. Frogs have nerve cells in the retina which are specialized for the detection of small objects moving across the visual field. These "bug detectors" enable the animal to respond quickly to flying insects – the frog's normal prey.

Specializations of sense organs are usually highly correlated with the animal's way of life. Most vertebrates have a hemispherical receptive surface (retina) behind the lens, ensuring that all parts of the visual field at the same distance from the animal are focused on the retina. In horses, however, the upper part of the retina is further from the lens than the lower half. This means that nearby objects lying below the level of the eye will be in focus at the same time as more distant objects above eye level. The effect of this arrangement is that the grazing horse can focus upon its food at the same time as keeping a look-out for predators.

The structure of the eye, and of the other sense organs, determines the limits of the animal's perceptual capabilities. We can imagine that the animal lives in three concentric worlds. The outermost is the physical world which includes all that it is possible for an animal to detect. Inside this is the world which the animal is capable of perceiving and this world is different for different species, for any one species the world of capability can move about within the physical world through evolutionary change. For instance, certain nocturnal moths (*Noctuidae*) which are preyed upon by bats have evolved the ability to hear the very high frequency pulses emitted by flying bats. Inside the world of capability is another world consisting of information which is either responded to or stored for future reference. Here we are distinguishing between what an animal can perceive and what it does perceive in particular circumstances. For example, Tinbergen (1951) and his co-workers discovered that male grayling butterflies (*Eumensis semele*) have marked color preferences when visiting artificial (scentless) flowers in search of food. During courtship, however, they behave as though they are completely color blind. Males prefer darker females, but take no notice of the color. For many years behavioral scientists maintained that cats were color blind. Neurophysiological investigations of the visual system, however, subsequently showed that cats ought to be capable of discriminating colors. Using improved behavioral testing techniques psychologists then demonstrated that cats are capable of color discrimination.

Stimulation of sense organs is of benefit to animals only in so far as they can interpret the information in terms of objects and events in the physical world. Most animals see coal as black and paper as white, even though brightly illuminated coal sends much more light to the eye than does a sheet of white paper in dim light. Animals must be able to interpret incoming signals in accordance with the context in which they occur and this must occur at higher levels in the nervous system. Experiments with animals show that many species are capable of accurate depth perception and judgment of distance. Squirrels leap unerringly from bough to bough, while frogs and chameleons (*Chamaeleontidae*) shoot out the tongue to the correct distance to catch an insect. Depth perception must result from processing of information in the central nervous system because each eye receives only a two-dimensional image. There are a number of cues that can be used by animals to form a three-dimensional representation of external objects: (1) Motion parallax occurs when the animal moves its head from side to side. Nearby objects are swept across the retina more quickly than distant ones, and many animals use this as a cue to distance. For examples, locusts (*Acridoidea*) characteristically move their heads in this way when preparing to jump across a gap. (2) The retinal image of an object is larger when the object is nearer to the eye. In laboratory experiments stationary objects can be made to increase in apparent size. Many animals, including crabs, frogs, chickens, kittens, monkeys and human infants, run away, duck or flinch when presented with such a stimulus. This indicates that they interpret the increase in size as meaning that the object is moving toward them. Thus it appears that increasing size of the retinal image, sometimes called the looming cue, is a widespread aspect of distance judgment among animals. (3) Each eye has a slightly different view of the world and there is therefore a disparity between the retinal positions of the image of an object in the outside world. This retinal disparity is greater when the object is nearer to the animal. It is known that some insects such as the praying mantis (*Mantis religiosa*) and some birds and primates use retinal disparity as a cue to depth. (4) The extent to which the eyes converge when fixating an object depends upon the distance of the object, and this information is used by chameleons as well as by man. Many of the cues which are used by animals in depth perception or in the judgment of distance require the use of both eyes and do not depend upon fixed properties of the sense organs themselves. Depth perception depends upon sophisticated processes in the central nervous system, based upon relatively simple information from the sense organs. Many aspects of perception, including the judgment of size, the localization of sounds, and the navigational abilities of animals, depend upon intelligent interpretation of sensory information which enables the animal to build up an inner representation of the outside world.

While many aspects of perception seem sophisticated others seem overly simple. Male European robins (*Erithacus rubecula*) attack other red-breasted robins that trespass on their territory. They will also attack a stuffed robin placed in the territory, but only if it has a red breast. It appears that the red breast is a powerful stimulus for labeling another robin as an intruder. Indeed the territory owner will vigorously attack a bunch of red feathers while ignoring a stuffed robin which has no red breast. No one doubts that a robin is capable of distinguishing between a real bird and a bunch of feathers, but in territorial defense robins appear blind to all attributes except the red breast. Such phenomena are common in animal behavior, and the relatively simple stimuli that elicit the animal's response are generally called SIGN STIMULI. The prime characteristic of sign stimuli is that the animal responds only to a small fraction of the stimulus complex that it is capable of appreciating.

It would, of course, be impossible for an animal to take note of every change in the environment that is monitored by the sense organs. Some selectivity is essential. An important aspect of this selectivity is attention. Three types of attention may be distinguished.

1. An animal may direct its sense organs toward a particular source of stimulation. A dog spying a rabbit directs his eyes, ears and nose to it, often turning head and body in the direction of the rabbit. This type of ORIENTING RESPONSE tends to result in the exclusion of other stimuli in the environment, partly as a result of the posture taken up by the dog.

2. An animal may attend selectively to some aspects of an object and ignore others. In the natural environment it is the sign stimulus that is generally the subject of this selective attention, but the phenomenon can be readily demonstrated in the laboratory where the significance of the stimuli is entirely learned (see ATTENTION).

3. The third type of attention is concerned with stimuli connected with a particular goal. An animal searching for food may have a SEARCH IMAGE of a particular type of food. The animal may pay particular attention to certain types of food, while ignoring other equally desirable foods. This phenomenon can be demonstrated both in the laboratory and in the field.

In addition to perceptual organization with respect to the external world, animals have to deal with the information from the sense organs that detect changes in their own body. To a large extent the coordination of muscular movements is automatic and does not involve higher nervous centers. Information from the skin and from sense organs in the muscles and tendons leads to reflex adjustments in posture and locomotion. To some extent also, messages from the internal sense organs that monitor the state of the blood (e.g. its pressure, temperature, osmosity, etc.) give rise to automatic physiological responses which form part of the general processes of HOMEOSTASIS. Nevertheless, humans can perceive some of the changes that occur in their own bodies, and pay attention to them from time to time. There is no reason to think that other animals are any different in this respect.   DJM

Bibliography

Ewert, J.P. 1980: *Neuroethology. An introduction to the neurophysiological fundamentals of behavior.* Berlin and New York: Springer-Verlag.

———, Capranica, R.R. and Ingle, D.J. eds. 1983: *Advances in vertebrate neuroethology.* New York and London: Plenum.

*Marler, P.R. and Hamilton, W.J. 1966: *Mechanisms of animal behavior.* New York: John Wiley and Sons.

McFarland, D. 1985: *Animal behaviour.* Pitman Books: London.

Tinbergen, N. 1969: *The study of instinct*. 2nd edn. Oxford: Clarendon Press.

pheromone A chemical smell substance released by one member of a species that has a highly specific effect on a conspecific. Pheromones are most highly developed in insects. For instance it has been shown experimentally that the antennae of the male silk moth are exceptionally receptive to just one chemical substance, bombykol, and are able to respond to a single molecule of it. Female silk moths release minute amounts of bombykol, and are located by males who fly upwind along the scent trail. Pheromones are used extensively by social insects such as bees, and ants. In bees there is a "queen substance" pheromone that actually controls the sexual development of colony females, rendering them infertile workers. Ants find their way to food along trail pheromones, and give up the food they bring back to the nest only to others emitting the correct pheromone.

Among mammals scent-signals are often implicated in sexual arousal, being most often given when a female is in estrus, i.e. sexually receptive. They have the effect of stimulating male sexual activity. This is true of primates such as the rhesus monkey.

(See also COMMUNICATION; REPRODUCTIVE BEHAVIOR.)   VR

Bibliography

Albone, E.S. 1984: *Mammalian semiochemistry*. Chichester: John Wiley.

Birch, M.C. ed. 1974: *Pheromones*. London: North Holland Publishing Company.

—— and Haynes, K.F. 1982: *Insect pheromones*. Studies in Biology. London: Edward Arnold.

Brown, R.E. and Macdonald, D.W. 1985: *Social odours in mammals*. Oxford: Clarendon Press.

phylogeny Representation of the evolutionary relationships of a collection of organisms.

play A type of activity which can be defined structurally by the re-ordering, exaggeration, repetition and fragmentation of behavior. Such characteristics would be uneconomic for goal-directed activity; therefore, functionally, play is usually described as having no clear immediate benefit.

Play has only been reliably documented in warm-blooded animals, and much more frequently and extensively for mammals than birds. Typically, play activities increase rapidly in frequency during the infancy period of mammalian development, peak, and decrease to low levels by sexual maturity. Play in adult mammals is usually with offspring. Adult monkeys may use play to distract youngsters from suckling, or from other companions.

The simplest kind of mammalian play takes the form of generalized physical activity; for example, rapid hopping back and forth in young wallabies (Kaufmann 1974). In addition, among the social mammals play fighting and/or chasing are commonly observed, the form depending on the particular species: for example, stalking, chasing, pawing and wrestling in lion cubs; rearing, pawing and biting in ponies; wrestling, biting and chasing in young rhesus monkeys. Sexual play has also been described in many species, and play mothering in monkeys. Manipulative play with objects has been documented, most noticeably with the higher primates. Manipulative play often follows exploration, but is distinguished from exploration by being less stimulus directed and more characterized by positive affect.

Lazar and Beckhorn (1974) have argued that play should not be seen as a separate kind of behavior, rather, activities of immature animals may be seen to be exaggerated, reordered or incomplete because this is an inevitable aspect of ontogenetic development, leading to adult behavior. This is a minority view although it may hold force for descriptions of play mothering, and perhaps sexual play. In the case of animal play fighting and chasing however, such activities may coexist developmentally with real fighting and chasing. The play activities may differ from the real activities according to structural criteria similar to those which Loizos proposed. Furthermore, sequences of play fighting and chasing are typically preceded by play invitation or marker signals (such as open-mouth face, exaggerated walk or bow) which only appear in such contexts and are not seen in adult non-play behavior.

The characteristics of playful behavior are compatible with a learning approach which emphasizes the reinforcing nature of sensory stimulation, especially varied and novel stimulation, for the young organism. This is usually coupled with an arousal-level model which postulates that sensory stimulation is only reinforcing if it keeps the organism within an optimal arousal zone (Baldwin and Baldwin 1977). This can explain age changes, but it would require supplementing by postulates as to why particular kinds of stimulation, such as those in play fighting, are so motivating.

Since play does not have clear immediate benefits to the animal, there has been considerable speculation as to its biological function. One approach has been to argue that play functions to maintain optimal arousal (Ellis 1973), but this merely defers the problem to explaining the benefits of arousal level, which can anyway be mediated by the other behavior. More plausibly, arousal level may be part of the proximal mechanism by which playful behavior develops, rather than the ultimate function for which playful behavior was selected. Associated theories are that play functions as a neural primer, and/or as a means of reducing information load (Hutt 1979).

Spencer's theory of "surplus energy" is now of only historical interest. "Surplus" energy can be stored, and there is no biological advantage in just getting rid of it. However a slight change in the logic produces the physical training hypothesis (Fagen 1981). This argues that active physical play serves to train muscle strength and general bodily capacity and stamina; it is further argued that there is a critical period for such training, during the infant/ juvenile period. The hypothesis is considered to explain certain design fea-

tures of play, notably its varied but repetitive nature, and the combination of short high-intensity with long low-intensity bouts. Increases in active play are predicted after physical confinement or exercise deprivation; there is some evidence for this.

The physical training hypothesis would not explain specifically social play, nor manipulative play with objects. Until recently, social play was thought by most ethologists to help in socializing the young into the group (see RELATIONSHIPS AND SOCIAL STRUCTURE). It was hypothesized to have social bonding functions, and/or to facilitate the learning of social DOMI-NANCE and of species-specific communication (Poirier and Smith 1974). Studies by Harlow and others found that monkeys deprived of social play in infancy, showed poor social adjustment later. However the inference that social play is essential for adjustment is suspect, as the monkeys were typically deprived of any kind of social interaction during isolation (Bekoff 1976).

The socialization hypotheses have been recently called into question. Firstly, naturalistic studies have found examples of some animal groups (e.g. some troops of squirrel monkeys) showing no social play, because of ecological circumstances such as food dispersal; yet these groups functioned normally in terms of cohesion, hierarchy and reproduction. Therefore, social play is not essential for socialization (Baldwin and Baldwin 1977). Secondly, socialization hypotheses do not explain the design features of social play, much of which is quasi-agonistic. Thirdly, socialization hypotheses assume that individual behavior is for the benefit of the social group. Recent thinking in SOCIOBIOLOGY directs more attention to competitive individual benefit in considering the adaptive function of behavior.

Developing these last two criticisms, Symons has carried out detailed studies of play fighting and chasing in rhesus monkeys, and elaborated an alternative functional hypothesis. The design features of play fighting are argued to be attempts to seek advantage, such as to play bite the partner without being bitten, resulting in unstereotyped competitive behavior which would serve as safe practice in juveniles for unstereotyped competitive aggression in adults. Such aggressive competition is important in REPRODUCTIVE SUCCESS, especially for adult males. It is therefore correctly predicted that play fighting is more frequent in juvenile males than females. Symons develops a corresponding argument that play chasing is practice for predator (avoidance) skills.

Manipulative play has been hypothesized to be functional in providing practice for adult TOOL USE, and also as a source of behavioral innovation (Fagen 1981). It is only commonly observed in the higher primates. In baboons and macaques, manipulative play is relatively infrequent in the wild and shows no regular pattern. It may not have been directly selected for, though Parker and Gibson (1977) suggest its importance for feeding activities.

This argument is stronger in the case of the cebus monkeys and great apes; notably for the chimpanzee, where manipulative play is quite frequent in the young, and may well be functional as practice for tool-using skills such as termite-fishing and leaf-sponging, which are important for subsistence (McGrew 1977). Here, manipulative play serves as practice for species-specific skills. The argument that play was selected for as a source of behavioral innovation suffers the drawback that significant beneficial innovations are rare in non-human species.   PKS

Bibliography

Baldwin, J.D. and Baldwin, J.I. 1977: The role of learning phenomena in the ontogeny of exploration and play. In *Primate bio-social development*, eds. Suzanne Chevalier-Skolnikoff and Frank E. Poirier. New York and London: Garland.

Bekoff, M. 1976: The social deprivation paradigm: who's being deprived of what? *Developmental psychobiology* 9, 497–98.

Ellis, Michael J. 1973: *Why people play*. Englewood Cliffs, N.J. and Hemel Hempstead: Prentice-Hall.

Fagen, Robert M. 1981: *Animal play behavior*. New York and Oxford: Oxford University Press.

Hutt, C. 1979: Play in the under-fives: form, development and function. In *Modern perspectives in the psychiatry of infancy*. Modern perspectives in psychiatry 8, ed. John G. Howells. New York: Brunner/Mazel.

Kaufmann, J.H. 1974: Social ethology of the chiptail wallaby. *Animal behaviour* 22, 281–369.

Lazar, J. and Beckhorn, G.D. 1974: Social play or the development of social behavior in ferrets (*Mustela putorius*)? *American zoologist* 14, 405–14.

McGrew, W.C. 1977: Socialization and object manipulation of wild chimpanzees. In *Primate bio-social development*. eds. Suzanne Chevalier-Skolnikoff and Frank E. Poirier. New York and London: Garland.

Parker, S.T. and Gibson, K.R. 1977: Object manipulation, tool use, and sensorimotor intelligence as feeding adaptations in cebus monkeys and great apes. *Journal of human evolution* 6, 623–41.

Poirier, F.E. and Smith, E.O. 1974: Socialising function of primate play. *American zoologist* 14, 275–87.

*Smith, P.K. ed. 1984: *Play in animals and humans*. Oxford: Basil Blackwell.

polygamy In anthropology, polygamy refers to forms of marriage where individuals of either sex have two or more spouses, usually simultaneously. The main forms of polygamy are polygyny, where a man has two or more wives, and polyandry, where a woman has two or more husbands. Both are contrasted to monogamy, where one man and one woman are married.

In ethology, by an intended analogy, polygamy and its related terms are applied to relationships between individuals as observed in animal behavior: however, the criteria are necessarily different, being based on sexual behavior rather than marriage, and sometimes applied to mating relationships that are successive within a breeding season rather than simultaneous. Sometimes cooperation of both sexes in rearing the young is considered a further criterion. Polygamous and monogamous mating relationships are both contrasted to promiscuous mating behavior, where restricted mating relationships of substantial duration are not evident. These mating systems occur with varying frequencies in different animal groups, and there have been attempts to describe and explain the ecological and social correlates of mating systems on the basis that they result from NATURAL SELECTION (see Krebs and Davies 1981; Davies and Lundberg 1984).

Biological and anthropological views of mating systems usually diverge. Nonetheless, behavioral definitions of polygamy and monogamy, based on the restriction of regular sexual activity, are sometimes applied to both humans and animals, reflecting a new approach which may offer new insights (see Hiatt 1980, Dickemann 1979). At present such approaches are at an exploratory stage.   RDA

Bibliography

Davies, N.B. and Lundberg, A. 1984: Food distribution and a variable mating system in the dunnock (*Prunella modularis*). *Journal of animal ecology* 53, 895–913.

Dickemann, M. 1979: The ecology of mating systems in hypergynous dowry societies. *Social science information* 18(2), 163–195.

Halliday, T.R. 1980: *Sexual strategy*. Oxford: Oxford University Press; Chicago: Chicago University Press (1982).

Hiatt, L.R. 1980: Polyandry in Sri Lanka: a test case for parental investment theory. *Man* 15, 583–602.

Krebs, J.R. and Davies, N.B. eds. 1981: *An introduction to behavioural ecology*. Oxford: Blackwell Scientific Publications; Sunderland, Mass.: Sinauer.

preparedness Certain combinations of stimuli, responses and reinforcers produce more rapid and effective CONDITIONING than others; this may be described, if not explained, by saying that organisms are prepared to associate certain combinations of events and not others. The best documented example is the conditioning of aversions to food. If rats are made ill after eating or drinking some novel substance, they show a marked aversion to the flavor of that substance, but not to other stimuli (auditory or visual) which accompanied its ingestion. But if they are

punished by a brief shock to the feet for eating or drinking this substance, they will show little or no aversion to its flavor, but be most reluctant to eat or drink anything in the presence of the auditory or visual stimuli present when they were punished. Flavors are readily associated with illness; auditory or visual stimuli with an external source of pain.   NJM

Bibliography

Seligman, M.E.P. 1970: On the generality of the laws of learning. *Psychological review* 77, 406–18.

Zeiler, M.D. and Harzem, P. eds. 1983: *Biological factors in learning*. New York: Wiley.

problem solving A test of animal intelligence. The problem solving abilities of animals have been the subject of considerable research particularly by early psychologists such as Thorndike (1911) and Köhler (1925). Much of this work was aimed at understanding cognition in animals, but its early promise has not been fulfilled. (See INSIGHT.)

Animals are so varied and have so many specialized abilities that it is difficult to come to any general conclusion about their INTELLIGENCE. For example a commonly investigated problem is that in which the direct and obvious route to a goal is blocked and the animal has to make a detour to arrive at it. Some animals have great difficulty with this. For example, a chicken presented with food on the far side of a short wire fence will persist in attempting to penetrate the fence and will only by accident discover the detour round the end of it whereas a dog would have little difficulty with this type of problem. Chameleons are particularly good at spatial detour problems, but they would not normally be considered to be especially intelligent. Many birds perform feats of navigation that would tax an able schoolchild given the same information.   DJM

Bibliography

Köhler, W. 1925 (1957): *The mentality of apes*. London: Pelican Books.

Lawick-Goodall, J. van 1970: Tool using in primates and other vertebrates. In *Advances in the study of behavior*, vol. 3, eds. D.S. Lehrman, R.A. Hinde and E. Shaw. New York: Academic Press.

Roitblat, H.L., Bever, T.G. and Terrace, H.S. eds. 1984: *Animal cognition*. Hillsdale, N.J.: Erlbaum.

Thorndike, E.L. 1911: *Animal intelligence*. New York: Macmillan.

R

reafference A theory that sets out to explain how animals distinguish between stimuli that result from their own behavior and those emanating from the environment. For example when we move our eyes in a voluntary manner the image moves on the retina, but we have no perception of movement, but when the image on the retina moves as a result of movement of an object in the environment, we do see movement. Reafference theory explains this difference by assuming that during voluntary movement the brain forms an image (known as the efference copy) of the expected consequences of the movement. If the actual (reafferent) consequences correspond to the expected consequences, no movement is perceived. Stimuli emanating from the environment (exafferent stimuli) do not correspond to any efference copy and so their perception is not cancelled.

The reafference principle was developed by von Holst and Mittelstaedt (1950) and has been applied to many aspects of animal behavior, including perception, orientation and motivation.

DJM

Bibliography

Ingle, D.J., Jeannerod, M. and Lee, D.N. eds. 1985: *Brain mechanisms and spatial vision*. Dordrecht: Martinus Nijhoff.

von Holst, Erich and Mittelstaedt, Horst 1950: Das Reafferenzprinzip: Wechselwirkungen zwischen Zentralnervensystem und Peripherie. *Naturgewissenschaft* 37, 464–76.

recognition In ethology this term is used most frequently to describe the perception of species specific characteristics. These are recognized both between and within species. Between species the

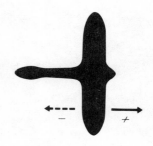

commonest forms of recognition occur between predators and their prey. Tinbergen (1951) illustrates a model of a bird used in experiments with young ducks and geese (see fig.).

When moved overhead to the left, this model produced no reaction, but when moved to the right it elicited escape responses. From this and many other similar experiments, it was concluded that most, if not all prey species have innate mechanisms for the recognition of predators, linked neurally to appropriate escape mechanisms.

In the case of recognition within species, the commonest forms concern species specific smells, sounds, and coloration. For instance rats recognize fellow group members by smell, sheep mothers recognize their offspring by smell, and wood ants recognize colony members by smell. Birds recognize conspecifics by their calls, as do certain insects such as crickets, and many mammals. Color patterns are important in recognition among birds, where the young often have particular coloration, and among mammals where the same is often the case; they are quite unimportant among insects such as ants. Owing to the existence of innate recognition mechanisms, many species have developed MIMICRY to protect themselves or further their own ends: eyespot mimicry among moths and butterflies has evolved by increasing the rate of survival of those individuals who were mistaken by predators for big-eyed creatures unsuitable for food.

In man recognition relates largely to inter-individual recognition, a phenomenon that definitely occurs in primates and among other mammal species. Studies of infant behavior by ethologists have, however, shown that human babies have an innate smile reaction to the shape of the face, together with a number of other reactions in which innate recognition mechanisms appear to be involved. At first these are non-specific, but individual recognition (of the parent) occurs as development proceeds.   VR

Bibliography

Gottlieb, G. 1971: *Development of species identification in birds*. Chicago: University of Chicago Press.

Lythgoe, J.N. 1979: *The ecology of vision*. Oxford: Clarendon Press.

Tinbergen, N. 1969: *The study of instinct*. 2nd edn. Oxford: Clarendon Press.

redirected activity A technical term of classical ethology which is sometimes confused with DISPLACEMENT ACTIVITY and with VACUUM ACTIVITY. A redirected activity is an activity, recognizable from its form as being usually directed toward a particular stimulus, but on this occasion directed toward another stimulus. The classic human illustration is the aggressive man slamming his fist into the table instead of into an opponent. Aggressive gulls may sometimes violently peck the ground instead of the rival. In motivational theories of classical ethology the aggressive drive was said to be prevented by fear from achieving its normal outlet – pecking the rival – and instead found outlet in the redirected activity – pecking the ground.
                                                RD

Bibliography

Hinde, R.A. 1982: *Ethology*. New York and Oxford: Oxford University Press.

reflex An automatic reaction to external stimulation. In a simple reflex the central nervous system receives a message from a sense organ and converts this directly into instructions for muscular contraction or glandular secretion. For example, an increase in illumination on the retina results in a reflex contraction of the iris so that the pupil of the eye becomes smaller, cutting down the amount of light falling on the retina.

Reflexes are particularly important in the COORDINATION of limb muscles. Changes in the length of muscles, measured by muscle spindles, or in muscular tension, measured by tendon organs, are automatically signaled to the spinal cord where there are connexions with the nerves responsible for controlling muscular tension. The postural reflexes enable muscles to adjust to the mechanical forces that result from shifts in the centre of gravity during LOCOMOTION. Such reflexes often work in reciprocation, so that incompatible sets of muscles can operate in succession, thus achieving smooth coordination of limb movements.

Pavlov discovered that, although many reflexes are inborn, some can be modified or established by CONDITIONING. The automatic depression of the brake pedal by a car driver in an emergency is an example of such a conditioned reflex.   DJM

Bibliography

Bush, B.M.H. and Clarac, F. eds. 1985: *Coordination of motor behaviour*. Cambridge and New York: Cambridge University Press.

Jenkins, H.M. 1984: The study of animal learning in the tradition of Pavlov and Thorndike. In *The biology of learning*, eds. P. Marler and H.S. Terrace. Berlin and New York: Springer-Verlag.

reinforcement The rewards and punishments obtained by animals during learning have the effect of strengthening and weakening the learning process. In the study of animal psychology the term reinforcement is used to describe these effects. A pigeon rewarded with food for pecking at a disk is likely to learn to repeat the response. The learning can be said to be positively reinforced. Conversely, a pigeon punished with a mild electric shock is likely to learn not to peck the disk in future and the pecking response is said to be negatively reinforced. For some psychologists the term reinforcement is synonymous with reward and punishment. Others reserve the term reinforcement for the processes of strengthening and weakening that occur as a result of the receipt of rewards and punishments. The situation is complicated by controversy over the question of whether reinforcement is necessary for learning. Some psychologists argue that all learning requires reinforcement since this is the process of strengthening and weakening stimulus-response connections. Others maintain that learning can occur in the absence of overt reward or punishment. IMPRINTING and song-learning in birds are cited as examples of this.

A major step in the development of ideas about reinforcement was Thorndike's Law of Effect.

The Law of Effect is that: Of several responses made to the same situation, those which are accompanied or closely followed by satisfaction to the animal will, other things being equal, be more firmly connected with the situation, so that, when it recurs, they will be more likely to recur; those which are accompanied or closely followed by discomfort to the animal will, other things being equal, have their connections with that situation weakened, so that, when it recurs, they will be less likely to occur. The greater the satisfaction or discomfort, the greater the strengthening or weakening of the bond . . . By a satisfying state of affairs is meant one which the animal does nothing to avoid, often doing such things as attain and preserve it. By a discomforting or annoying state of affairs is meant one which the animal commonly avoids and abandons (Thorndike 1911, pp. 244–5).
(See also LEARNING: THORNDIKE'S LAWS.)

An important feature of Thorndike's theory is that it emphasizes connections between situations and responses (S–R connections). For THORNDIKE, reinforcement strengthened (or weakened) a connection between a preceding response and the stimulus situation in which it had occurred. For PAVLOV, on the other hand, reinforcement elicited a pattern of behavior which was associated with the prevailing environmental stimuli, and would subsequently be elicited by stimuli preceding the reinforcer (S–S connections). These two principles of reinforcement, Thorndike's law of effect and Pavlov's principle of stimulus substitution remain the most important analyses of reinforcement to this day. (Mackintosh 1974.) (See also CONDITIONING.)

Thorndike's law of effect was extended by SKINNER, who saw reinforcement as any contingency which causes the behavior to increase (or decrease) in frequency. Thus if delivery of food is made contingent upon a particular response and the response is observed to increase in frequency, delivery of food counts as reinforcement. Skinner also assumed that the nature of the reinforcement, of the response, and of the prevailing stimulus are essentially arbitrary. For Skinner, the connection between any stimulus and any response can be strengthened by any means of reinforcement provided the response is within the animal's repertoire and the stimulus within its sensory range. There have been two major developments which throw serious doubt on Skinner's position. The first is the discovery that the relationship between response and reinforcement is not arbitrary, and the second is that even in classical Skinnerian situations the reinforcement does not necessarily have to be contingent upon the response.

Modern evidence indicates that a given type of reinforcement is more effective in strengthening (or weakening) a response if the response is already motivationally related to the reinforcement. Rats readily learn to avoid food with a particular flavor if consumption of the food is followed by vomiting, but if it is followed by electric shock they usually fail to associate the flavor with the subsequent punishment.

Pigeon inspects the square illuminated key on which a stimulus is projected, pecks it and obtains a food reward delivered into a hopper located below the keys.

Similarly, if different response patterns of the golden hamster are systematically followed by the presentation of food, certain responses are reinforced but others are not. Moreover those responses which are susceptible to reinforcement by food are those, such as digging and rearing, which the animal would normally show when deprived of food. Responses which are resistant to food reinforcement, such as face-washing and scent-marking, are not normally associated with food or hunger (Shettleworth 1973).

The techniques of operant conditioning can be used to train animals to perform particular behavior patterns or tasks. Suppose we wish to train a pigeon to peck an illuminated key to obtain food reward. After one or two days of food deprivation in its home cage, the pigeon is placed in a small cage equipped with a mechanism for delivering grain. The key is situated on the wall of the cage at about head height as illustrated. Delivery of food is signaled by a small light which illuminates the grain. The pigeon soon learns to associate the switching on of the light with the delivery of food and approaches the food mechanism whenever the light comes on. The next stage is to make food delivery contingent upon some aspect of the animal's behavior. Pecking is frequently used and is encouraged by limiting rewards to movements which become progressively more similar to a peck at the illuminated disk. This procedure is called shaping. When the pigeon has learned to approach the key for reward it is rewarded only if it stands upright with its head near the key. At this stage the pigeon usually pecks the key spontaneously: slow learners can be encouraged to do this with a grain of wheat temporarily glued to the key. When the pigeon pecks the key it closes a sensitive switch in an electronic circuit which causes the food to be delivered automatically. From this point on the pigeon is rewarded only when it pecks the key and manual control for reward is no longer required.

This method is similar to that used in training circus animals and it is also used by psychologists in training animals to perform for television commercials, etc. One such team of psychologists reported on behavioral peculiarities which often occur during such training sessions. A pig was trained to pick up large wooden coins and place them in a money box. The pig was required to deposit a number of coins to obtain a reward. It learned the task easily, but with increasing practice it developed the habit of dropping the coins and rooting at them before placing them in a box. It seemed that the pig was treating the coins as though they were food items and responding to them in an instinctive manner. This type of instinctive drift has been described in a number of species (Breland and Breland 1961).

Laboratory investigations show that animals often respond to reinforcement in a motivationally biased manner. In the case of the key-pecking pigeon mentioned above, film analysis shows that the pigeon pecks the key with a typical food-getting peck. Under a water reinforcement regime pigeons peck the key with a different style of peck reminiscent of that used when they take droplets of water. Once the pigeon has associated the key with food it behaves toward it as though it were food. Key-pecking behavior can be obtained from a naive bird without any shaping at all. All that is necessary is that food should be presented soon after the pigeon's attention is drawn to the key. This can be done by switching on the key light and then presenting food. If this is repeated many times the pigeon comes to peck the key. This procedure, generally called auto-shaping, can be explained in terms of

Pavlovian conditioning in which the key becomes directly associated with food (S–S learning), without any recourse to the notion that the pecking response is necessary for learning to occur (S–R learning). If a pigeon is allowed to see its mate for a short period after illumination of a light, and this procedure is repeated many times, it starts to direct its courtship behavior toward the light, as though the light were a pigeon of the opposite sex. Demonstrations such as these have led some psychologists to doubt the role of reinforcement in establishing S–R connections. As every operant conditioning situation provides an opportunity for Pavlovian conditioning it may be that S–S connections are all that is necessary in an account of reinforcement (Moore 1973). Whatever the theoretical interpretation of autoshaping experiments it is clear that Skinner was incorrect in asserting that reinforcement is arbitrary in the sense of establishing connections between any type of stimulus and any element of the animal's behavior repertoire.   DJM

Bibliography

Breland, K. and Breland, M. 1961: The misbehavior of organisms. *American psychologist* 16, 661–64.

Hinde, Robert A. and Stevenson-Hinde, Joan eds. 1973: *Constraints on learning*. London and New York: Academic Press.

*Mackintosh, N.J. 1974: *The psychology of animal learning*. London and New York: Academic Press.

Mackintosh, N.J. 1983: *Conditioning and associative learning*. Oxford and New York: Oxford University Press.

Moore, B.R. 1973: The role of directed Pavlovian reactions in simple instrumental learning in the pigeon. In Hinde and Stevenson-Hinde.

Shettleworth, S.J. 1973: Food reinforcement and the organization of behavior in golden hamsters. In Hinde and Stevenson-Hinde.

*Tapp, Jack T. ed. 1969: *Reinforcement and behavior*. New York and London: Academic Press.

Thorndike, Edward Lee 1911: *Animal intelligence*. New York: Macmillan. Reprinted 1965. New York and London: Hafner.

relationships and social structure

Two abstract hierarchical levels invoked in the description of societies and derived from behavioral interactions between individuals (Hinde 1979). According to Hinde a relationship results from sequences of interactions between two individuals. The nature of any interaction will be influenced by other interactions in that relationship and reflect properties inherent in both participants. The kind of patterning of all relationships realized by individuals interacting over a period of time will produce the structure of the group.

On describing relationships and structures

Traditionally, the descriptive units of social behavior exhibited by a species are enumerated and empirically classified into different categories, for example, agonistic or sociopositive behavior, on the basis of their temporal and/or functional associations. This allows us to describe relationships and social structures in terms of absolute and relative frequencies of behavioral units or categories which occur among individuals. In addition, proximity data portray relationships and subgroups by representing the spatial arrangement of individuals. Demographic parameters such as group size and sex/age composition are also used in characterizing social organizations. The more comprehensive list of social qualities compiled by Wilson (1975) draws attention to more abstract properties of social structures, such as the network of communication, the permeability or openness of a group, the degree of behavioral specialization among the group members and the kinds of subgroups. McBride's questionnaire (1976) lists an even larger number of parameters useful in the characterization of animal social groups. While illustrating the diversity of social phenomena in animals, such descriptions do not reflect the fact that similar surface structures may result from entirely different processes involved in their formation.

Most of the traditionally-used measures convey a static picture of what in reality constitutes a continuously changing system where even apparently stable properties will rely on processes conserving them. Individuals enter and leave relationships and groups while kinds of relationships and structures are preserved over generations. The framework developed by Hinde (1975) for studying relationships and structures includes the notion of historically developed entities, the current state of which cannot be understood without reference to the past.

Hinde's framework involves three levels: interaction, relationships and structure. Interactions consist of behavioral exchanges between individuals: one participant directs a particular behavior toward another that may or may not show an immediate response. What an individual does to a partner will partly depend on the identity of this partner. Interactions, therefore, have properties not present in the behavior of either participant alone. Relationships are operationally defined in terms of the content, quality and temporal patterning of their constituent interactions. Labels like "mother-child", "dominant-subordinate" or "male-female" refer to the types or content of the interactions realized in the respective relationship. Relationships not only vary in what the participants do together but also in how they are doing it, for example, in the intensity of an interaction or in its coordination between the partners. Relationships develop over time. The attributes of the partners that primarily govern the interaction pattern are likely to change. At early stages, external qualities such as sex and size will draw individuals together, while more hidden qualities, such as skills and idiosyncrasies may shape the interactions of mature relationships. A social structure is seen by Hinde as the content, quality and patterning of relationships. Mason, in contrast to Hinde, considers the operation of factors external to the social group (Mason 1978). He distinguishes three levels: an individual's behavioral repertoire and social propensities define its potential contribution to the structure of the group. The expression of this potential will be modified by the social setting of the group and the expression of their social attributes.

Finally, the environment of the whole social system includes non-social factors that affect individual behavior and group structure.

An animal relationship often begins with aggressive interactions; in time it may proceed to ever more intimate interactions such as mutual grooming. It may eventually develop into a bond. The stage reached is in part predictable by the sex, age and DOMINANCE status of the two individuals. Experimental addition of a third individual may cause the original relationship to regress permanently to an earlier stage, illustrating the mutual influence among relationships within a social structure (Kummer 1975). Some animal social structures are stratified. In the four-level society of hamadryas baboons (Abegglen 1984) members of the same lower-level unit (e.g. families) interact more frequently and at more intimate stages than individuals sharing only the highest unit (the troop).

Causal aspects of relationships: learning paradigms

Hinde (1979) reviews how three classical learning paradigms relate to interindividual relationships: exposure learning, and classical and operant CONDITIONING. For both humans and animals, it has been shown that the mere repeated perception of another individual may induce a change in behavior towards that individual. Mutual attraction is the likely outcome of increased familiarity even in the absence of positive reinforcement and may thereby create possibilities for interactions (see KINSHIP).

Individualized relationships are not a prerequisite of complex social structures, as the example of the social insects shows. Individual behavior may be directly affected by the composition of the group. For example, the sex reversal in some fish species is contingent upon the sex composition of the social group. The tasks performed by an individual social insect are influenced by other colony members and the caste composition of the colony. In primates, interindividual preferences may co-vary with the sex composition of the

131

group and the effect of relationships on one another may range from mediation to suppression: a female's ability to interact with an infant may depend on the nature of her relationship with her mother whereas a male hamadryas baboon having observed that two conspecifics form a pair is inhibited from interacting with either of them (Kummer et al. 1974).

Functional aspects of relationships

Kummer (1978), in his heuristic scheme, discusses the value of primate social relationships for the reproductive survival of the individual member. A relationship is seen as a potential for useful interactions in the future, built by interactions in the past. An individual monitors the general qualities, the behavioral tendencies and the availability of a companion, and presumably improves them by the longterm effects of his own contributions to the interactions. It also defends the availability of the companion, since one of the problems faced by a personal relationship is that it must resist the impersonal sign stimuli displayed by other group members. Ethological research on social monitoring and longterm effects of particular interactions is still in its initial phase.

Since social animals are both cooperators and competitors, conflicts of interest are frequent, and the asymmetry of attachment and interests in the dyad may change over time. Yet completely asymmetric exploitative relationships are rare and transient, presumably because either member disposes of evolved strategies that aim at an optimal cost-benefit ratio in terms of its individual fitness (see SOCIOBIOLOGY). Relationships of long standing may be more efficient than newly-formed ones in problem-solving and in terms of the number of young reared by a pair.

Group structure is ultimately determined by individual behavior and component relationships and will not, in animals, take on an existence and value of its own (Hinde 1974). The social structure is the statistical summation of individual behavioral strategies. Social behavior that benefits the whole group can mostly be explained as behavior evolved for the benefit of the actor.   HK

Bibliography

Abegglen, J.J. 1984: *On socialization in Hamadryas baboons. A field study*. Lewisburg: Bucknell University Press.

Hinde, R.A. 1974: *Biological bases of human social behavior*. New York and London: McGraw-Hill.

——— 1975: Interactions, relationships and social structure in nonhuman primates. In *Proceedings from the symposia of the fifth congress of the International Primatological Society*, eds. Shiro Kondo et al. Tokyo: Japan Science Press.

*——— 1979: Towards understanding relationships. *European monographs in social psychology* 18. London and New York: Academic Press.

——— 1983: *Primate social relationships: an integrated approach*. Oxford: Blackwell Scientific Publications.

Kummer, H. 1975: Rules of dyad and group formation among captive gelada baboons (*Theropithecus gelada*). In *Proceedings from the symposia of the fifth congress of the International Primatological Society*, eds. Shiro Kondo et al. Tokyo: Japan Science Press.

——— 1978: On the value of social relationships to nonhuman primates: a heuristic scheme. *Social science information* 17, 687–705.

——— , Götz, W. and Angst, W. 1974: Triadic differentiation: an inhibitory process protecting pairbonds in baboons. *Behaviour* 49, 62–87.

Mason, W. 1978: Ontogeny of social systems. In *Recent advances in primatology*, vol. 1, eds. D.J. Chivers and J. Herbert. New York: Academic Press.

*McBride, G. 1976: The study of social organization. *Behaviour* 59, 96–115.

Wilson, E.O. 1975: *Sociobiology: the new synthesis*. Cambridge, Mass.: Harvard University Press.

relearning Occurs when a training or acquisition experience is repeated some time after original learning. If the training is carried out in the same way on both occasions, the degree to which relearning is accomplished more rapidly than the original (savings) can be used as a measure of retention of the original. Conversely, in so far as relearning is necessary, forgetting of original learning can be inferred.

Sometimes, even when there is no sign that the ability to perform a task has been retained, the more sensitive relearning test may reveal some memory. Relearning rates are also used to assess the effects of an intervening treatment, e.g. a brain lesion, upon retention of a task.   DJM

releasers Are social stimuli which are especially effective in producing a response by another individual. The term also implies that both the stimulus features and the responsiveness have become mutually adapted during the course of their evolution. The term was originally used in early ethological writings when it was linked with energy models. It is closely related to other ethological concepts such as SIGN STIMULUS. (See INNATE RELEASING MECHANISM (IRM) AND RELEASERS.)   JA

Bibliography

Hinde, R.A. 1982: *Ethology*. New York and Oxford: Oxford University Press.

reproductive behavior Encompasses the many and varied activities shown by animals which promote the production and rearing of offspring. It includes not only behavior directly associated with mating, but also aggressive behavior directed toward obtaining mates and the resources essential for successful reproduction, and parental behavior by which the young are fed and protected. So diverse are the behavior patterns subsumed under the heading of reproductive behavior, that it is difficult to draw a clear distinction between reproductive behavior and other major behavioral categories. For example, when AGGRESSION is directed toward the defense of a territory that contains the food resources required to feed the young, it becomes essentially a matter of opinion whether such aggression should be labelled as reproductive behavior or, together with behavior shown in other contexts, included under the general category of aggression (see also TERRITORIALITY).

Since the crucial variable upon which NATURAL SELECTION acts is the number of progeny that an individual organism leaves in succeeding generations, it could be argued that virtually all behavior patterns can be described as reproductive behavior, since anything an animal does may affect its chances of surviving and reproducing. However, a distinction is usually made between those activities which directly promote reproduction and those which maintain the survival and growth of the individual. Other categories of behavior, such as aggression or feeding, cut across this dichotomy. On some occasions an animal may be fighting or feeding to maintain its own survival, on others to promote its reproductive output.

In the great majority of animals, but with the exception of hermaphrodites (animals capable of producing male and female gametes), individuals show very different forms of reproductive behavior depending on whether they are male or female. The biological basis of all other gender differences is the difference between female and male gametes, eggs and sperm. Since sperm are relatively very small and thus metabolically cheap to produce, they are typically produced in much larger number than eggs. As a result, males have a greater reproductive potential than females. In many animals this difference in potential is expressed in very disparate forms of reproductive behavior. Whereas females commonly devote much of their time to the care, nourishment and protection of their offspring, males tend to direct much of their effort toward competing with one another for matings. This pattern is not, however, seen in all species. In some, males and females share the parental components of reproductive behavior, and in a minority of animals, it is the males which devote greater effort to the care of the young and the females which compete with one another for access to males.

How the various aspects of reproductive behavior are apportioned between the sexes varies greatly from one species to another and depends on a complex interaction between several factors. For each species, reproductive behavior takes place within a distinctive set of social interactions called the mating system of that species. In a monogamous mating system, males and females form pair bonds of varying durability. In polygynous animals certain males mate with several females, and in a polyandrous species individual females may mate with several males. Promiscuity is a term sometimes used to describe systems in which both males and females mate with several partners.

The nature of the mating system largely determines the forms of reproductive behavior shown by each sex. In monogamous species, males and females typically share such activities as nest-building and parental care. In many polygynous animals, males carry out little or no parental care but devote nearly all their effort to fighting with other males for the possession of females. Polyandry is associated with sex role "reversal", females tending to be the more dominant sex, competing for males which carry out most of the parental care.

Monogamy is more common among birds than other groups of animals. This is probably because, for birds more than for other groups, males can enhance their own REPRODUCTIVE SUCCESS significantly by staying with one female and sharing the parental duties with her, rather than by seeking to mate with other females. In birds, males can incubate eggs and feed chicks just as effectively as females. In mammals monogamy is rare and polygyny more common. Only female mammals can produce the milk on which the young are reared and males can offer only protection to the developing offspring.

Another factor that can determine the form of the mating system is the nature of the mating act. For example, among fishes there is a tendency for the parental role to be the prerogative of the male rather than the female in those species in which the eggs are fertilized outside the female's body. Conversely, female care is commoner in species in which fertilization is internal to the female. Essentially, parental care falls on the partner that is closest to the eggs when they are fertilized.

Virtually all animals show marked periodicity in their reproductive behavior. In many species there is an annual breeding season which, in extreme cases, is limited to one or two days each year. The timing of the breeding season is typically linked to seasonal changes in the environment so that reproduction occurs at the most propitious time for the successful production and rearing of offspring. In most birds that breed in temperate climates, egg laying is timed to precede the dramatic increase in the availability of plant and insect food that occurs in the spring and summer. In some mammals, including humans, there is little or no seasonal periodicity, but a continually cycling system, in which females regularly become reproductively active (come into estrus). Whatever the periodicity of reproductive behavior, cycles are physiologically controlled by reproductive hormones secreted within the body by various endocrine glands. Hormone production, particularly in species which breed annually, is triggered by a variety of external influences such as temperature, day-length and the behavior of members of the opposite sex. HORMONES commonly have a range of physiological effects, influencing many aspects of reproductive behavior. For example, testosterone has a major influence on both mating activity and aggression in males, as well as playing a role in sperm production. Female sex hormones, such as estrogen and progesterone, can be involved in the control of nest-building, mating and parental care. In general, the role of sex hormones in reproductive behavior is to bring the whole physiology of males and females into a state of reproductive preparedness and receptivity. The exact timing of the various components of reproductive behavior, and of mating in particular, is typically a function of behavioral interactions occurring between males and females.

The critical point in the reproductive process is the act of mating which is usually associated with a category of reproductive behavior referred to as COURTSHIP. Courtship involves the coordination of male and female behavior necessary for successful mating and, in some species, provides an opportunity for animals to choose their mating partners from among a wide range of potential mates. In monogamous animals which form durable mating partnerships, courtship may continue after mating has occurred and can be important in maintaining the pair bond during the parental phase of the reproductive process.

In a few animals the reproductive behavior of parents is augmented by the efforts of other individuals which act as helpers. In a number of birds, helpers provide food for the young and assist in defense of the brood against predators and other enemies. In most cases, but not all, helpers are genetically related to the individuals they are assisting. They may, for example, be previous offspring of one or both parents and thus be full or half-siblings of the young for whom they are caring. Such cooperative breeding groups are essentially extended families (see ALTRUISM). (See also SEXUAL BEHAVIOR.) TRH

Bibliography

Bateson, P. ed. 1983: *Mate choice*. Cambridge and New York: Cambridge University Press.

Halliday, T.R. 1980: *Sexual strategy*. Oxford: Oxford University Press; Chicago: Chicago University Press (1982).

Daly, M. and Wilson, M. 1978: *Sex, evolution and behavior*. North Scituate, Mass.: Duxbury.

Hutchison, J.B. ed. 1978: *Biological determinants of sexual behaviour*. New York and Chichester: Wiley.

McFarland, D. 1985: *Animal behavior*. London: Pitman Publishing Ltd.

reproductive effort Time and energy allocated directly to producing progeny. It can be measured by the fraction of time and energy at a given age that is devoted to reproduction. In a Darwinian sense all animal activity must be related ultimately to REPRODUCTIVE SUCCESS, but it is often helpful to differentiate between effort that results directly in the production and care of progeny (reproductive effort) and effort that, although ultimately contributing to this end, is not itself directly concerned

with progeny. Maximum reproductive success will result from a trade off between the two forms of effort. Those interested in the study of life history strategies are much concerned with the timing and extent of reproductive effort. GAP

reproductive success A measure of the number of offspring produced by a given individual which manage to survive to a given age. Lifetime reproductive success is the sum of all the annual reproductive successes of a given individual. Relative lifetime reproductive success is a measure of individual FITNESS. If individuals show heritable differences in relative reproductive success, selection will be acting to favor genes that confer higher than average reproductive success. Absolute reproductive success is less important than relative reproductive success in determining the outcome of selection. GAP

resource-holding potential (RHP) A measure of the ability of one of a pair of animal contestants to win or to score against its opponent in a fight, assuming both were to employ the same strategy (see EVOLUTIONARILY STABLE STRATEGIES). Thus RHP defines how contest costs will accrue to each opponent if they fight in similar fashion. This parameter, introduced by Parker (1974), is important in the modeling of animal contests, since disparities in RHP will affect the payoffs achieved by opponents in a dispute. It is clear that RHP is often equivalent simply to fighting ability, which is itself a reflection of size, strength and experience. However, in many instances environmental features may also affect an individual's ability to win a score against its opponent. For example, in fights between male insects for the possession of a female, the male originally in possession may have much better prospects (owing to its prior grasp on the female) than the attacker, even though the attacker may be larger (Sigurjonsdottir and Parker 1981). Riechert (1978) has suggested that RHP may best be defined as "relative holding power", since it is the relative difference between the two opponents that is important in determining payoffs. GAP

Bibliography

Parker, G.A. 1974: Assessment strategy and the evolution of fighting behavior. *Journal of theoretical biology* 47, 223–43.

Riechert, S. 1978: Games spiders play: behavioral variability in territorial disputes. *Behavioral ecology and sociobiology* 3, 135–62.

Sigurjonsdottir, H. and Parker, G.A. 1981: Dung fly struggles: evidence for assessment strategy. Behavioral variability in territorial disputes. *Behavioral ecology and sociobiology* 8, 219–30.

reversal learning Learning the opposite of a DISCRIMINATION that has previously been acquired; having learned to choose A not B from a pair AB the reversal would be learning to choose B. Like EXTINCTION, reversal does not result in mere "unlearning" of the original response; for example, relearning of the initial task following reversal is often more rapid than original learning. Ease of reversal learning is affected by the extent of practice on the original discrimination; paradoxically, overtraining on the original task sometimes (not always) speeds up reversal. This may occur because reversal, while superficially seeming to represent pure negative transfer, contains elements of positive transfer in that the reversal involves similar attention or orienting behavior to the original task. If the same discrimination is repeatedly reversed and reinstated (serial reversal) the rate of learning improves progressively (reversal learning set) in most species, rats and monkeys for example being capable eventually of reversing a simple discrimination reliably after a single error. EAG

Bibliography

Mackintosh, N.J. 1983: *Conditioning and associative learning*. Oxford and New York: Oxford University Press.

rhythms Periodically repeated features of behavior which may recur over time scales of any duration. Rhythms can arise as a result of clock-driven behavior, as a result of responses to rhythmically occurring external stimuli, or as relaxation oscillations which arise as a result of the physiological or mechanical organization of the animal.

Clock-driven rhythms result from the endogenous time-keeping ability of animals, and may give rise to circannual, circalunar or circadian periodicity in behavior. The timing of annual migration and hibernation is organized in this way, as are the daily routines of many animals.

Responses to exogenous rhythmicity occur in adjustment to the seasons, the weather and daily fluctuations in the availablity of food. Relaxation oscillations occur whenever there is a build-up and release of behavioral potential, as in hunger and in many aspects of locomotion. (See CLOCK-DRIVEN BEHAVIOR.) DJM

Bibliography

Cloudsley-Thompson, J.C. 1980: *Biological clocks*. London: Weidenfeld and Nicolson.

ritual and ritualization In anthropology, ritual refers to a prescribed formal pattern of cultural behavior, usually symbolic and often religious or ceremonial in character (see Keesing 1981).

In ethology, by an intended analogy, ritual refers to a pattern of animal behavior, such as reproductive DISPLAY, which has a distinctively stylized quality: and ritualization is the evolutionary and developmental process which brings a ritual into existence (see Immelmann 1980). Hypothetically, evolutionary ritualization originates with a non-ritual movement such as feeding, and proceeds by a gradual modification of the movement in which it also acquires the function of a social signal. The modified form of the movement may be exaggerated, formalized and repetitive, and may include the display of conspicuous colors or structures: these changes are considered to enhance the clarity of the communication involved (see also STEREOTYPY; TYPICAL INTENSITY).

Discussions between ethologists,

anthropologists and others (e.g. Hinde 1972) have raised many issues of interest, but have also demonstrated that the different disciplines use "ritual" and "ritualization" in very different senses.　　　RDA

Bibliography

Hinde, R.A. ed. 1972: *Non-verbal communication.* Cambridge, New York, Melbourne: Cambridge University Press.

Immelmann, K. 1980: *Introduction to ethology.* New York, London: Plenum Press.

Keesing, R.M. 1981. *Cultural anthropology: a contemporary perspective.* 2nd ed. New York and London: Holt, Rinehart and Winston.

Tinbergen, N. 1952: Derived activities: their causation, biological significance, origin and emancipation during evolution. *Quarterly review of biology* 27, 1–32.

RNA, DNA The two major nucleic acids in virtually all living organisms. DNA (deoxy-ribonucleic acid) is found primarily in the nucleus of all cells and contains the genetic blueprint for the entire organism. It is present as a double-stranded helix whose backbone is comprised of an alternative arrangement of sugar and phosphate molecules. The stairs of the helix are formed by pairing four bases: cytosine, guanine, thymine and adenine. Base pairings are always complementary, with adenine binding to thymine and cytosine to guanine. A linear arrangement of these four bases forms the genetic code, which is read as a series of triplets, each coding for one amino acid. During transcription the two strands of DNA separate, breaking the base pairings, and a single stranded molecule of RNA (ribonucleic acid) is transcribed in complementary fashion from the DNA template. In RNA, uracil replaces thymine. The messenger RNA thus formed migrates to the cytoplasm and associates with ribosomes to initiate protein synthesis, a process called translation. A separate species, transfer RNA, brings molecules of amino acids over to the ribosomes in an order specified by the sequence of bases in the messenger. These amino acids are joined sequentially by peptide bonding to form a polypeptide. When translation is complete, the polypeptide breaks away from the ribosome and assumes the configuration of a protein.

　　　GPH

role A pattern of behavior that is characteristic of individuals holding a particular position within a social structure. The role concept is useful only if the behavior in question benefits other group members (Bernstein 1966). An example is the exploratory behavior of a peripheral animal. In introducing the role concept to primate ethology Bernstein emphasized that the functions of animal social positions are not entirely defined by DOMINANCE. An animal may begin or cease a role behavior within days of a change of group structure. The assumption of a role may result from the evolved behavioral tendencies of the member and may be influenced by social interactions. Whereas human role behavior is partly enforced by group expectations, animals more often seem to suppress than to enforce role behavior in a group member.　　　HK

Bibliography

Bernstein, I.S. 1966: Analysis of a key role in a capuchin (*Cebus albifrons*) group. *Tulane studies in zoology* 13, 49–54.

S

search image A term with a variety of meanings. It is sometimes used in the context of a predator becoming more likely to eat a particular kind of prey as the result of experience: it might be said, for instance, that a bird which had learnt that a certain type of insect was good to eat had "adopted a search image" for that insect. The term is also used in a more restricted sense, reserving it for cases where there is evidence of a predator actually improving its ability to see camouflaged prey against its background. "Adopting a search image" here would be equivalent to learning to "break the camouflage" of the prey and implies a definite perceptual change on the part of the predator. MSD

Bibliography

Dawkins, M. 1971: Shifts of "attention" in chicks during feeding. *Animal behaviour* 19, 575–82.

———— 1974: Perceptual changes in chicks: another look at the Search Image concept. *Animal behaviour* 19, 566–74.

Krebs, J.R. 1973: Behavioral aspects of predation. In *Perspectives in ethology*, eds. P.P.G. Bateson and P.H. Klopfer. New York: Plenum Press.

Lawrence, E.S. 1985: Evidence for search image in blackbirds (*Turdus merula l.*). *Animal behaviour* 33, 929–37 and 1301–9.

Sutherland, N.S. and Mackintosh, N.J. 1971: *Mechanisms of animal discrimination learning.* New York: Academic Press.

selfishness In human psychology the word is used with its normal meaning, but evolutionary biologists sometimes use it in a technical sense: selfish behavior increases the welfare of the individual at the expense of the welfare of others. "Altruistic" behavior is the opposite. A third technical term is sometimes defined in a similar way: a "spiteful" act is one that harms the perpetrator, but harms some other individual(s) even more. Mathematical models suggest that SPITE is unlikely to evolve in nature. Whether ALTRUISM is likely to evolve depends upon how welfare is defined. If it is taken to mean survival, ordinary parental care qualifies as an altruistic act. But if welfare is taken to mean Darwinian FITNESS or REPRODUC-TIVE SUCCESS, parental care is not necessarily altruistic since a parent only achieves reproductive success through the survival of its offspring. Much the same can be said of apparent altruism towards other close genetic relatives. The history of the Darwinian study of altruism has been, in a sense, a process of explaining away apparent altruism at the level of the individual by showing that it follows from a more fundamental genetic selfishness. This has no connection with another kind of "explaining away" in the field of human motives: we may dismiss an apparently altruistic man as secretly selfish, doing good for his own ends. Darwinian explanations of selfishness at the genetic level make no reference to subjective motives. They are concerned solely with the effects of actions. RD

Bibliography

Dawkins, R. 1976: *The selfish gene.* Oxford: Oxford University Press.

senses: chemical The capability of identifying chemical substances and of determining their concentration. Nerve endings that are sensitive to chemicals, or chemoreceptors, are widespread amongst animals and occur on the body surface, on specialised appendages and among the internal organs. In vertebrates chemoreceptors are of considerable importance in providing information to the brain about the physiological state of the body. They occur in the intestine, in blood vessels, etc.

Taste and smell are chemical senses which are directed towards the external environment. In vertebrates the chemoreceptors occur in the region of the nose and mouth, but in other animals they may be found on other parts of the body. Many insects have taste receptors on their antennae and legs. The two senses are distinguishable in vertebrates by the fact that different peripheral nerves carry the information to the central nervous system, and also by the fact that taste involves direct contact with the source of stimulation. In aquatic species, however, the latter distinction is not relevant, because all the environmental chemicals are water born. In land vertebrates taste stimuli must be water soluble whereas olfactory stimuli must be volatile. In non-vertebrates there is no clear difference between taste and smell.

The qualitative aspects of taste in humans are really due to stimulation of the olfactory system, the sense of taste proper being confined to perception of four qualities: sweet, sour, salty and bitter. Other tastes result from a combination of these. Flavor is a combination of taste and smell. Thus the flavor of onion is indistinguishable from that of apple, if a small piece is placed on the tongue while the nose is held closed.

There are thought to be seven basic odors which are determined by structural shape of the volatile molecules: floral, peppermint, musk (e.g. angelica root), comphoraceous (e.g. moth repellent), ethereal (e.g. dry-cleaning fluid), pungent (e.g. vinegar) and putrid (e.g. bad egg). Most everyday odors result from a combination of several of these primary odors.

Although the sense of smell is not very important in man, in some animals it is paramount and highly developed. For example, the olfactory sense of the male moth (*Bombyx mori*) is specifically attuned to the PHEROMONE produced by the female, and is capable of detecting the presence of a single molecule.   DJM

senses: electromagnetic The ability to detect electric or magnetic fields. Many fish are capable of electroreception. For example, dogfish and sharks have electroreceptive sense organs, called *ampullae Lorenzini*, which are distributed over the body surface and usually concentrated in the region of the head. Some dogfish even when buried under sand, can detect prey by the local distortion of the geophysical electric field.

Some fish, especially the gymnotid eels, generate their own weak electric fields and are sensitive to distortions of their own field caused by objects in the environment. They usually live in conditions of poor visibility. The fish are sensitive to the electric discharges of other members of the species, and may communicate with each other through this medium.

Fish such as the electric ray and the electric eel produce strong electric discharges capable of stunning prey and some predators. However, they do not seem to be capable of electroreception.

Many different animals are sensitive to magnetic fields. Orientation to magnetic north has been found in bacteria, flatworms and snails. Magnetic sensitivity is also used in navigation in pigeons and in bees. Pigeons and other birds effectively have a magnetic compass which they deploy when the sun is obscured by clouds, or when navigating at night.   DJM

Bibliography

Ewert, J.P. 1980: *Neuroethology*. Berlin: Springer-Verlag.
Gould, J.L. 1980: The case for magnetic-field sensitivity in birds and bees (such as it is)! *American scientist* 68.

senses: mechanical The detection of mechanical disturbances in the environment and within the animal's body. Mechanoreceptors are involved in many senses, including hearing, balance, pressure detection and touch.

Information from mechanoreceptors in the limb joints and muscles is particularly important in COORDINATION and LOCOMOTION. Postural reflexes are triggered by receptors in the limbs and in the maculae, the organs of balance in the vertebrate ear. Invertebrates often have analogous mechanisms. Thus the statocysts of the octopus are analogous to the maculae of vertebrates and enable the animal to maintain its orientation with respect to gravity.

The array of mechanical senses with which an animal is equipped is partly determined by its way of life. Pigeons have a small vesicle in the ear which gives them a high sensitivity to barometric pressure. This organ is especially well developed in diving birds and is also found in sharks. Other fish detect hydrostatic pressure by means of mechanoreceptors attached to the swim bladder, an organ which does not occur in sharks. DJM

Bibliography

Schwartz, E. 1974: Lateral-line mechanoreceptors in fishes and amphibians. In *Handbook of sensory physiology*, vol. 3, ed. A. Fessard. New York: Springer-Verlag.

sensory deprivation and enrichment Rearing in either enriched or deprived multi-sensory environments may produce significant effects upon the adult nervous system, including biochemical, anatomical and behavioral changes. For example cells in the cortex show greater dendritic branching, more dendritic spines, and larger synaptic regions in animals reared in complex environments relative to littermates reared in impoverished environments. There is also a consistent increase in the overall cortical thickness of rats reared in enriched environments, which is accompanied by a greater cortical weight. The increased weight is at least partially due to greater protein and RNA content in brain tissue, and there is a greater ratio of RNA to DNA, suggesting increased metabolic activity.

At the behavioral level, selective rearing in an enriched environment produces more efficient maze learning, but the results on tasks such as visual discrimination learning are less consistent. In general, the evidence supports the conclusion that differential rearing produces behaviorally different animals, but it may be misleading to use terms like "intelligence" to refer to such differences. Selective rearing is known to produce longlasting effects upon emotionality and exploration: multi-sensory deprivation decreases exploratory tendencies and increases diffused, undirected fear reactions, whereas enrichment conditions produce more purposeful patterns of exploratory and avoidance behavior. It is these changes which may account for the deprived animal's inferior performance on learning tasks. BER/RCS

Bibliography

Henderson, N.D. 1980: Effects of early experience upon the behavior of animals: the second twenty-five years of research. In *Early behavior: implications for social development*, ed. E.C. Simmel. New York: Academic Press.

sequential analysis A family of research methods which detect and summarize the regularities with which one event or behavior follows another. The commonest techniques begin by calculating transitional probabilities, the conditional probabilities with which each type of event occurs given the types of immediately preceding events. In the simplest case a Markov chain is formed – a sequence of events having as its defining regularity a fixed pattern of probabilities of occurrence for each event, conditional only upon the one event immediately before.

Such methods require three assumptions to be met, which may frequently be a problem with real behavioral data: stationarity (meaning that the transitional probabilities are fixed parameters of the pattern); homogeneity (meaning that the probabilities have not been produced by the unwitting mixture of several different behavior patterns); and order (meaning that probabilities have been used which are conditional on the appropriate number of preceding events).

Other approaches to sequential analysis

variation between species. Some sleep at night, some during the day, while others are active only at sunrise and sunset. Sleep is no different from many other aspects of behavior in fitting into a daily routine that is characteristic of the species in its natural environment. The timing of sleep is partly influenced by the animal's endogenous clock and partly by other aspects of the state of motivation. Animals do not usually sleep until they have found a suitable site, free from disturbance by predators or rivals.

The duration of sleep also varies widely from one species to another. Some mammals, such as the two-toed sloth, armadillo and opossum, sleep up to twenty hours per day. At the other extreme, Dall's porpoise and the swift appear not to sleep at all, being constantly on the move. Herbivores generally sleep less than carnivorous animals, and this is probably due to their need to spend a large proportion of the day feeding. Herbivores are often vulnerable to predators when asleep and their need for vigilance is therefore higher than that of an animal which can sleep in a safe place.

Differences between species are sometimes difficult to interpret, because of lack of knowledge arising from the difficulty of diagnosing sleep under natural conditions. While sleep can be readily identified in the laboratory, by EEG or arousal tests, it cannot be claimed that sleep follows a natural pattern under laboratory conditions. On the other hand there have been very few studies of sleep in the natural environment which have used proper diagnostic tests. In one study arousal tests were administered to herring gulls in the wild and it was discovered that a certain rate of eye-blink was characteristic of sleep with a raised threshold of arousal. Sometimes the animals adopted a sleep posture, but did not have raised thresholds of arousal or show the typical eye-blink rate (Amlaner and McFarland 1981). By using the eye-blink criterion to distinguish between true and pseudo-sleep, it was discovered that the sleep patterns of herring gulls are different in different phases of the breeding cycle. The birds

sleep less during the courtship phase, when territorial defense is at a premium, than they do during the incubation phase. It is also thought that migrating birds sleep less than usual, both in the wild and if they are confined to the laboratory during the migratory period. It appears that sleep patterns adapt to the animal's way of life, even when this changes markedly with the seasons of the year.

In animals other than birds and mammals EEG diagnosis is not possible, and assessment of sleep must be based upon behavioral considerations. Some reptiles show obvious symptoms of sleep, but others, including alligators, crocodiles, and snakes, may remain immobile for days without giving much clue to their motivational state. The chameleon (*Camaeleo melleri*) retires to a branch at sunset and adopts a typical sleep posture with its eyes closed. Some reptiles and amphibians have a lowered respiration rate during sleep and are less easily disturbed during such periods. Fish spend long periods immobile, some at night and others during the day. Color changes occur in some fish, probably to enhance camouflage during sleep. By similar behavioral criteria, some insects would appear to sleep. Moths and butterflies rest at specific sites which offer good camouflage. They often adopt a typical rest posture and may sometimes be touched without being disturbed.

Arousal in animals may range from deep sleep, through various waking stages, to great excitement. The term is also used to denote the degree of responsiveness to particular types of stimulation.

Prolonged periods of torpid immobility are found in many animals, especially during periods of unfavorable climate, such as the desert summer or the arctic winter. In the torpid state the animal is able to conserve energy, as in hibernating mammals, or conserve water, as in aestivating desert rodents. It has been suggested that sleep also enables animals to conserve energy at times when activity is not likely to be profitable, as when food is unattainable or predators prevalent. Many small birds reduce their body temperatures at night and this enables them to reduce energy expenditure on THERMO-REGULATION. Some small mammals sleep in a warm insulated nest which serves a similar purpose. Sleep can therefore be seen as a means by which animals conserve energy and avoid danger.

The whole question of the function of sleep is, however, controversial. Traditionally, sleep has been seen as a restorative process, necessary for the maintenance of some as yet unknown brain process. Animals and people deprived of sleep become irritable and aggressive. When allowed to sleep after deprivation they to some extent catch up on the sleep they have missed. In these respects sleep seems to be like hunger and thirst, part of the physiological HOMEOSTASIS.

All sleep researchers recognize that there is a mechanism which induces an increasing tendency to sleep, which is satisfied by periods of sleeping. However, this does not necessarily mean that sleep is an essential recuperative process. It shows only that animals can have a strong motivation to sleep. Some scientists doubt the recuperative theory because of the great variation in sleep duration that is found when different species are compared. Careful studies have shown that there is no correlation between sleep pattern and intelligence or degree of evolutionary development, as might be expected if sleep were important in the regulation of brain activity. Sleep is thought to be of great evolutionary age and sleep patterns appear to be carefully tailored to the life-style of the animal. Animals in danger of predation either sleep less than other animals or take trouble to sleep in an especially safe place. As mentioned above, sleep patterns generally complement the periods when foraging opportunities are good, and they appear to vary as the demands on the animal's time vary with the seasons.

The ecological view of the function of sleep, that it has evolved to keep animals out of trouble at certain times of day, does little to explain the complex alternation of quiet and active sleep that is found in birds and mammals. It has been suggested that sleep may have evolved as an aid to time-budgeting, but acquired secondary functions among the more advanced animals. So it is possible that both sides of the argument may be justified.   DJM

Bibliography

Amlaner, C.J.Jr. and McFarland, D.J. 1981: Sleep in the herring gull (*Larus argentatus*). *Animal behaviour* 29, 551–56.

Mayes, A. 1983: *Sleep mechanisms and functions in humans and animals – an evolutionary perspective.* Wokingham: Van Nostrand Reinhold.

Orem, J. and Barnes, C. 1980: *Physiology in sleep.* New York: Academic Press.

social ethology Biological study of social behavior.

social structure *See* relationships and social structure.

smell *See* senses: chemical.

sociobiology The study of the biological basis of social behavior. Although the word was being used in the early 1960s (Altmann 1962), the birth of sociobiology as a discipline is clearly identified with the publication of Wilson's major review (1975).

The field is derived from two separate biological traditions, evolutionary biology and ethology. Sociobiology is properly concerned with the causation and development of social behavior, as well as with functional and evolutionary questions which ask how specific traits serve as adaptations. Research on the causation and ontogeny of social behavior is reviewed by Hinde (1970). However the impetus for Wilson's "new synthesis" came from theoretical considerations of apparent evolutionary anomalies.

NATURAL SELECTION acts on individuals and results in changes of population gene frequencies. Genes which cause the FITNESS of their bearers to be enhanced are selectively favored. A tradition in ETHOLOGY, evident in the writings of Lorenz, has been the belief that animals behave for the benefit of the group or the species rather than in their own individual interests. Selection among groups was seen as a potent evolutionary force. Wynne-Edwards (1962) was explicit about the importance of group selection as a force moulding social behavior. He argued that animals restrict their population density and rate of reproduction so that the maximum sustainable yield is maintained from the available food supplies. He postulated the existence of epideictic displays (see CONVENTIONAL AND EPIDEICTIC BEHAVIOR) which allow members of a population to assess the density of the population. Although group selection *is* an evolutionary force, it is a weak one compared with individual selection: biologically unacceptable models of population structure have to be envisaged for group selection to outweigh the importance of individual selection (Maynard Smith 1976).

If animals are generally selected to behave in their own selfish interests, why is ALTRUISM such a common component of many animal societies? Although both Fisher and Haldane anticipated his result, Hamilton (1964) described a mechanism whereby genes coding for altruistic behavior would be selectively favored: an individual helping a close relative may be favoring the spread of its own genes because kin are particularly likely to share copies of the altruist's genes through identity by descent. Indeed, parental investment might be seen as one manifestation of such kin selection theory. Another may be that the peculiar kind of inheritance found among some social insects (the hymenoptera – ants, bees and wasps) whereby sisters share more genetic material than do mothers and daughters, predisposes these animals to develop societies founded on altruistic behavior. Not all cases of altruism result from kin selection. Trivers (1971) suggested that under certain conditions reciprocal altruism may evolve in which one animal helps another to its own disadvantage in the expectation that the altruism may be reciprocated later. This process is distinct from mutualism (see SYMBIOSIS) where there is no delay between giving and receiving help.

The currency of sociobiology is units of fitness. Since the advantages of social behavior will result from the summation of individual interactions it is important to understand that the best strategy for an animal to adopt in a social context will depend upon the behavior of others. This realization has led to the identification of the EVOLUTIONARILY STABLE STRATEGY.

Sociobiologists cannot assume that patterns of behavior are inherited (see BEHAVIOR GENETICS). Many will be learned or culturally transmitted. Since it is often impractical to determine the heritability of variation in social behavior among animals sociobiologists normally recognize adaptation by a difference between two phenotypic traits which leads to a difference in fitness between the individuals possessing them. The animal with the higher fitness is said to be more adapted than the other. This reasoning does not imply that adaptations necessarily have genetic causes since adaptation is defined by its effects rather than its causes.

The scientific methodology used by sociobiology has been criticized by Lewontin (1979). In addition to cautioning against genetic assumptions he argues that hypotheses are too often accepted without test, and points out that a functional approach to the interpretation of social behavior and the difficulty of testing hypotheses can often lead to the "imaginative reconstruction" of evolutionary scenarios which are later accepted as facts. Furthermore he claims that if the results of tests, when made, do not closely fit predictions the hypotheses are not discarded but merely modified since animals are thought to optimize their behavior. Lewontin calls this technique "progressive ad hoc optimization".

Functional explanations for patterns of variation in social behavior almost always claim some degree of generality and are, therefore, testable. When similar selective forces act on independently evolving lineages we might expect convergent evolution to produce traits that are correlated in similar ways within different taxonomic groups. This is the nub of the comparative method that was extensively used by DARWIN to test functional evolutionary hypotheses. Constellations of functionally related characters are expected to recur in similar ecological circumstances among different taxonomic groups. For instance, in different mammalian families group structures correlate with the distribution of resources. In turn males respond to and influence grouping patterns in their attempts to gain mating access to females. The breeding systems that result correlate with differences in morphology between the sexes (Clutton-Brock and Harvey 1978).

However, there is a tendency among sociobiologists to treat all behavioral differences as adaptive. This is an unfounded assertion, and Lewontin (1979) lists several causes for non-adaptive evolution. One of the major methodological problems facing sociobiologists (and evolutionists in general) is that, although it is often possible to demonstrate the adaptive nature of a character difference, it is not possible to be sure that a particular difference is non-adaptive.

Wilson (1975) saw sociobiology as a potential unifying discipline embracing both social psychology and sociology. It is conceivable that cross-cultural analyses will demonstrate correlates of social life and ecology among humans, while comparison with other mammalian groups might suggest the importance of universals in human societies. It must be understood that human social behavior is extremely malleable, and that behavioral differences among individuals from various cultures probably result from cultural rather than genetic transmission.　　　PHH

Bibliography

Altmann, S.A. 1962: A field study of the sociobiology of rhesus monkeys (*Macaca mulatta*). *Annals of the New York Academy of Sciences* 102, 338–435.

Barash, D.P. 1982: *Sociobiology and behaviour*, 2nd edn. London: Hodder and Stoughton.

*Clutton-Brock, T.H. and Harvey, P.H. 1978: Mammals, resources and reproductive strategies. *Nature* 273, 191–95.

Greenwood, P.J., Harvey, P.H. and Slatkin, M. 1985: *Evolution: essays in honour of John Maynard Smith*. Cambridge and New York: Cambridge University Press.

Hamilton, W.D. 1964: The genetical evolution of social behaviour. *Journal of theoretical biology* 7, 1–52.

Hinde, R.A. 1970: *Animal behaviour: a synthesis of ethology and comparative psychology*. New York: McGraw-Hill.

*Lewontin, R.C. 1979: Sociobiology as an adaptationist program. *Behavioral science* 24, 5–14.

Maynard Smith, J. 1976: Group selection. *Quarterly reviews of biology* 51, 277–83.

Trivers, R.L. 1971: The evolution of reciprocal altruism. *Quarterly reviews of biology*. 46, 35–57.

*Wilson, Edward O. 1975: *Sociobiology: the new synthesis*. Cambridge, Mass.: Harvard University Press.

Wynne-Edwards, V.C. 1962: *Animal dispersion in relation to social behaviour*. Edinburgh: Oliver and Boyd; New York: Hafner.

spacing The term used in ethology to refer to the distance an animal puts between itself and a fellow member of its own group. When there is no spacing, as for instance in the mother-infant relationship in mammals, we can speak of a bond between the two individuals. In most species, spacing distributes the members of a group in such a way that they are in sensory contact with each other but do not infringe each other's personal space. This is the case, for instance, in birds that form flocks and shoaling fish. The actual mechanisms by which spacing is maintained in these species are still not fully understood, but in some fish it is clear that fry do not show the precisely aligned spacing characteristic of adults, and it is probable that learning is at least partly involved in the ontogeny of spacing.

In territorial species, spacing may be very pronounced. Birds of prey lay claim to a large hunting ground and defend it against all other birds of prey, not merely their own species. For predators, spacing is a permanent state, whereas for other species, such as grouse, it may be a complex phenomenon, related mainly to distribution during the breeding season.

Studies of primates have shown that when spacing is insufficient, (a condition that can be called "crowding"), the frequency of aggressiveness increases. (See also TERRITORIALITY; CONVENTIONAL AND EPIDEICTIC BEHAVIOR.)   VR

Bibliography
Davies, N.B. and Houston, A.I. 1984: Territory economics. In *Behavioural ecology*. 2nd edn., eds. J.R. Krebs and N.B. Davies. Oxford: Blackwell Scientific Publications; Sunderland, Mass.: Sinauer.

species and speciation In modern evolutionary biology, species usually refers to the biological species concept, whereby a species is a set of actually or potentially interbreeding natural populations that is reproductively isolated from other such sets (see Mayr 1963). In practice, the existence of reproductive isolation cannot always be determined directly, and other features such as differences in form may be used to distinguish between species: but generally these criteria are intended as reflections of reproductive isolation, not as good criteria in themselves.

Speciation refers to the evolutionary processes whereby species originate – usually, the splitting of one species into two or more distinct ones. The mechanism usually thought responsible is geographic speciation – the development of reproductive isolation between populations during a period of geographic isolation. Other mechanisms, however, are sometimes proposed (White 1978). (See also EVOLUTION; NATURAL SELECTION.)
                                                    RDA

Bibliography
Mayr, E. 1963: *Animal species and evolution*. Cambridge, Mass.: Harvard University Press.
White, M.J.D. 1978: *Modes of speciation*. San Francisco: W.H. Freeman.

spite Behavior that lowers the genetic fitnesses of both the perpetrator and the target animal. Spite has to be understood in relation to kin selection. Since only behavior that increases an individual's fitness will spread, spiteful behavior would normally be selected against. If, however, spite is directed against an unrelated individual, related ones may benefit, and genes underlying the behavior will proliferate. In practice spite is difficult to demonstrate in nature, though efforts have been made (Hamilton 1970). Spite in animals clearly differs from the lay usage with its wider implication of any harmful action perpetrated by an individual who feels himself to have been harmed.   VR

Bibliography
Hamilton, W.D. 1970: Selfish and spiteful behaviour in an evolutionary model. *Nature* 228, 1218–20.

statistical methods Procedures for the planning of data collection in experiments and surveys together with techniques for describing and summarizing sample data so that inferences may be made about populations from which the samples were taken. They offer a rigorously based approach to the design and analysis aspects of investigations. Methods for analysis are usually pre-determined by the particular experimental or survey design employed and its implementation. Knowledge of (a) the design and its characteristics, (b) the methods of analysis which may be associated with the design, (c) the amount of precision required for estimation and (d) the variation in the population may be used to determine the sample sizes which will be necessary for a satisfactory investigation.

Following the collection of statistical data the first requirement is usually a description. In the light of the nature of the variables, whether they are nominal, ordinal, interval or ratio in character, appropriate graphical methods are used for presentation. For the first two types of variable a bar chart, pie chart or pictogram is normally used whereas for the last two a histogram or a frequency diagram suffices. Certain probability distributions may be confirmed by plotting sample frequencies on special graph paper. Multivariate data are treated by plotting scatter diagrams or frequency contours for two variables at a time. Graphical methods are used for exploratory data analysis and residual analysis which allow the validity of assumptions made by classical methods to be examined and appropriate action taken.

Following graphical descriptions, statistical measures are calculated from the observations to provide estimates of population characteristics. These may be quantities which describe the distribution of the values of a variable in the population in terms of its location (e.g. mean, median, mode, mid-range) or its dispersion (e.g. standard deviation, mean deviation, range, semi-interquartile range) or its shape (e.g. skewness, kurtosis). Where single values are calculated to represent these population characteristics, the estimates are called "point estimates". More useful are "interval estimates" which consist of two values between which the true value of the population parameter in question will be expected to lie with some stated probability. Such intervals are known as "confidence intervals".

Whereas it is possible to proceed to make inferences about hypotheses involving population parameters using confidence intervals, it is more common to compute "test statistics" for this purpose. These are quantities calculated from samples which are standardized so that their distributions over repeated samples can be derived theoretically and "critical values" obtained and tabulated for use in statistical tests.

Statistical tests are said to be "parametric" if they refer to the form of the underlying distribution of the observations and "nonparametric" or "distribution-free" if they do not. Parametric tests are concerned with hypotheses which mention the population values of parameters of this underlying distribution. The most common parametric tests are based on the sample mean and test a hypothesis regarding the population mean (e.g. normal z-test, Student's t-test) whereas non-parametric tests often use the ranked sample values for testing a hypothesis about the population median (e.g. Mann-Whitney U-test, Wilcoxon test, sign test). The advantage of the latter is that the specific test used will be more valid over a wide range of underlying distributions and the main disadvantage, where both may apply, will be a loss of power. Parametric tests often assume that the sample values follow a normal distribution, or at least that the sample mean is approximately normally distributed and this is true in practice unless the sample sizes are very small because of the Central Limit Theorem.

Non-parametric tests are used for testing the goodness-of-fit of an observed distribution to a theoretical one or may compare two observed distributions. The chi-square (χ^2) test and the Kolmogorov-Smirnov tests are both suitable for these purposes with the latter being more sensitive to the largest deviation between two distributions. Where individuals are classified into categories by two attributes the resulting contingency table may be analysed using a chi-square test for association between the attributes. Fisher's exact test is used in this situation for small frequencies. Where the samples are correlated, another non-parametric test, McNemar's, is used to test for a difference between the proportions in the categories.

Tests of means for a single population or for two populations are based on the standard normal z- or the t-distribution according as the variance in the population sampled is known or unknown. Tests for proportions use a test statistic which is taken to be approximately normal for large samples. Where there are more than two populations, an analysis of variance is applied using an F-statistic for difference between means or a chi-square statistic for a difference between proportions.

As well as providing for the testing of means of several samples, the analysis of variance, due to R.A. Fisher, is used to test for the effects of several factors which are varied in a systematic way in the same experiment. Such uses of the analysis of variance are examples of linear models which describe the measured response in terms of a sum of effects due to the factors and the interactions between them. For a single factor the simplest design is known as the "completely randomized" design in which the levels of the factor (or treatments) are applied randomly to the experimental units. Where these units are arranged in groups or "blocks" and complete sets of treatments are applied in each block the design is known as a "randomized block design". This very commonly used design allows for independent testing of treatment and block effects by means of an analysis of variance.

Whereas the randomized block design may be seen to exploit the heterogeneity of experimental units in one dimension, an extension of the design known as the "Latin Square" design caters for two dimensions. If the two dimensions are thought of as "rows" and "columns" then the rows constitute blocks within which all treatments appear and the columns likewise. This balanced but restricted design allows for independent tests of the "rows", "columns" and treatments factors. Extensions of the randomized block design provide for additional treatment factors and for incomplete blocks containing subsets of the available treatments. The latter include confounded designs in which main effects are estimated with full precision and only those interactions which are of interest are deliberately estimated in the analysis. In balanced incomplete designs, some of the interactions may be estimated with lower precision than main effects. This is also achieved by "split-plot" designs in which less important factors are applied at the level of plots within blocks and more important factors are applied to sub-plots which are formed by splitting main plots. Whereas factorial designs in which all levels of all factors appear in every possible combination are known as "crossed" designs, the split-plot design is an example of a "hierarchical" or "nested" design.

The analysis of variance F-tests are based upon underlying assumptions that the observations are normally distributed and have equal variance within groups. When these assumptions are untenable recourse is made either to transformation of the variable to restore the desired properties or to ranking and a non-parametric test. In the single factor experiment the Kruskal–Wallis test is used and

for several factors, Friedman's test for matched samples is applied for each factor separately.

Where the factors may be expressed in the form of quantitative variables, the analysis of variance may be used to test the significance of the trend or response function. The levels of a factor may be equally spaced on an appropriate scale and it is then convenient to consider the response function by fitting orthogonal polynomials. For a factor with two levels, a linear component is tested, with three levels, a quadratic component, etc. If there are several factors of this type operating simultaneously, interactions between these components are investigated also.

As well as the response variable, a concomitant variable is sometimes measured. Adjustment for the effect of this concomitant variable is by an analysis of covariance. This procedure is able to deal with several concomitant variables.

Regression and correlation methods are applied to investigate the relationships between two or more variables. In the case of simple regression, one variable which is statistically varying is seen to depend upon another mathematical variable which is not subject to statistical variation. There are applications, however, where both variables involved are statistical but the "dependent" variable is subject to more variation than the "independent" one. The form of the relationship is most often linear but can also be a higher degree polynomial or exponential or any other mathematical continuous function. Correlation refers more generally to the relationship or interdependence between two variables and therefore applies to situations where regression may be inappropriate. Measures of correlation include the "product–moment correlation coefficient" which measures the degree of linear correlation between two continuous variables and, for ranked variables, Kendall's "tau" and Spearman's "rho".

Multiple linear regression is a method for fitting a relationship in which the "dependent" variable is a linear function of several "independent" variables Multiple correlation refers to the degree of interdependency between variables in a group and is often calculated as a coefficient in the multiple regression context where it represents the measured correlation between observed values of the dependent variable and the values predicted by the multiple regression equation.

Factor analysis and associated techniques in multivariate analysis seek to explain the relations between the variables in a set, using the correlation matrix for the set. Principal component analysis establishes a set of uncorrelated combinations of the original variables which explain in decreasing order of magnitude the variation in the sample. Ideally, most of the variation is accounted for by the first few components and the remainder may be discarded. Where the set of original variables is structured with two subsets, one "regressor", the other "independent", canonical analysis is relevant. Discriminant analysis deals with the problem of a single set of variables which have different mean values but identical correlations in two or more populations. A discriminant function is estimated using individuals from known populations and then used to classify unknown individuals. Other techniques such as multi-dimensional scaling and cluster analysis are employed to explore the structural relationships between individuals for whom multiple observations are available.

Finally, it should be remarked that some research workers prefer to incorporate "prior" information with experimental evidence in a formal way when making inferences. Bayesian inference, which originates from a theorem of Thomas Bayes on inverse probability, provides for this by requiring a specification of the prior distribution of parameters. This can involve some complicated mathematics and non-Bayesians are concerned by the difficult and arbitrary choice of this prior distribution. The arguments for Bayesian analysis are that this generalizes the inferential procedure so that nothing of the conventional approach is lost, that it encourages the formulation of prior knowledge and that it provides a decision-theoretic approach which is relevant to many situations. Bayesians and non-Bayesians all use prior information and mostly arrive at the same conclusions despite the differences in approach.   RWH

Bibliography

Conover, W.J. 1980: *Practical non-parametric statistics*. New York: John Wiley.

Fisher, R.A. 1935: *The design and analysis of experiments*. Edinburgh: Oliver and Boyd.

Guilford, J.P. and Fruchter, B. 1956: *Fundamental statistics in psychology and education*. New York: McGraw-Hill.

Marriott, F.H.C. 1974: *The interpretation of multiple observations*. London: Academic Press.

Siegel, S. 1956: *Non-parametric statistics for the behavioral sciences*. New York: McGraw-Hill.

Winer, B.J. 1962: *Statistical principles in experimental design*. New York: Holt, Rinehart and Winston.

stereotypy Stereotyped behavior patterns are those which show a high degree of fixity or constancy from one occasion to the next or even from one individual to another. The courtship patterns of ducks, which are typical of each species and are often performed with "clockwork" regularity, are a classic example. In fact, many animal signals have a fixed character, often being repeated with little variation (see TYPICAL INTENSITY).

Stereotypies may, however, emerge in a completely different context. Animals (particularly active ones like monkeys and wolves) may sometimes develop stereotyped actions such as bobbing up and down or pacing out a fixed path if they are confined in small cages. It has been argued that such stereotypies can be used as an indication that the animals are suffering from their confinement.   MSD

Bibliography

Barlow, G.W. 1977: Modal action patterns. In *How animals communicate*, ed. T.A. Sebeok. Bloomington: Indiana University Press.

stress a physiologically recognizable syndrome that results from extreme environmental pressure, whether physical or social. Climatic factors, captivity, social deprivation and social bullying can all lead to stress in animals. The symptoms of stress include ABNORMAL BEHAVIOR, loss of appetite, and changes in HORMONES which disrupt the normal HOMEOSTASIS. Stress is particularly associated with enlargement and over-activity of the adrenal cortex. Excessive stress can cause gastric ulcers, heart failure and other disorders. DJM

supernormal stimulus A stimulus, commonly artificial, evoking a stronger response than the stimulus to which the response normally occurs. Supernormal stimuli often exaggerate aspects of SIGN STIMULI. Thus an elongated yellow pencil shape with two red rings near the tip will evoke more food soliciting pecks from a herring gull chick than the parent's bill, which is broader and carries a single red spot. Some experiments have shown that an animal's responsiveness to certain stimuli can be open-ended: many birds prefer to incubate larger than normal eggs; even huge eggs larger than the bird's own body are preferred. Some male fish will always choose to court the larger of two females and hence females of a foreign species may prove abnormally attractive. The supernormal, bright orange gape of a young cuckoo is one of the means whereby its foster parents are induced to feed it, often to the exclusion of their own young. (See also PARASITISM.) AWGM

Bibliography

Tinbergen, N. 1969: *The study of instinct.* 2nd ed. Oxford: Oxford University Press.

survival value The alleged contribution of a characteristic to the probability of the survival of an organism.

symbiosis In evolutionary biology, a relationship of close ecological dependence between members of two different SPECIES. Generally the relationship is of a complex kind, and probably reflects adaptation in each species to the presence of the other. Three kinds of symbiosis are distinguished: commensalism, where one partner benefits and the other is not greatly affected; PARASITISM, where one partner benefits and the other is disadvantaged; and mutualism, where both partners benefit. Sometimes symbiosis is used in a narrower sense, equivalent only to mutualism as just defined. Symbioses are often seen at the level of ecological and behavioral interactions between individuals, but symbiotic relationships have also been described involving whole societies, and these cases are referred to as social symbioses. See Wilson (1975). RDA

Bibliography

Barash, D.P. 1982: *Sociobiology and behaviour.* 2nd edn. London: Hodder and Stoughton.

Wilson, Edward O. 1975: *Sociobiology: the new synthesis.* Cambridge, Mass.: Harvard University Press.

T

taste *See* senses: chemical.

teleology The study of purpose; also the claim that a phenomenon exists for a purpose (extrinsic teleology), or has a purpose of its own (immanent teleology). Explanations in terms of purpose have a peculiar logic: doubts about their scientific validity used to be common among psychologists. With the rise of cybernetics and artificial intelligence since the second world war, goal-directed animal behavior has come to be better understood.

The new paradigm recognizes that an intelligent problem-solver must be able to represent internally the desired state of affairs, and the actual state of affairs, and must construct a possible route from the actual to the desired. The old problems of teleology, such as "How can the future affect the present?", are replaced by problems about representation, such as "How does the system represent alternative possible futures, and how does it select between them?".

A further advance has been the clearer separation made between the concept of goal-directedness and the concept of functional adaptiveness. Natural functionality can be understood in purely biological terms with the help of Darwin's theory of NATURAL SELECTION, without the need for cognitive notions like "goal" or "internal representation".   ARW

Bibliography

Blackman, D.E. 1983: On cognitive theories of animal learning: extrapolation from humans to animals? In *Animal models of human behavior*, ed. G.C.L. Davey. Chichester and New York: Wiley.

Miller, G.A., Galanter, E. and Pribram, K. 1960: *Plans and the structure of behavior*. New York: Holt, Rinehart and Winston.

Wiener, N. 1949: *Cybernetics, or control and communication in the animal and the machine*. New York: Wiley.

Woodfield, Andrew 1976: *Teleology*. Cambridge and New York: Cambridge University Press.

territoriality The tendency of animals to defend a particular area, usually against members of the same species. The concept was first elaborated by Howard (1920) with particular reference to birds, and this group remains the most studied.

Territories vary enormously in size: among birds the least flycatcher (*Empidonax minimus*) has a feeding territory of just 0.07 ha while the golden eagle (*Aquila chrysaetos*) defends almost 10,000 ha. Territories are most easily seen where there is overt aggression between animals, but often this is not the case, and territory boundaries are maintained by conventional signals; under these circumstances the best indication of territoriality will be the distribution of animals on the ground, which will not be random.

Animals may occupy a territory singly, as for example male ruffs (*Philomachus pugnax*) on the breeding ground, as a pair (eagles), or in much larger groups, such as the herds of African buffalo (*Syncerus caffer*) that divide up the savannah plains. Animals often invest considerable resources in territory defense, which will be profitable only if in the long run the benefits to be had are even greater. These benefits will not be the same in all cases, and for convenience one may divide territories into those maintained primarily for feeding and those for breeding (predator avoidance may also be important).

Comparative studies of a wide range of species have shown that territory is often intimately linked to food supply. In the case of birds, for example, there is a strong relationship between body weight and territory size, which implies that the territory is being used to supply the animal's food requirements – bigger animals need more food (Schoener 1968). Territoriality also varies with food availability within a single species. The dunlin (*Calidris alpina*) is a small wading bird that breeds (among other places) in Alaska. Holmes (1970) discovered that in an arctic area, where they are few ponds and an unpredictable food supply, the territories were considerably larger than in a subarctic area where there were more ponds and where the food was more abundant.

Davies (Davies and Houston 1984) has made a thorough study of the economics of feeding and territoriality. His own work on the winter feeding territories of the pied wagtail (*Motacilla alba yarrellii*) reveals the nice balance struck between the costs of defense and the benefits gained as a result. The pied wagtail eats insects washed up onto the banks of small streams, defending its riparian rights to a stretch of stream. The size of the territory is such that by the time the bird has searched methodically along both banks a fresh supply of insect food has been washed ashore. When food is less abundant the wagtail will abandon its territory and go off to feed in a flock elsewhere, though it returns from time to time to chase intruders and reassess the availability of insects. When food is particularly abundant it may permit another bird, often a juvenile, to share the territory, but if the supply should diminish it chases the satellite bird away.

The pied wagtail balances food and defense accurately, and the same probably applies to other species. Nectar feeding sunbirds defend territories that vary greatly in size but nevertheless contain a similar number of flowers, and the number of flowers is just sufficient to supply the bird's daily energy needs (Gill and Wolf 1975).

Breeding is a second reason for the defense of territories. It may be that the male is able to defend some resource that the female needs; by controlling that resource the male gains access to females.

Female elephant seals (*Mirounga angustirostris*) haul out on beaches to give birth, and mate shortly after parturition. Males defend the beach against all comers and so gain the right to mate with the females.

In many birds the female needs a good nest-site, or ample food for the nestlings, or both. Males that can offer these resources within the territory will attract females. If the resource is very patchily distributed it may pay a female more to be the second female on a good territory than the only one on a poor territory, and hence territoriality can influence the development of specific mating systems, in this case polygyny.

Territory size may influence breeding success. In the stickleback (*Gasterosteus aculeatus*) males with bigger territories do better. This is because a primary source of danger for the eggs in the male's nest is other male sticklebacks, and a larger territory keeps intruders at bay. Females prefer to mate with a male with a larger territory (van den Assem 1967).

Some breeding territories are very small and contain no resources. These include the tiny nesting areas of gulls, spaced apart by the distance that two incubating adults can stretch. These territories are a compromise between the advantages of colonial nesting in terms of mass defense against predators and the disadvantages of such behavior as cannibalism. A small territory may contain only the male defending it. Such aggregations of males are called leks, and they are found in many species. The lekking ground is often maintained from season to season over many years, succeeding generations adhering to the tradition. Usually it is the males occupying central positions in the lek who attract the most females, but the peripheral males may gain some matings and will also, as they grow older, come to control central territories.

The female's role in lek behavior is not clear. She may prefer to visit certain territories, or to mate with certain males. In the Uganda kob (*Kobus kob*) there is no discernible difference in the display of central and peripheral males, and the females continue to visit the central territories even after the males that formerly occupied them have been removed. Probably in leks the females' preference for the central places sets up an artificial prize for which males compete. Once the males have sorted out their relative worth the females confer the ultimate prize – reproduction – on the winners.

Territoriality often seems to regulate population numbers. In red grouse (*Lagopus scoticus*) individuals who do not acquire a territory not only fail to breed, but also pay the ultimate cost and die. When territory holders are removed, their places are taken by non-territorial birds, who now survive, and so Watson (1967) suggested that territorial behavior set an upper limit on population size. Population regulation may be a consequence of territoriality, but cannot be its function, because this would require natural selection to act at the level of the group, and there are good theoretical reasons why this is seldom the case.

Territories are defended by means of a series of specialized behavior patterns. Many animals, particularly carnivores, mark the boundaries of the territory with urine, faeces, or the secretions of special scent glands. Neighbors respect these signs and intruders too will avoid fresh scent marks.

In general there are three tiers to territorial defense. A long-distance signal – scent or specific warning vocalizations – serves to keep intruders away. In one study (Krebs et al. 1978) great tits (*Parus major*) were removed from their territories and replaced by loudspeakers that broadcast great tit song. Intruders were kept away by song alone, whereas they quickly invaded territories with no song broadcast. If an intruder should ignore the signals of the occupant there will often be a display, and in the case of persistent intruders this will escalate into a fight. At almost all stages the resident has a clear advantage, by virtue of its knowledge of the territory. Sometimes, as in the case of the speckled wood butterfly (*Pararge aegeria*), this advantage is absolute; the resident always wins (Davies 1978). In other cases there is an overwhelming "home field" advan-

tage to the resident. The red-winged blackbird (*Agelaius phoeniceus*) will dominate a rival on its own territory but succumb on the rival's territory (Yasukawa 1979).

A concept related to territoriality is that of individual distance. Rather than a fixed geographic area, this is a space around the animal within which others are not permitted. Individual distance is exemplified by large flocks of starlings (*Sturnus vulgaris*) sitting at regular intervals along a telephone wire (see SPACING). Such behavior may prevent interference in escape or when feeding and hinder the spread of parasites.   JJCh

Bibliography

Assem, J. van den. 1967: Territory in the three-spined stickleback (*Gasterosteus aculeatus* L). *Behaviour*, Supplement 16, 1–164.

Davies, N.B. and Houston, A.I. 1984: Territory economics. In *Behavioural ecology: an evolutionary approach*. 2nd edn, eds. J.R. Krebs and N.B. Davies. Oxford: Blackwell Scientific Publications: Sunderland, Mass.: Sinauer Assoc.

*Davies, N.B. 1978: Territorial defence in the speckled wood butterfly (*Pararge aegeria*): the resident always wins. *Animal behaviour* 26, 138–47.

Gill, F.B. and Wolf, L.L. 1975: Economies of feeding territoriality in the golden-winged sunbird. *Ecology* 56, 333–45.

Hinde, Robert A. 1982: *Ethology*. London: Fontana; New York and Oxford: Oxford University Press.

Holmes, R.T. 1970: Differences in population density, territoriality and food supply of dunlin on arctic and subarctic tundra. In *Animal populations in relation to their food resources*, ed. A. Watson. Oxford: Blackwell Scientific Publications.

Howard, H. Eliot 1920: *Territory in bird life*. London: John Murray; reprinted 1978: New York: Arno Press.

Krebs, J.R., Ashcroft, R. and Webber, M. 1978: Song repertoires and territory defense in the great tit (*Parus major*). *Nature* 271, 539–42.

Schoener, T.W. 1968: Sizes of feeding territories among birds. *Ecology* 49, 123–41.

Watson, A. 1967: Population control by territorial behavior in red grouse. *Nature* 215, 1274–75.

Yasukawa, K. 1979: A fair advantage in animal confrontations. *New scientist* 84, 366–68.

excludes cases where food items are dropped onto a hard surface to smash them open, which is common among birds, or where the animal scratches itself by rubbing against a tree, although it includes cases where the animal picks up a stick to scratch itself, as has been observed in elephants and horses (Lawick-Goodall 1970). A bird's nest could be considered as a tool for rearing the young, but this is not really a short-term goal.

Tool using involves problem solving, particularly where a tool is not readily available. Some animals display intelligence in fashioning suitable tools. Thus the Galapagos woodpecker finch (*Lactospiza pallida*) probes for insects in crevices by means of a twig or cactus spine held in the beak. The birds select a tool that is appropriate to the task and may even break a twig to a convenient length.   DJM

Bibliography

Box, H.O. 1984: *Primate behaviour and social ecology*. London: Chapman and Hall.

Izawa, K. 1978: Frog-eating behaviour of wild black-capped capuchin. *Primates* 21, 443–67.

Lawick-Goodall, von J. 1970: Tool-using in primates and other vertebrates. In *Advances in the study of behaviour*, eds. D.S. Lehman, R.A. Hinde and E. Shaw. New York and London: Academic Press.

transfer of learning The effect of a previous learning episode or episodes upon performance in a later task. Transfer may be positive, if later performance is facilitated by previous learning, or negative if it is impaired. Transfer may be specific, when the same knowledge is applied in detail in two situations; it may result from GENERALIZATION, where the second task is similar to the first in some way; or it may be abstract or conceptual, where performance on the second task is based on some general principle or rule which the two tasks share. LEARNING SETS provide a classic example of the latter; so does the "learned helplessness effect" where previous experience of response-independent reinforcement results in difficulty in learning a wide range of response-reinforcer relations. Finally, transfer may depend on inference, previously learned information being combined with new information to generate novel behavior.   EAG

Bibliography

Mackintosh, N.J. 1983: *Conditioning and associative learning*. Oxford and New York: Oxford University Press.

typical intensity The high degree of STEREOTYPY observed in many patterns of behavior that have a communicative function. Display movements or sounds are generally much more stereotyped in form than the behavior patterns from which they have evolved. For example, many male woodpeckers drum on dead branches to signal their possession of a territory to other males and to attract females. Display drumming is performed with a characteristic rhythm which shows much less variation than the sound made by a male excavating a nest hole, the behavior from which the drumming display is apparently derived. The adaptive significance of typical intensity is that it means that animal signals convey unambiguous information. Typical intensity is one of the properties that displays acquire during the process of ritualization and is a particularly important feature of displays that indicate an individual's species. (See also COMMUNICATION; TERRITORIALITY.)   TRH

Bibliography

Hinde, R.A. 1982: *Ethology*. Oxford and New York: Oxford University Press.

U

Umwelt (pl. *Umwelten*) The portion or aspect of the environment which is significant for a human or animal being. First introduced into biology by Jacob von Uexküll, it was meant to signify the subjective environment corresponding to the structure and state or "inner world" of an organism. As sensory (*Merkwelt*) as well as motor environment (*Wirkwelt*) the *Umwelt* is species-and organism-specific. Generalized to the human level (by Uexküll himself) *Umwelt* has now become the technical term for the subjectively meaningful surroundings of an individual or group. That is why social scientists emphasize the social character of *Umwelten* as ensembles of meaning (Harré 1979).

In every-day German *Umwelt* is equivalent to environment in differential psychology – the whole class of external factors capable of influencing behavior, as contrasted with hereditary influences. CFG

Bibliography

Harré, R. 1979: *Social being: a theory for social psychology*. Oxford: Basil Blackwell; Totowa, N.J.: Littlefield Adams.

von Uexküll, J. 1909: *Umwelt und Innenwelt der Tiere*. Berlin: Springer.

*——— 1957: A stroll through the worlds of animals and men. In *Instinctive behavior*, ed. C.H. Schiller. New York: International Universities Press.

V

vacuum activity Behavior manifested in the absence of any appropriate stimulus, as a result of abnormally high motivation. In practice it is never possible to be certain that no stimulus is present, but this is unimportant for the term draws attention to the extreme lowering of thresholds of responsiveness which can result if an instinct is thwarted over a long period. In such cases, it has been argued, there is an accumulation of a specific DRIVE relating to the activity. The original example described by LORENZ related to captive starlings performing the full sequence of fly-catching activities in the absence of any fly and when fully fed in their cage. Paired Bengalese finches at the nest-building stage of their reproductive cycle but deprived of nesting material will attempt to carry items of food or even their own droppings to the chosen nest site. In a completely bare cage they can be observed to go through all the movements of carrying material, placing and weaving it into the nest, with nothing in their bills.

AWGM

vigilance A state of readiness to detect specific unpredictable events in the environment. Vigilance is closely related to ATTENTION and the type of event that is most likely to be detected may vary according to motivation.

In humans the prototype was the wartime development of radar and sonar: an operator was required to pay attention to a "noisy" situation and very occasionally a signal appeared just above the noise level – a blip on the screen or an echo in the earphones. Vigilance became important in psychology after the classical experimental studies of N.H. Mackworth who discovered that in conditions requiring vigilance there was a marked deterioration in human performance in a relatively short time – less than half an hour. The problem proved to be susceptible to analysis by a specialized form of decision theory known as signal detection theory which emphasizes the distinction between two kinds of errors: those due to the missing of stimuli which did appear, and those due to responding to stimuli which in fact had not appeared. It also led to an interest in the concept of AROUSAL.

Vigilance has recently become the subject of study in animals. For example, resting herring gulls attend preferentially to alarm calls from other members of the species. Vigilance in foraging for food may take the form of a specific SEARCH IMAGE, as a result of which the animal pays attention to certain types of food items, while ignoring other equally palatable ones. Vigilance is particularly important in social situations, where a few members of the herd or flock keep watch for predators while the others feed or sleep.   DJM/WTS

Bibliography

Broadbent, Donald E. 1971: *Decision and stress*. London and New York: Academic Press.

Lendrem, D.W. and McFarland, D. 1985: Selective attention and vigilance. In *Attention and vigilance*, eds. D.W. Lendrem, and D. McFarland. London: Pitman.

voluntary behavior Behavior in which the animal seems, to some extent, a free agent. Some behavioral scientists believe that voluntary behavior is the product of a free will, but others take a more deterministic attitude. Many psychologists equate voluntary behavior with operant behavior that is produced in order to attain some goal. Physiologists regard it as being the product of the somatic nervous system, in contrast to the autonomic activity which is reflex and involuntary. The somatic nervous system supplies the striated skeletal muscles responsible for the movement of limbs, etc.

Although the major part of overt behavior is controlled through the somatic nervous system, it is by no means all voluntary. Examples of involuntary somatic reflexes are the startle response and the ORIENTING RESPONSE. Other involuntary reflexes may be the result of CONDITIONING. Voluntary behavior does not include automatic responses to a situation, but scientists disagree as to whether observed behavior, however apparently voluntary, is always an inevitable consequence of the stimulus situation and the animal's internal state (see MOTIVATION).   DJM

Bibliography

Bolles, R.C. 1975: *Theory of motivation* 2nd edn. New York: Harper and Row.
Toates, F.M. 1983: Models of motivation. In *Animal behaviour*, vol. 1. *Causes and effects*, eds. T.R. Halliday and P.J.B. Slater. Oxford: Blackwell Scientific Publications.

von Frisch, Karl Born in Vienna in 1886 and educated in the Universities of Vienna and Munich. He has been Professor in Zoology at a number of universities, notably Munich. Initially working in fish biology, his interest in color changes in fish led him to research in color vision, especially in lower organisms. His researches on the sensory physiology of honeybees were facilitated by his discovering how to train bees to forage at artificial feeding stations. It became clear that odor information could be passed to other bees by foragers returning to the hive. Later, von Frisch concluded that returning foragers use a "dance language" to communicate the distance and direction of the food source, by means of the speed and orientation of the dance (see COMMUNICATION). This work in particular (von Frisch 1967) raised profound issues about the nature of symbolic communication, although criticisms and re-interpretations have not been lacking (e.g. Rosin 1980). It led to his sharing the Nobel Prize for physiology and medicine in 1973 with Lorenz and Tinbergen.   PKS

Bibliography

Dyer, F.C. and Gould, J.L. 1983: Honey bee navigation. *American scientist* 71, 587–97.
Rosin, R. 1980: Paradoxes of the honey-bee "dance language" hypothesis. *Journal of theoretical biology*, 84, 775–800.
von Frisch, K. 1967: *The dance language and orientation of bees*. Cambridge, Mass.: Harvard University Press.

W

Watson, John Broadus (1878–1958).

The founder of the psychological school known as BEHAVIORISM. This doctrine was first stated in Watson's classic paper "Psychology as the behaviorist views it" (1913) and developed during a relatively short academic career. Watson's own words from this paper best summarize his position and also illustrate the vigor with which he set out the new psychology.

Psychology as the behaviorist views it is a purely objective branch of natural science. Its theoretical goal is the prediction and control of behavior. Introspection forms no essential part of its methods, nor is the scientific value of its data dependent upon the readiness with which they lend themselves to interpretation in terms of consciousness. The behaviorist, in his efforts to get a unitary scheme of animal response recognises no dividing line between man and brute. The behavior of man, with all of its refinement and complexity, forms only a part of the behaviorist's total scheme of investigation.

This captures the essence of Watson's new departure: psychology as a natural science, of the continuity in nature and the form of study of animal and man, and antimentalism (opposition to the belief that understanding mental events is central to understanding behavior). One further element present in his scheme was reductionism, the doctrine that behavior is ultimately explicable in terms of physiology. In this respect Watson's thinking was more subtle than that of some of his followers. He warned that though it may be taken for granted that the organism is a machine, "the machine should not be made too simple for the multitudinous demands" that the behaviorist's findings require.

Watson was born in Greenville, South Carolina and entered the town's Baptist University, Furman, at the age of fifteen. In 1900 he joined the psychology department of Chicago University to read for his doctorate. He graduated as the university's youngest ever PhD in 1903 and his thesis was published in the same year. Watson's early work bore some of the hallmarks of his later doctrine: close observation and an absence of ANTHROPO-MORPHISM. During his stay at Chicago, where he was appointed instructor, he worked feverishly both on his research and to support himself. He was plagued by a shortage of money for much of his academic life. During this period he began to win public recognition and started to edit the *Psychological bulletin*. In 1908, at the age of twenty-nine he was appointed Professor of Psychology at Johns Hopkins University. In 1910 he published an article in *Harpers* in which he argued for a "new science of animal behavior", using only observation and experiment and refraining from absurd speculations on animal consciousness.

The turning point in Watson's career and, indeed, in academic psychology came in 1913. In a series of lectures at Columbia University he delivered the lecture which was published as "Psychology as the behaviorist views it" and was in effect a manifesto for the new science.

Watson was reacting against not only the introspectionism of Titchener and Wundt but also the dominant school of animal psychology, functionalism. This Watson considered to be anthropomorphic and therefore unscientific. He wanted to end the distinction between animal and human psychology and place them both in the evolutionary tradition of Darwinian biology.

Watson regarded behavior as the product of the interplay of heredity and environment. The task of psychology is to determine what is instinctive and what is learned. (The extreme environmentalism for which he became notorious was expounded in his later popular articles).

Watson's book *Psychology from the standpoint of a behaviorist* (1919) further elaborated the behaviorist program. In it he reported his observations of children and attempted to show how behaviorism could deal with the most diverse and complex human actions.

In 1920 Watson divorced his wife in favor of a student many years his junior. The scandal caused by this forced him to resign his chair and he never returned to an academic post. He took up a second career with the advertising agency J. Walter Thompson where he made a considerable contribution to the developing business of advertising, rendering it much more psychological in character. During the 1920s Watson became a great popularizer of psychology and *The psychological care of infant and child* (1928) became a best seller. Two years later he produced a revised edition of *Behaviorism*. Among the revisions was the adoption of a more strongly environmentalist position, judging conditioning to be more important than heredity.

After his wife's death in 1936 Watson gradually withdrew from active life and retired in 1947. He was treated with hostility, derision and indifference by many of his academic contemporaries for much of his career, but in 1957, the year before he died, the American Psychological Association honored its past Presidents, including Watson. Its tribute to him remains an apt summary: "To John B. Watson, whose work has been one of the vital determinants of the form and substance of modern psychology. He initiated a revolution in psychological thought and his writings have been the point of departure for continuing lines of fruitful research."   APO

Bibliography

Boakes, R. 1984: *From Darwin to behaviourism: psychology and the minds of animals.* Cambridge and New York: Cambridge University Press.

Cohen, D. 1979: *J.B. Watson: the founder of behaviourism.* London and Boston: Routledge and Kegan Paul.

Larson, C.A., Harris. B. and Semelson, F. 1981: On the other hand. *Contemporary psychology* 26, 62–4.

Watson, J.B. 1913: Psychology as the behaviorist views it. *Psychological review* 20, 158–77.

―――― 1919: *Psychology from the standpoint of a behaviorist.* 1st edn. Philadelphia: Lippincott.

―――― 1930: *Behaviorism.* Rev. edn. New York: Norton.

Index

The figures in **bold** index the main article on that subject. Columns (designated a & b) are only differentiated where the subject is restricted to one column on any page.